Dedicated to

Bobby Heagerty, whose vision and
commitment to family caregivers made
The Caregiver Helpbook a reality.

Adalie Haas
845 - 255 - 0614

The Caregiver Helpbook

Powerful Tools for Caregiving

Vicki L. Schmall, PH.D.

Marilyn Cleland, R.N.

Marilynn Sturdevant, R.N., M.S.W., L.C.S.W.

LEGACY
Health System

Legacy Caregiver Services
Legacy Health System
Portland, Oregon

Some materials on pages 12–13 are adapted from *The Arthritis Helpbook,*
Fourth Edition, by Kate Lorig, R.N., DR.P.H. and James F. Fries, M.D.,
copyright © 1995 by Perseus Books, L.L.C. Reprinted by permission of
Perseus Books Publishers, a member of Perseus Books L.L.C.

ISBN 0-9679155-4-6

Printed in the United States of America

Text design and layout by Jonathan Wills Graphic Design and
Mike Staudinger, Legacy Health System Marketing & Creative Services.
Cover design by Jonathan Wills.

First Printing: March 2000

10 9 8 7 6 5 4 3 2 1

Table of Contents

❦

FOREWORD

The Caregiver Helpbook was developed as part of a six-week caregiver educational program, "Taking Care of You: Powerful Tools for Caregiving." This book, and an accompanying Class Leader's Guide, are the result of a three-year project funded by the Meyer Memorial Trust, Portland, Oregon. The project began with ten focus groups of diverse caregivers and professionals who work with family caregivers. The book is based on what caregivers told us were their needs and concerns. Caregivers stated that one of their greatest challenges was maintaining their own health and wellbeing while managing caregiving responsibilities.

The Caregiver Helpbook is designed to provide caregivers with the "tools" to increase their self-care and their confidence to handle difficult situations, emotions, and decisions. These tools include:

◆ Tools for reducing personal stress.

◆ Tools for changing negative self-talk.

◆ Tools to help a caregiver best communicate his or her feelings and needs to others.

◆ Tools that can help a caregiver set limits and ask for help.

◆ Tools for dealing with emotions such as anger, guilt, and depression.

◆ Tools for making tough caregiving decisions.

◆ Tools for dealing with difficult situations, such as when a family member is having problems managing money, can no longer live alone, or is exhibiting unsafe driving.

Underlying assumptions of *The Caregiver Helpbook* are:

1) When a caregiver practices self-care, the care receiver also benefits.

2) An optimistic attitude is one of the most important tools a caregiver can have. A pessimistic attitude makes the job of caregiving even harder. What a caregiver thinks and says to himself or herself affects how he or she feels and reacts to situations.

The Caregiver Helpbook can't take away caregiving problems, but it can help caregivers to manage them better, and to seek and find solutions. The goal is to help caregivers to thrive as individuals.

The six-week educational program is based on the results of the focus groups, a review of research on caregiving, and the successful Chronic Disease Self-Management Program developed by Dr. Kate Lorig and her colleagues at Stanford University's Patient Education Research Center. Many of Dr. Lorig's ideas were adapted to the special needs and concerns of family caregivers.

Although the educational program was developed for family members who are caregivers to someone with Parkinson's disease, Alzheimer's disease or a similar disorder, or stroke, *The Caregiver Helpbook* is beneficial for anyone who is providing support or caregiving to a parent, spouse, or other older family member.

One final note: Throughout the book we have used only masculine pronouns, solely for reasons of convention and consistency. This in no way diminishes our recognition of the many women who give countless hours caring for family members, or that the challenges of aging affect males and females equally.

For information about *The Caregiver Helpbook* or the curriculum for the class, "Taking Care of You: Powerful Tools for Caregiving," contact:

Legacy Caregiver Services
1015 NW 22nd Avenue, Suite N300
Portland, Oregon 97210
(503) 413-7706

ACKNOWLEDGEMENTS

Many people made *The Caregiver Helpbook* possible. First, we gratefully acknowledge the work of Dr. Kate Lorig and her colleagues at Stanford University's Patient Education Research Center whose pioneering work in patient education and chronic disease self-management formed the foundation for our work. Dr. Lorig's advice and encouragement was invaluable. We are particularly appreciative that Dr. Lorig and Bull Publishing of Palo Alto gave us permission to use and adapt materials on goal setting, contracting, and problem solving from the book, *Living a Healthy Life with Chronic Conditions*.

We are most indebted to the Meyer Memorial Trust, Portland, Oregon, for the generous grant to support the development of *The Caregiver Helpbook* and the caregiver educational program, "Taking Care of You: Powerful Tools for Caregivers."

Many chapters in the second half of *The Caregiver Helpbook* would not have been possible without the generosity of the Oregon State University Extension Service, which gave us permission to to use and adapt five of their age-related publications.

We also appreciate the generosity of the American Society on Aging for allowing us to use photographs from their collection, including photographs by Steven W. Brummel, Faye J. Clark, Lena Sexton, Don Huff Photography and Susan M. Knechtel.

A special thank you goes to the many family caregivers and professionals who helped us to identify the needs and concerns of family caregivers, participated in pilot testing of program materials, and reviewed chapters of *The Caregiver Helpbook*. We could not have reached our goal of developing a book that makes a difference for caregivers without their participation and insights.

Special gratitude also goes to:

◆ Bobby Heagerty who first envisioned this project and made it a reality. Bobby also directed the project for two years.

◆ Leslie Congleton who served as the project coordinator and trainer and provided extensive review of *The Caregiver Helpbook*.

◆ Joyce Beedle who served as a project trainer and provided input and reviewed chapters.

◆ Linda Boise who served as project evaluator and directed the project in its third year.

◆ Louise Dunn and Mary Goodwin for their writing of the grant proposal.

◆ Karen Skjei who served as editor.

◆ Rod Schmall, for photographs and word processing.

◆ David Gorsek for photographs.

◆ Legacy Creative Services for help with formatting, graphics, and publishing of this book.

◆ Jonathan Wills Graphic Design for design and computer production of this book.

Many cooperating agencies have been supportive throughout the project. A special thank you to the Oregon Trail Chapter of the Alzheimer's Association, Oregon Stroke Association, Will-Cope Parkinsonian Society, and the Parish Nurse Association. Many professionals from cooperating organizations provided extensive review of selected chapters. These included:

◆ Elizabeth Baxter, Program Coordinator, Legacy Chronic Care Initiatives

◆ George Bingham, family caregiver

◆ Barbara Block, family caregiver

◆ Sally Bowman, Ph.D., Family Development Specialist, Oregon State University

◆ Leah Eskenazi, Manager, Legacy Caregiver Services

◆ Len and E.J. Greger, co-presidents. Will-COPE Parkinsonian Society

◆ Sally Madden, family caregiver

◆ Elizabeth McKinney, Executive Director, Oregon Trail Chapter, Alzheimer's Association

◆ Tim Nay, M.S.W., Attorney at Law, specializing in elderlaw

◆ Joseph Quinn, M.D., Neurologist, Alzheimer's Disease Center, Oregon Health Sciences University

◆ Howard Shapiro, facilitator, Men's Caregiver Support Group, Legacy Health System

◆ Arleen Slive, LCSW, Medical Social Worker, Legacy Stenzil Skilled Nursing Unit

◆ Mark Tillson, Ph.D., Psychologist, Rehabilitation Institute of Oregon

◆ Daniel G. Vorhies, RKT, CDRS, Kinesiotherapist/Driver Rehabilitation, Portland Veterans Administration Medical Center

◆ Katherine Wild, Ph.D., Psychologist, Aging and Alzheimer's Clinic, Oregon Health Sciences University

◆ Oregon Senior & Disabled Services Division for program support and contribution for printing *The Caregiver Helpbook*

CHAPTER ONE

Taking Care Of You

Caregiving involves many challenges. You often need to master new skills. You may need to develop new ways of relating to a family member if his or her ability to communicate or remember is compromised by illness. You may have to make tough decisions. But often one of the greatest challenges is taking care of yourself.

Too often caregivers neglect their own health and wellbeing, and put their own needs "on the back burner." Sometimes caregivers become a second victim of the disease that afflicts their family member. It's sad when someone says, "My mother was the ill person, but her illness destroyed my father." Usually, we cannot stop the impact of a chronic illness on a family member. However, we are responsible for our own self-care.

When you board an airplane, the flight attendant gives several safety instructions. One of them is, "If oxygen masks drop down, put on your oxygen mask first before helping others." This is because if you don't take care of yourself first, you may not be able to help those who need your help. It's the same thing with caregiving. When you take care of yourself, everyone benefits. Ignoring your own needs is not only potentially detrimental to you, but it can also be harmful to the person who depends on you.

THE CAREGIVER HELPBOOK

The Caregiver Helpbook was designed to help you maintain personal wellbeing while providing quality care to your family member. The first half of the book focuses on several tools to help you to take care of *you*. These tools will help you to:

- set goals and make action plans.

- identify and reduce personal stress.

- make your thoughts and feelings work for you, not against you.

- communicate your feelings, needs, and concerns in positive ways.

- cope with difficult situations, including asking for help and setting limits.

- deal with emotions, especially feelings of anger, guilt, and depression.

- make tough caregiving decisions.

Chapters in the second half of the book address special concerns and decisions you may face as a caregiver. These include what to do when a family member is no longer a safe driver, hiring in-home help, using community services, how to communicate with and respond to a family member who is memory impaired, options available when a family member is having problems managing his money, coping with depression, and making a decision about a care facility. You can turn to these chapters for guidance and resources when you face a specific decision or concern.

MANAGING SELF-CARE

Managing our self-care means that as caregivers we:

- **Take responsibility.** We realize we are responsible for our personal wellbeing and for getting our needs met. This includes maintaining activities and relationships that are meaningful to us.

- **Have realistic expectations.** We fully understand our family member's medical condition and we are realistic about what our family member can and cannot do.

Ask yourself the following questions about your caregiving:

Yes No

- ❐ ❐ Do you ever find yourself trying "to do it all?"

- ❐ ❐ Do you ever say to yourself "I should be able to …," "I can never…," or similar statements?

- ❐ ❐ Do you ever ignore your feelings or find that they are overwhelming?

- ❐ ❐ Do you ever get frustrated because of something you can't change or someone who won't change?

- ❐ ❐ Do you resist seeking, asking for, or accepting help?

- ❐ ❐ Do you feel that your family or others just don't understand what you are going through as a caregiver?

A "yes" answer to any of these questions indicates an area of self-care you might want to work on.

The more you know about your family member's medical condition, the better you will be able to plan successful caregiving strategies. Knowledge is power.

It's also important to look at your definition of a "good caregiver." Unrealistic expectations can set you up for feelings of failure, resentment, and guilt. Placing burdensome expectations on yourself does not make you a better caregiver. In fact, you are much more likely to become an exhausted, irritable, and resentful caregiver...and then to feel guilty!

◆ **Focus on what we can do.** It's important to be clear about what you can and cannot change. For example, you will not be able to change a person who has always been demanding and inflexible, but you can control how you respond to that person's demands. You can accept— "let go" of—the things you cannot change. Managing your self-care also means you seek solutions to what you can change.

◆ **Communicate effectively with others.** These include family members, friends, health care professionals, and the care receiver. Don't expect others to know what you need. Recognize it is your responsibility to tell others about your needs and concerns. Communicate in ways that are positive and avoid being demanding, manipulative, or guilt-provoking when you make requests.

◆ **Learn from our emotions.** Realize there will be emotional ups and downs. Listen to your emotions and what they are telling you. Don't bottle up your emotions. Repressing or denying feelings decreases energy; causes irritability, depression, and physical problems; and affects your judgment and ability to make the best decisions. Also, don't strike out at others. You are in control of your emotions; your emotions don't control you.

◆ **Get help when needed.** An important part of self-care is knowing when you need help and how to find it. Help can be from community resources, family and friends, or professionals. Most important is that you do not wait until you are "hanging at the end of your rope" before you get help. Don't wait until you are overwhelmed or exhausted, or your health fails. Reaching out for help, when needed, is a sign of personal strength.

◆ **Set goals and work toward them.** Be realistic in the goals that you set and take steps toward reaching those goals. Seek solutions to the problems that you experience. Changes do not need to be major to make a significant difference.

In summary, self-care means that you seek ways to take better care of yourself. As a caregiver, you don't just survive. You thrive!

Trying To Do It All

One problem that caregivers frequently experience is trying to do it all and doing it all alone. Is it possible to do it all? The answer to the question can be both "yes" and "no." It really depends on you. What is critical is how you define what it means to "do it all." And, whether or not your definition of "doing it all" includes taking care of yourself so that you thrive, and not just survive.

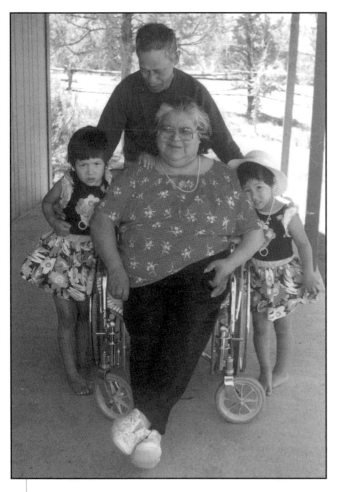

To Maxine, the answer to the question "Is it possible to do it all?" was "no." She says, "Mother's needs are endless and no matter what I do, I can never make her happy." Yet, at the same time, Maxine was trying to do it all. Her mother's care dominated Maxine's life.

Another caregiver, Maria, answered "yes" to the question, "Is it possible to do it all?" She explained that "All that needed to be done for my mother was done."

A major difference between Maxine and Maria was the rules by which they operated. Maxine operated by the rule, "I must do everything for my mother." The rule had become, "I must help Mama at all costs." As a result, her relationships with other family members suffered and Maxine found herself becoming increasingly resentful. Maxine's feelings of wanting to do everything is legitimate, but the actions associated with her feelings usually are impossible to carry out. As a result, Maxine experiences feelings of failure and lack of success.

Maria was more realistic. She recognized that the things she wanted to be done—whether they were her desires, her mother's desires, or the desires of others—were not the same as the things that needed to be done. Maria's goal was to make her mother as comfortable as possible, without sacrificing herself and the other important relationships in her life. She also got help from family and a community agency in meeting her mother's needs. Maria said:

> To some degree I recognized that caregiving was like a job and my goal was to find the best way to get the job done. A friend also told me that doing any job well—including the job of caregiving—requires four things:
> 1. Recognizing you can't do everything yourself—you work with others.
> 2. Taking daily breaks.
> 3. Taking vacations to renew oneself.
> 4. Being realistic about what you can do.

There was another difference between Maxine and Maria. Maxine felt it was selfish to think of herself. Maria, on the other hand, viewed that if she was going to be there for the long haul, she must take care of herself, and make sure that she had pleasurable moments in her life.

As a caregiver, you are more likely to "be there" for your family member who needs your care and to be a more loving and patient caregiver when you meet some of your own needs. It's important to "fill your own cup" and not allow it to "run dry."

It's not being selfish to focus on your own needs and desires when you are a caregiver to a family member who has a chronic or progressive illness. It's important to ask yourself, "If my health deteriorates, or I die, what will happen to the person I provide care for? If I get emotionally drained, become deprived of sleep, or become isolated because I am trying to do it all, how loving am I likely to be to my family member?"

Taking Time for Yourself

Do you value yourself and your personal needs? What do you do for personal renewal? Do you save some time for yourself out of each day? Do you take occasional extended breaks? Or are you so involved with caregiving tasks that you have little or no time for yourself?

What activities do you enjoy? What would you like to do that would give you a lift? When was the last time you gave yourself a treat?

Breaks in caregiving are a must. They are as important to health as diet, sleep, rest, and exercise. It's important not to lose sight of your personal needs and interests. Studies show that sacrificing yourself in the care of another and removing pleasurable events from your life can lead to emotional exhaustion, depression, and physical illness. You have a right—even a responsibility—to take some time away from caregiving.

Regular breaks from the tasks of caregiving are essential. Decide on the time, date, and activity—then follow through. Breaks don't have to be long to make a positive difference. It's important to plan some time for yourself in every day, even if that time is only for 15 minutes or half an hour. Most important is to do something that "fills your cup" and helps you to feel better and to thrive.

If you have difficulty taking breaks for yourself, consider taking them for your family member. Care receivers also benefit from caregivers getting breaks.

SETTING GOALS

An important tool in taking care of yourself is setting goals. A goal is something you would like to accomplish in the next three to six months. What would you like to do to take better care of yourself and to help yourself to thrive? This might be to get a break from caregiving for a week, get help with caregiving tasks, be able to walk three miles, or quit feeling guilty.

Goals often are difficult to accomplish because they may seem like dreams or they may be overwhelming. As a result, we may not even try to accomplish them or we may give up shortly after we get started. We will address this problem shortly. For now, take a moment and write your goals here:

Goal 1 _____

_____

_____

Goal 2 _____

_____

_____

Goal 3 _____

_____

_____

Put an asterisk (*) next to the goal you would like to work on first.

After identifying a goal, the first step is to brainstorm all of the different things you might do to reach your goal. Identify and write down all possible options.

Option 1 _____

_____

_____

Option 2 _____

_____

_____

Option 3 _____

_____

_____

Option 4 _____

_____

_____

Option 5 _____

_____

_____

The second step is to evaluate the options you have identified. Which options seem like possibilities to you? It's important not to assume that an option is unworkable or doesn't exist until you have thoroughly investigated it or given it a try. Assumptions are major self-care enemies.

Put an asterisk (*) next to two or three options you would like to try. Select one to try.

The third step is to turn your option into a short-term plan, which we call *making an action plan.*

MAKING ACTION PLANS

An action plan is a specific action that you are confident you can accomplish within the next week. It's an agreement or contract with yourself.

Action plans are one of your most important self-care tools. An action plan is a step toward reaching your long-term goal. It is to be something you want to do. It is *not* to be something you feel you *should* do, *have to* do, or *need to* do. The intent of making an action plan is to help you to feel better and to take better care of yourself. Remember, an action plan is a "want to do."

Here are the five steps for making an action plan:

1. Decide what you want to do.
2. Make your plan behavior-specific.
3. Make a specific plan.
4. Determine your confidence level.
5. Write down your action plan.

Decide What You Want To Do

Think about what is realistic for you to accomplish within the next week. It's important that an action plan is reachable; otherwise, you are likely to experience frustration. An action plan is to help you experience success—not frustration, increased stress, or failure. An action plan starts with the words, "I will…." If you find yourself saying "I will try to…," "I have to…," or "I should…," then re-examine your action plan. It probably is not something that you truly want to do.

Make Your Plan Behavior-Specific

The more specific your action plan, the greater your chances of accomplishing it. For example, "taking better care of myself"

<table>
<tr><td>

PARTS OF AN ACTION PLAN

1. It's something you want to do.
2. It's reachable (something you believe you will be able to accomplish during the next week).
3. It answers these questions:
   —What?
   —How much?
   —When?
   —How often?
4. It has a high confidence level. (You are certain that you will be able to complete your *entire* action plan during the next week.)

</td></tr>
</table>

is not a specific behavior. However, making an appointment for a physical check-up, walking three times a week, getting a massage on Thursday afternoon, or asking someone to stay with your family member for one morning are all specific behaviors. "I will relax" also is not a specific behavior; however, reading a book, listening to your favorite music, or puttering in the garden are specific behaviors.

Make a Specific Plan

Making a specific plan is often difficult, yet it is the most important part of making an action plan. A specific plan answers these four questions:

1. **What are you going to do?**
   Examples: I will read (*book name*) for pleasure. Or, I will walk.
2. **How much will you do?**
   Examples: Will you read one chapter or will you read for a half hour? Will you walk two blocks or for 20 minutes?

3. **When will you do this?**
   Examples: Will you read the first thing in the morning when you awaken, before you go to bed, when the care receiver is sleeping, or…? If your plan is to walk, when during the day will you do it ?

4. **How often will you do this activity?**
   Example: Three times a week on Monday, Wednesday, and Friday.

A common mistake is to make an action plan that is unreachable within the time frame. For example, if you plan to do something every day, you might fail. Caregiving, and life in general, has its surprises. Although well-intentioned, it's often not possible to do something every day. It's better to plan to do something once or twice a week and exceed your action plan than to plan to do something every day and fail because you only did it six days, rather than seven. Remember, an action plan is meant to help you to take better care of yourself and to experience success. The last thing you need is additional pressure, disappointment, and stress.

Here are two recommendations for writing an action plan that can help you achieve success.

1. **Start where you are or start slowly.** If there's a book you've been wanting to read, but just haven't found the time, it may not be realistic to expect to read the entire book in the next week. Instead, try

reading for a half hour twice during the week. If you haven't been physically active, it may be unrealistic to make an action plan to start walking three miles. It is better to make your action plan for something that you believe you can accomplish. For example, make your plan for walking three blocks or a half mile, rather than three miles.

2. **Give yourself time off.** We all have days when we don't feel like doing anything. That's the advantage of saying you will do something three days a week, rather than every day. That way, if you don't feel like doing something on one day, or something develops that prevents you from doing it, you can still achieve your action plan.

Determine Your Confidence Level

Once you've made your action plan, ask yourself the following question: On a scale of 0 to 10, with 0 being not at all confident and 10 being totally confident, how confident am I that I can complete my action plan?

If your answer is 7 or above, your action plan is probably realistic and reachable. However, if your answer is 6 or below, it's important to take another look at your action plan. Something probably needs to be adjusted.

Ask yourself, "What makes me uncertain about accomplishing my action plan? What problems do I foresee?" Then, see if you can either find a solution to the problems you identified or change your action plan to one in which you feel greater confidence.

Write Down Your Action Plan

Once you are satisfied with your action plan, write it down. Putting an action plan in writing helps us to remember, keep track of, and accomplish the agreement we have made with ourselves. Keep track of how you are doing. Write down the problems you encounter in carrying out your action plan. Check off activities as you accomplish them. If you made an adjustment in your action plan, make a note of what you did.

At the end of the week, review your action plan. Ask yourself, "Am I nearer to accomplishing my goal?" "How do I feel about what I did?" What obstacles or problems, if any, did I encounter?" Taking stock is important. If you are having problems, this is the time to seek solutions.

See page 12 for a sample action plan. See page 13 for an action plan form that you can duplicate and use to develop your own action plans.

PROBLEM-SOLVING: A SOLUTION-SEEKING APPROACH

Sometimes you may find that your action plan is not workable. You may encounter unusual circumstances that week and need to give the plan a try for at least another week. Or you may need to make adjustments in your original plan. The following solution-seeking approach can help you identify solutions to problems.

- **Clearly identify the problem.** This is the first and most important step in the solution-seeking approach. It also can be the most difficult step.

- **List ideas to solve the problem.** Family, friends, and others may be helpful in giving ideas. When you ask for ideas, just listen to each suggestion. It's best not to respond as to why an idea is or isn't likely to work. Just focus on getting the ideas.

- **Select one to try.** When trying a new idea, give it a fair trial before deciding that it won't work.

- **Assess the results.** Ask yourself, "How well did what I chose work?" If all went well, congratulate yourself for finding a solution to the identified problem. If the first idea didn't work, try another idea. Sometimes an idea just needs fine-tuning. It's important not to give up on an idea just because it didn't work the first time.

If you have difficulty finding a solution that works, utilize other resources. Share your problem with family, friends, and professionals and ask them for possible ideas. If you still find that suggested solutions do not work, you may need to accept that the problem is not solvable right now.

Remember, just because there doesn't seem to be a workable solution right now doesn't mean that a problem can't be solved later, or that other problems can't be solved in the same way. It may be helpful to go back to the first step and consider if the problem needs to be redefined. For example, a caregiver had thought that her problem was "I am tired all of the time." However, the real problem was the caregiver's beliefs that "No one can care for John like I can," and "I have to do everything myself." As a result of these beliefs, the caregiver was doing everything herself and getting worn out. When she redefined the problem and focused on changing her beliefs and view of the caregiving situation, she found a workable solution. Sometimes, too, a problem may be easier to work on if you break it down into smaller problems.

Most of the time if you follow these steps, you will find a solution that solves the problem. It's important to avoid making the mistake of jumping from step 1 to step 7 and thinking "nothing can be done."

SUMMARY OF THE SOLUTION-SEEKING APPROACH

1. Identify the problem.
2. List ideas to solve the problem.
3. Select one idea to try.
4. Assess the results.
5. Substitute another idea if the first one didn't work.
6. Utilize other resources if your solutions don't work.
7. Accept that the problem may not be solvable now.

REWARD YOURSELF

Accomplishing action plans is often a reward in itself. However, it's also important to find healthy pleasures that add enjoyment to your life. Rewards don't have to be fancy or expensive or take a lot of time. One caregiver, for example, regularly goes to a movie or a play as a gift to herself from her husband. She said:

> When my husband was well, he would take me out Friday nights to a movie or a play at least twice a month. Because of his medical condition, he is no longer able to do so. Now a friend and I go to a movie or a play at least once a month. I consider this is a treat that my husband is still giving to me.

Another caregiver said:

> Before my wife's illness, I would go golfing with my buddies on Saturday morning. When Carmela needed more care, I quit golfing. I now treat myself to Saturday golfing, while my daughter or a friend visits with Carmela. This gives me something to look forward to each week and I feel more alive when I return home. I'm also finding I am more patient with Carmela. My daughter says I am always happier and calmer when I return home. So, I look at Saturday golfing as my treat not only to me, but also to Carmela.

SUMMARY

In review, a caregiver who practices self-care does the following:

1. Sets goals.

2. Identifies a variety of options for reaching a goal.

3. Makes an action plan toward accomplishing the goal.

4. Carries out the action plan.

5. Assesses how well the action plan is working.

6. Makes adjustments, as necessary, in the action plan.

7. Rewards himself or herself.

Not all goals are achievable. Sometimes we must accept that what we want to do is not possible at this time, and we must let go of the idea. Be realistic about goals and don't dwell on what can't be done.

Consider what is likely to happen to the caregiver who is driven by a goal to make her mother happy. Given her mother's personality, this goal may be completely unachievable. Such a goal creates a heavy burden and a caregiver is not likely to achieve it. However, an achievable goal might be to provide a pleasurable activity for her mother at least once a week—perhaps taking her to get her hair done, visiting a friend, watching a comedy on television, or working together on a project her mother enjoys.

Remember, what is important in care-giving is not just to survive, but to thrive! This book is designed to give you a set of tools to help you take care of yourself. This in turn will help you provide better care.

MY ACTION PLAN — *Sample*

When writing an action plan, be sure it includes:

1. **What** you are going to do.

2. **How** much you are going to do.

3. **When** you are going to do it (i.e., what time of day).

4. **How often** you are going to do it.

Example: This week I will read a favorite book (what) for a half hour (how much) in the mid-afternoon when my spouse sleeps (when), three times—Monday, Wednesday, and Friday (how often).

This week I will _____ read a book _____ [what]

_____ half an hour _____ [how much]

_____ mid-afternoon, when my spouse naps _____ [when]

_____ 3 days – Monday, Wednesday, Friday _____ [how often]

How confident are you that you will complete your entire action plan during the week?
(*Circle*)   0   1   2   3   4   5   6   ⑦   8   9   10
        not at all confident   *totally confident*

Check off each day you accomplish your plan		**Comments:**
Monday	✓	Felt good to read for pleasure
Tuesday	____	
Wednesday	____	Granddaughter came over. Nice visit!
Thursday	✓	Read for an hour – refreshing!
Friday	✓	Read for 15 minutes, fell asleep.
Saturday	✓	Awakened early; read while drinking coffee – a good way to start the day
Sunday	____	

MY ACTION PLAN

When writing an action plan, be sure it includes:

1. **What** you are going to do.

2. **How** much you are going to do.

3. **When** you are going to do it (i.e., what time of day).

4. **How often** you are going to do it.

Example: This week I will read a favorite book *(what)* for a half hour *(how much)* in the mid-afternoon when my spouse sleeps *(when)*, three times—Monday, Wednesday, and Friday *(how often)*.

This week I will _____[what]

_____[how much]

_____[when]

_____[how often]

How confident are you that you will complete your entire action plan during the week?
(Circle) 0   1   2   3   4   5   6   7   8   9   10
    not at all confident   *totally confident*

Check off each day you accomplish your plan   Comments:

Monday _____   _____

Tuesday _____   _____

Wednesday _____   _____

Thursday _____   _____

Friday _____   _____

Saturday _____   _____

Sunday _____   _____

Adapted from *The Arthritis Helpbook*, Fourth Edition, by Kate Lorig, R.N., DR.P.H. and James F. Fries, M.D. Reprinted by permission of Perseus Books Publishers, a member of Perseus Books L.L.C.

CHAPTER TWO

Reducing Personal Stress

The philosophy of Virginia Satir, noted family therapist, sets the tone for this chapter on the stresses and challenges of caregiving. She reminds us that how we perceive and respond to an event is a significant factor in how we adjust and cope with it.

This chapter explores the stress of caregiving. It will help you identify and understand your particular stressors, challenges, and strengths. You can then plan strategies that help you cope, change, and reduce stress. A basic premise of this chapter is that each of us has a reservoir of strength. The challenge is to identify our strengths and build on them.

Life is not the way it's supposed to be. It's the way it is. The way you cope with it is what makes the difference... I think if I have one message, one thing before I die that most of the world would know, it would be that the event does not determine how to respond to the event. That is a purely personal matter. The way in which we respond will direct and influence the event more than the event itself.

Virginia Satir

THE STRESS OF CAREGIVING

There has been so much written about stress it has become a household word. Studies show that a certain amount of stress is helpful. It can challenge us to change and motivate us to do things we might not do otherwise. However, when the amount of stress overwhelms our ability to cope with it, we feel "distress" or "burnout."

According to Webster's Dictionary, distress is "suffering of mind or body; severe physical or mental strain." As a caregiver, you no doubt have increased stress in your life, whether you are caring for a mother with early Parkinson's disease, who is still able to care for her personal needs, or a spouse who doesn't recognize you because of advanced Alzheimer's disease.

Each caregiving situation is unique. What is stressful for you may not be stressful for someone else. In his book *The Survivor Personality*, Al Siebert says, "there is no stress until you feel a strain." Since the feeling of stress is subjective and unique to each individual, it is difficult to define objectively. The stress you feel is not only the result of your caregiving situation, it is also your perception of it. Your stress will increase or decrease depending on how you perceive your circumstances. And your perception will affect how you respond.

Factors That Affect Stress

Your level of stress is influenced by many factors, including:

◆ whether your caregiving is voluntary or not.

◆ your relationship with the care receiver.

◆ your coping abilities.

◆ your caregiving situation.

◆ whether support is available.

Whether your caregiving is voluntary or not

Many people become caregivers voluntarily. Others acquire the role because no one else is available. When you become a caregiver voluntarily, you are making a choice. However, if you "inherited" the job and feel you had no choice, the chances are greater for experiencing strain, distress, and resentment. Nancy became a caregiver because no one else was available.

Nancy couldn't have been more surprised when the visiting nurse asked her if she was the primary caregiver for her mother-in-law, Joan. Nancy was fond of Joan. She called and stopped by frequently to see how Joan was managing, but hadn't thought of herself as the primary caregiver. It was apparent that Joan's medical condition was worsening and she was becoming increasingly weak. Nancy realized there were no other children or relatives available, so she agreed, although somewhat reluctantly, to be Joan's caregiver. Nancy felt anxious and uncertain about what it meant to be a primary caregiver and whether she had the necessary skills to perform the role.

Luckily, Nancy and Joan had a good relationship and they were able to communicate openly, minimizing some of the potential for stress. You can't always think about a caregiving relationship in advance, but if you can, it has greater potential for success.

Your relationship with the care receiver

If your relationship with the care receiver has been difficult, becoming a caregiver is more of a challenge. If the care receiver has always been demanding and controlling, you will probably feel more stress, anger, and resentment.

Sometimes people are caregiving with the hope of healing a relationship. The healing may or may not happen. If healing doesn't happen, the caregiver may feel regret, depressed, and discouraged. A professional counselor, spiritual advisor, or trusted friend can help deal with such feelings and emotions.

Your coping abilities

How you have coped with stress in the past predicts how you will cope now. Did you find constructive ways to manage your stress? Perhaps you were able to find time to exercise regularly and generally take care of yourself. Or did you rely on alcohol or drugs to help you cope? Sometimes people rely on medications and alcohol in times of stress, which only makes matters worse.

It is important to identify your current coping strengths and build on them. Learning new coping skills also will help make your caregiving situation less stressful.

The caregiving situation

What does your caregiving situation require of you? Does it require 24-hour-a-day availability? Or do you just need to make an occasional telephone call to check on the person? What disease does the care receiver have? Does he have a mental or physical disability, or both?

Certain caregiving situations are more stressful than others. For example, caring for someone who has a dementia such as Alzheimer's disease is often more stressful than caring for someone with a physical limitation. Also, stress tends to be highest when:

◆ the caregiving situation continues for a long time.

◆ the care receiver's needs gradually increase.

◆ caregivers feel they have limited or no support.

◆ caregivers have their own health/physical problems.

Whether support is available

Caregivers who feel isolated and without adequate support usually experience a higher level of stress. Support may be lacking for several reasons:

◆ The caregiver may resist accepting help, even when he or she needs it.

◆ Others may be willing to help but don't offer because they are uncomfortable around the ill person, frightened of the illness, or don't know what they can do.

◆ Others don't want to interfere, especially if the caregiver seems to have everything under control and has refused help in the past.

Caregiver stress is influenced by many factors, including the need to adapt to ongoing changes and losses caused by the care receiver's illness. These changes cause you to redefine your life. What was normal has changed. You are living with a new reality.

STEPS TO MAINTAIN HEALTH AND AVOID DISTRESS

Whatever causes stress in your life, too much of it can lower your resistance to disease and lead to "burnout." Current research shows that there is a close connection between stress and health. Unrelieved stress is one of many factors that cause illness. Research also shows that thoughts and emotions affect the immune system, which is the first line of defense against disease. It is possible to strengthen the immune system by reducing stress. The following four steps will help you maintain your health and avoid distress:

1. Recognize your warning signs of stress.

2. Identify your sources of stress.

3. Identify what you can and cannot change.

4. Take action to manage your stress.

Each of these steps will be discussed in detail.

Step 1: Recognize Your Warning Signs of Stress

The first step in managing stress is to be aware of how it affects you. What are your warning signs and symptoms of stress?

The following are signs that may occur when you experience an unusual amount of stress. Answering these questions can help you identify your own warning signs.

What is usually your earliest sign of stress? It's important to recognize stress early and do something about it, before it

---

Yes No

☐ ☑ Do you feel a loss of energy or zest for life?

☑ ☐ Do you feel tired or exhausted much of the time?

☐ ☑ Do you feel out of control, exhibiting uncharacteristic emotions or actions?

☐ ☑ Do you feel tense, nervous, or anxious much of the time?

☐ ☑ Do you lack interest in people or things that were formerly pleasurable?

☐ ☑ Are you becoming increasingly isolated?

☐ ☑ Are you consuming more sleeping pills, medications, alcohol, caffeine, or cigarettes?

☐ ☐ Are you having increased health problems: for example, high blood pressure headaches, ulcers, upset stomach, or other difficulties with digestion?

Yes No

☑ ☐ Do you have sleep problems, such as difficulty falling asleep at night, awakening early, or sleeping excessively?

☐ ☑ Are you experiencing appetite changes?

☑ ☐ Do you have problems with concentration or memory?

☑ ☐ Are you increasingly irritable or impatient with others?

☐ ☑ Do you have feelings of helplessness or hopelessness?

☐ ☑ Are you abusing or neglecting to provide care to the care receiver?

☐ ☑ Do you have thoughts of suicide?

A "yes" answer to even one or two of these questions can indicate stress that has become debilitating.

causes you serious problems. For one caregiver, the early sign might be increased irritability. For another, it might be lying awake for hours before falling asleep. For another, it might be fatigue and a lack of energy.

Sometimes, too, when we are involved in a situation, we may not listen to our early warning signs, but they are voiced in the words of others: "You look so tired," "You get upset so easily lately," "Why are you snapping at me?" If you hear such statements, it is a "red light" warning sign. Just as a flashing red light on your car's dashboard warns you that something is wrong with your car, we also display warning signals. What happens if we ignore the early red flashing light on the car's dashboard? What happens if we ignore our personal early warning signals?

Do you listen to your early warning signals? What are they? And what do you do about them? Warning signs usually mean we need to stop, evaluate what's happening, and make some changes. The earlier warning signals are recognized, the greater the chance of avoiding or reducing the destructive effects of stress.

Step 2: Identify Your Sources of Caregiving Stress

The second step in managing stress is to recognize what causes your stress. Not all stressors are the result of caregiving. Other sources can affect your ability to be a caregiver. The following questions include many common sources of stress. Answering these questions can help you recognize some of your own sources.

Yes No

☑ ☐ Are you experiencing many demands on your time, energy, or money? What are they?

☑ ☐ Do you feel you have conflicting responsibilities? Which ones?

☑ ☐ Are there differences in expectations between your family, your boss, the care receiver, and yourself? What are they?

☑ ☐ Do you feel others don't understand the care receiver's mental or physical condition?

☐ ☑ Do you have difficulty meeting the care receiver's physical or emotional needs?

☐ ☑ Are you pressured by financial decisions and lack of resources?

☐ ☐ Do you feel a loss of freedom, to the point of feeling trapped?

☑ ☐ Is there disagreement among family members?

☑ ☐ Do you feel that other family members aren't doing their share?

☐ ☑ Does the care receiver place unrealistic demands and expectations on you?

☐ ☑ Is there a lack of open communication between you and the care receiver?

☐ ☑ Do other family members have negative attitudes that create difficulty for you?

☑ ☐ Is it painful to watch the care receiver's condition get worse?

☐ ☑ Are there other problems with children, marriage, job, finances, or health? What are they?

Consider your "yes" answers carefully. The sources of stress you have identified are indicators for change. Use the awareness you have gained in the first two steps to make helpful changes.

The following story is an example of a caregiver who recognized the source of her distress and made changes to better manage the situation.

> Ernestine was increasingly fatigued, irritable, and depressed with the responsibility of caring for her husband, Richard, who had Parkinson's disease. Richard's condition was steadily getting worse. He was bedbound and needed help with many functions. Other family members hadn't offered to help, and Ernestine felt abandoned, alone, angry, and overwhelmed. A few friends and neighbors had offered to help but Ernestine refused. When she started having health problems, it became clear that something had to change. She had to have help.
>
> Because Ernestine had difficulty asking for help, she devised a simple plan that would give others an opportunity to help without having to be asked. She made a list of tasks she needed help with and posted it on the refrigerator. The list included such things as vacuuming the living room, grocery shopping, staying with Richard so she could go to church, weeding the garden, picking up audio books at the library, picking up medications at the pharmacy, and preparing food. When visitors offered to help, Ernestine referred them to the list, suggesting they choose a task that suited them. This proved to be a successful plan for everyone.

It's important to identify the causes of your stress before they overwhelm you. Don't wait until you develop health problems, as Ernestine did. Many caregivers keep going until they become ill. You can only be an effective caregiver if you are healthy. Self-sacrifice to the point of illness benefits no one and is not required or recommended.

Step 3: Identify What You Can and Cannot Change

A major challenge of caregiving is to not only survive, but to rebuild your life and thrive. This is possible once you know the sources and signs of your stress. Then you can determine those you can do something about and those that are beyond your control. Step three is to identify what you can and cannot change.

Identifying what you can change gives you a sense of control over events. However, it isn't easy to determine what can and cannot be changed. Too often people try to change things they have no control over. For example, someone who focuses on trying to change another person usually ends up more frustrated. The only person you can change is yourself. You may be able to change a situation, how you respond to it, or your perception of it, but you can't change another person. It wastes valuable time and energy trying to change what is outside of your control.

Some situations can't be changed. However, you may be able to manage them better if you change your outlook about a situation, or decide to "roll with the punches."

The frustration and hopelessness that result from trying to change the unchangeable are self-defeating and can adversely affect a relationship, as in the case of Hal and Sue.

Sue and Hal had been a socially active couple. Sue was diagnosed with early Parkinson's disease and gradually started backing out of social plans because she didn't feel up to it. Since the beginning of the disease Sue has been on a roller coaster of having good days and bad days. Hal encourages Sue to go out when she doesn't feel like it, urging her to "snap out of it." He wants things to remain as they were.

Hal is frustrated in his attempts to change the effect of the disease on their lives. By not accepting Sue's feelings, he is adding stress to their relationship. But recently he has learned more about Parkinson's disease and is trying to be more realistic and flexible about what he can and cannot change. Flexibility is crucial. A Japanese saying is:

In a storm, it is the bamboo, the flexible tree, that can bend with the wind and survive. The rigid tree that resists the wind falls, victim of its own insistence on control.

Bending with the wind is crucial to surviving the winds of change, including those involved in caregiving. At times, both you and the care receiver may feel a loss of control over your lives. While feeling in control is important, sometimes it can become a problem because the more we try to control, the less control we seem to have. Being flexible can help us keep a positive attitude, despite hardships.

Use the following guidelines to look at your situation and to determine what can and cannot be changed:

1. Accept the reality of your caregiving situation.

2. Educate yourself about the care receiver's disease.

3. Identify unrealistic expectations, especially your own.

4. Seek and accept support.

5. Identify what you still have, rather than focus on what is lost.

6. Let go of what cannot be changed.

Accept the reality of your caregiving situation

When making changes it is necessary, but not always easy, to accept reality. We often deny things that hurt, and that can keep us from seeing a situation as it really is.

Jane heard the doctor tell Joe that he had a serious illness. He also told Joe he would need more rest and help with certain daily activities. Still, Jane found herself feeling annoyed when Joe took frequent naps, especially since she was taking on more responsibility for managing things at home. It took time for Jane to stop denying, and start accepting, the full impact of the disease. It was then that she was able to see realistically what could and couldn't be changed.

Jane is coping in a more adaptive way. However, Joe's mother denied the seriousness of the disease long after Jane came to terms with it. Family members may take different lengths of time to accept reality, which can add to the stress of caregiving.

Educate yourself about the care receiver's disease

You will be better able to identify what you can and cannot change when you understand the disease. For example, without knowledge about the communication abilities of someone with Alzheimer's disease, you may try to reason with the person or expect him to tell someone something you consider easy to remember. This will probably frustrate both of you.

There are many sources of information about specific diseases, including your personal physician, medical libraries, and associations related to specific diseases, such as Alzheimer's and Parkinson's disease. If you have access to a computer that is linked to the Internet, you can find a wealth of current information on diseases and disease-related associations.

Identify unrealistic expectations, especially your own

You can make changes successfully only when your expectations are realistic. How realistic are yours? Do you often feel anxious because you expect more of yourself than you can achieve? Many caregivers listen only to the "shoulds" they have been raised with. Women, especially, often believe they "should" be able to do everything themselves, and when that isn't possible, they feel guilty or depressed. If you have unrealistic expectations of yourself, then your expectations of what can be changed probably will be unrealistic also.

The following story is an example of a caregiver, Rosa, who with her husband, Dean, made constructive changes in what was a difficult, stressful situation.

Rosa was devastated when Dean, her husband of 40 years, suffered a sudden, severe stroke that left him partially paralyzed on one side of his body and unable to speak. The stroke was a shock. Rosa's initial response was to become overly protective and do everything for Dean. She was afraid to leave him alone for fear something terrible would happen.

Before the stroke, Rosa and Dean had been making retirement plans, which included extensive travel. Those plans were forsaken as they both felt increasingly overwhelmed, fearful, isolated, and depressed.

Rosa became extremely fatigued and irritable as Dean became increasingly dependent on her. The visiting nurse talked with them about what Dean could and could not do for himself. She emphasized the importance of Dean maintaining as much independence as possible. It became apparent that Dean could do many things for himself, including writing letters to family and friends. Dean felt better as he became more independent. Rosa was able to be more realistic in her expectations. She realized that Dean's dependence on her was detrimental to their relationship.

As Rosa and Dean gradually adapted to living with the stroke, they became less fearful and more hopeful. They began looking at the quality of their remaining life together. They wanted, more than anything, to travel together and decided to take a short trip to see how it would go. The first trip was successful and they felt encouraged to travel more. Rosa found a travel agent who helped them plan trips that accommodated Dean's disabilities. They enjoyed several trips before Dean's death 12 years later.

Rosa and Dean responded to this challenge by gaining an understanding of the disease, accepting reality, setting realistic expectations, and changing what could be changed.

Seek and accept support

Many caregivers find it difficult to ask for help. Rosa initially refused help from friends and neighbors. She did everything herself until she started feeling distressed. The expectations she had for herself were overwhelming and unrealistic. It wasn't until she began seeking support from the visiting nurse, travel agent, and others that she was able to find a way to make changes. Often you can make changes only with the help of others. Seeking and accepting support may be the single most important factor in making constructive changes.

Identify what you still have, rather than focus on what is lost

When Rosa and Dean decided to look for "what remained" in their situation, they hoped that they still had quality in their life together. They looked at what they still had, rather than focusing on what had been lost, and they made changes that were still possible.

They found an unexpected "gift" as they made changes and adapted to the illness. Rosa said, "I never would have asked for the stroke to happen, but it was because of it that Dean and I learned what love was all about. I am a different person than I was. I am more understanding, patient, caring, and sensitive to the pain of others."

Many caregivers, as they learn more about themselves, experience personal growth. That is the "gift" that can often be found in difficult times.

Let go of what cannot be changed

It is natural to want to hold on to things as they were. But letting go of what you cannot change is accepting the situation as it is. It releases you from the need to control what you cannot change. Letting go is a way to cooperate with the inevitable. It releases new energy for accepting reality and seeing new possibilities. Sam is a prime example of someone who is learning to let go.

Sam had always been an intense athletic competitor, and sports had been the driving force in his life. At age 45 he had a slight stroke which left him mildly affected. Sam's problem wasn't that he had a stroke; the problem was that he couldn't let go of wishing that he hadn't had one. He continuously wanted things to be as they had been. This made him feel angry and frustrated. Fortunately, Sam reached a point of wanting to learn to live with the stroke and to let go of wanting life to be as it had been before.

Sam was unable to live in the present until he let go of his desire for things to be as they were. The "if onlys" and "what ifs" were a source of suffering. When Sam let go, he learned to live with the stroke and made changes that helped him develop a satisfying life. What Sam learned also applies to caregivers, as shown in the case of Marsha and Bud.

Marsha was the caregiver for her husband, Bud, who had Parkinson's disease. Bud's condition worsened and he and Marsha were unable to do many of the things they had done in the past. Marsha continually wanted things to be the way they had been. "If only" became her constant thought: "If only Bud could dress himself," "If only we could go dancing like we used to," "If only Bud had more energy," "If only he could still drive us places."

Marsha's unhappiness caused a strain in their relationship. It was only when she and Bud were having a good time playing cards with friends one day that she realized how much valuable time she was wasting by constantly wanting things to be different. She began to let go of "if only" and to accept "what is." In letting go, she found acceptance and peace of mind.

As you reflect on your challenges as a caregiver, consider these questions. What can I change? What must I accept? What can I improve? The challenge is beautifully written in "The Serenity Prayer."

The Serenity Prayer

...grant me Serenity to accept the things I cannot change, Courage to change the things I can, and Wisdom to know the difference.

Reinhold Niebuhr, 1934

Step 4: Take Action to Manage Your Stress

The fourth step points the way for you to manage and reduce your stress. There are many different tools for managing stress. But you must find what is most effective for you. Proven ways to manage and reduce stress include:

◆ managing your thoughts, beliefs, and perceptions.

◆ practicing self-care.

◆ getting social support.

◆ using techniques that lower stress.

◆ developing plans of action.

◆ finding hope and meaning.

Managing your thoughts, beliefs, and perceptions

Thoughts and beliefs are the foundation of experience. They are not only reactions to events but our thoughts and beliefs can also influence events. What we think and believe affects what happens. Managing our thoughts means we have control over how we view things. As a caregiver, there may be times when the only thing you can change is how you view a situation.

There are several tools for managing thoughts, beliefs, and perceptions. Two that can be helpful are reframing and self-talk.

Reframing. Your frame of reference is the window through which you view the world. It gives meaning to your world. You see things one way, but someone else sees the same circumstances differently. Situations become more stressful when you view them in a negative way.

Reframing is learning to look at things in a different way, for example, finding something

positive about a difficult situation. Some examples of reframing include:

◆ A caregiver who views the behavior of someone with Alzheimer's disease as "purposefully behaving that way to get to me" versus taking the view that "the behavior is a part of the disease."

◆ A caregiver who is angry at her brother for helping only once a month versus taking the view that "any help, no matter how little, will lighten my load."

◆ A caregiver who puts the situation into a religious or philosophical framework, such as "This is happening because God is angry with me" versus taking the view that "God is giving me an opportunity to learn and grow."

People who are able to reframe difficult situations generally feel less burden and more in control. Feeling a greater degree of

control often leads to acting in control. Clara is a good example.

Clara had difficulty taking breaks from caregiving. Before becoming a caregiver, she had worked in a demanding position and had realized the importance of taking weekends off and vacations to refresh herself and cope better with work demands. When she started to view caregiving as a job, it made a difference in how she viewed breaks in caregiving. They became not only more acceptable, but a necessity.

Julie also found that reframing a difficult situation reduced her stress and helped her act in new ways.

Julie felt resentful and burdened with the increasing demands of caring for her mother. She had no help, feeling that as a good, dutiful daughter she should do it all. A social worker told her about available resources and suggested she think of herself as a personal care manager as a way to find help in caregiving. Julie gained a sense of control over the situation once she realized she didn't have to provide all of the care herself, but could oversee her mother's care.

As a caregiver, you may feel overwhelmed and burned out, especially if you are assuming responsibility for most of the caregiving. Changing your perception of your role from a caregiver to care manager is a way of reframing. As a care manager you still get the job done, but you don't have to provide all the care yourself. The role of care manager means that you:

◆ coordinate and supervise another's care needs. This includes using available support.

- are aware of available community resources.
- plan and prioritize care.
- understand the disease of the care receiver and what to expect.
- participate as an equal partner with other health care professionals.
- are knowledgeable about the health care system.

As a care manager you assume an active role and reach beyond giving hands-on care, to planning and coordinating care and using available resources. You will feel an increased sense of mastery as a successful care manager.

Self-talk. Most stress management courses include learning how to use self-talk to promote health. Self-talk is what we say to ourselves. As Ralph Waldo Emerson said, "A man is what he thinks about all day long."

What do you think about all day long? What do you say to yourself? It's especially important to notice your self-talk when you suffer setbacks and when you feel anxious, angry, discouraged, or distressed. Negative self-talk statements often begin with the following phrases:

- I just can't do…
- If only I could (or didn't) do…
- I could never…
- I shouldn't have done…
- I should have…

Negative self-talk is defeating. It can lead to depression and a sense of failure, because with negative self-talk we tend to focus on:

- what we did not do versus what we have done.
- what we can't do versus what we can do.
- Our mistakes and failures versus our successes.

You want your self-talk to work for you, not against you. If your self-talk is negative or unhelpful, challenge it. Learn to change the negative things you say to yourself into positive statements, such as affirmations.

Affirmations are positive, supportive statements that counteract the effects of negative thinking. When positive statements are repeated several times a day, they begin to replace negative thoughts. This helps to change one's attitude, promote relaxation, and reduce stress. Karen's story is an example of changing negative self-talk to positive self-talk with the use of affirmations:

> Karen felt angry and discouraged when her mother didn't eat the tasty, nutritious meals she prepared for her. She didn't accept the fact that her mother's lack of appetite was caused by the illness. Karen constantly told herself, "No matter what I cook, it is never good enough for mother."

This is an example of negative self-talk. Karen became aware that she often thought she was not doing good enough, especially in caring for her mother. These thoughts made her feel like a failure.

With determination, patience, and practice, you can change your self-talk from negative to positive. The following steps lead to change:

1. Identify your negative thoughts. Listen to what you say to yourself, especially during difficult times.

2. Write your negative thoughts down on paper. This helps to identify and clarify them.

3. Challenge your negative thoughts. Give them a good argument.

4. Write a simple, positive statement for each thought you want to change.

5. Memorize and repeat the chosen statements. This helps establish the habit of positive self-talk.

6. Put your written statements where you see them frequently. This is a helpful visual reminder.

Karen chose the affirmation, "I am preparing nutritious food. That is enough." In fact, the statements, "I am doing my best. It is good enough," became her frequent affirmation and counteracted her negative thoughts of "not doing good enough."

These statements have the dual purpose of affirming what Karen is doing and helping her let go of the idea that she has control over her mother's appetite. Accepting that was important. Telling herself that she is doing her best and it is enough is a positive way of saying she is changing what she can and letting go of what she cannot change. Karen's expectations for herself have become more realistic.

Practice over time will change negative, habitual thinking. Repeat this activity frequently to identify other negative self-talk. Remember, thoughts and attitudes create your reality. Changing your negative thoughts will help you focus on the positive things in your life, rather than on what you don't have.

CHALLENGING YOUR SELF-TALK

Identify an example of your negative self-talk and the situation when it is most likely to occur. Be as clear and as detailed as possible. Write it down.

1. My negative statement:

3. I will replace the negative thought with this positive statement:

2. I say this to myself when:

4. Repeat the chosen affirmation whenever the above situation occurs.

There will be times when you will find it hard to shake off negative thoughts. This is normal. However, paying attention to the frequency and content of these thoughts is the beginning of self-awareness and the possibility of change.

Practicing self-care

To be an effective caregiver you need to maintain your own health and spirit, and to nurture yourself. All too often caregivers put their own needs last. Studies show that sacrificing yourself in giving care to another can lead to emotional exhaustion, depression, and illness.

Maintaining your health and spirit can reduce your level of stress. It is critical to find activities that help you to stay healthy and nurture yourself. These activities are different for each individual. What works for one person may not work for another. You must find stress-reducing methods that work best for you.

We can learn a lot from a self-care program in Florida called "Getting Well." This is a group of people who are supporting each other in learning to live and feel better. They take part in life-affirming activities such as "laughing, juggling, playing, meditating, painting, journal writing, exercising, and eating nutritiously." They demonstrate the necessity of associating with others who help you maintain your spirit and help you feel loved and supported.

To manage stress, it is essential to take breaks from caregiving. Plan them into your schedule, starting immediately, if you have not done so already. Studies show that caregivers often don't take breaks until they are at the "end of their rope" or "burned out."

ARE YOU TAKING CARE OF YOURSELF?

Yes No

☐ ☐ Are you uncomfortable putting yourself first at times?

☐ ☐ Do you think you should always meet the needs of other people before your own?

☐ ☐ Do you feel you should be a "perfect caregiver"?

☐ ☐ Do you minimize or deny that you have needs?

If you answered "yes" to any of these questions, you may be ignoring your own needs.

This serves no one's best interest as your ability to function can be seriously affected. To avoid problems, it is your responsibility to take time off from caregiving to refresh yourself.

It is important to the wellbeing of care receivers that you take breaks. If you don't, they may become increasingly dependent on you. If you take breaks, they will be less isolated and will benefit from having contact with other people. They also need breaks from you. (This is an example of reframing your perception of a situation.)

You are responsible for your own self-care. Practicing self-care means that you:

◆ learn and use stress reduction techniques.

◆ attend to your own health care needs.

◆ get proper rest and nutrition.

◆ exercise regularly.

◆ take time off without feeling guilty.

◆ participate in pleasant, nurturing activities.

◆ reward yourself.

◆ seek and accept the support of others.

◆ seek supportive counseling when you need to, or talk with a trusted counselor, religious advisor, or friend.

◆ identify and acknowledge your feelings.

◆ tell others what you need. Don't assume "they should know."

◆ change the negative ways you view situations.

◆ set goals and prioritize.

Reflect on what it means to practice self-care. Consider the items above. How do you fare? Are you caring for yourself as well as you are caring for another? Remember, it is only when we love and nurture ourselves that we are able to love and nurture another.

As a caregiver, appreciation and "thank yous" for what you do may be lacking. For example, a person with Alzheimer's disease may be unable to show appreciation for what is done. Everyone has a need for approval. It motivates us to keep going. If you don't receive appreciation from other people, find a way to give it to yourself.

What would be helpful for you? Consider the following suggestions:

◆ Acknowledge and take satisfaction in those things you do well.

◆ Reward yourself on a regular basis.

◆ Involve yourself in an activity that will provide positive feedback.

Carol found a creative way to reward herself for a job well done when her mother could no longer express appreciation.

Carol's mother, Irene, had Alzheimer's disease. Irene often expressed frustration and anger at Carol, in spite of the fact that Carol was her mainstay. Carol understood the disease process and successfully avoided taking her mother's attacks personally. To give herself a gift of appreciation, Carol bought flowers regularly. She said, "I considered the flowers a gift from Mom to me. It's something she would have done for me if she were well."

Memories of past generosity and love from her mother sustained Carol. In buying herself flowers she reminded herself weekly that the gift of love and caring she gave to her mother had first been given to her. At a difficult time she found a way to nurture herself.

What are you doing to nurture yourself? Are you choosing healthy activities? Or are you relying on drugs, alcohol, cigarettes, and tranquilizers to handle the emotional and physical burdens of caregiving? According to the National Institute on Drug Abuse, millions of people abuse these drugs to reduce tension and to relax. It is in your best interest to choose healthy, nurturing ways of coping with the difficulties of caregiving.

Getting social support

Caregiving can be a lonely experience. According to the National Family Caregivers Association, caregivers often report that they feel alone and isolated.

Support from family, friends, and others is an important stress buffer. Something as simple as a two-minute telephone call can make you feel cared about and supported. It helps to share your experiences and burdens with a person you trust—a friend, family member, counselor, religious advisor, or support group member—who will listen and understand.

Support groups can be helpful when you're going through a difficult time. Sharing with others who are going through similar experiences is a way to give and receive support, and take time out from caregiving duties. You can learn new ways of coping from others in the group, which may include learning to look at the light side of difficult situations with a bit of humor. Sharing lightens the load. A support group is a place to express thoughts and feelings in a confidential setting. Most important, you learn that you are not alone. This can be a wonderful relief.

Support groups are available for caregivers and for people with various chronic illnesses. Local hospitals and disease-related associations often have groups available.

Using techniques that lower stress

It is of little help to identify your stressors if you don't take action early to reduce them. Recognize obstacles to taking action. These may include:

◆ Not giving yourself permission to take care of yourself.

◆ Lacking awareness of stress-reduction techniques.

◆ Choosing unrealistic stress-reduction techniques for example, those that are too complicated, lengthy, or difficult for you.

◆ Delaying or postponing a stress-reduction activity. For example, planning a break or trip too far into the future to be of help now, when you need it.

Take care of yourself daily. Use "tried and true" stress reduction tools that work for you. In addition, learn and incorporate new stress-reducing techniques into your life. There are many worthwhile techniques available. We offer some quick and easy ones that you can fit into your busy life.

Basic wellness practices. It is vital to maintain your health and wellbeing. Ask yourself the questions in the box below.

Yes	No	
❐	❐	Do you participate in physical activity at least three times a week?
❐	❐	Do you get enough sleep daily so that you feel rested in the morning?
❐	❐	Do you eat balanced, nutritious meals?
❐	❐	Do you take time to sit down and eat your meals?
❐	❐	Do you take care of your own physical health (e.g., get regular medical check-ups and take care of yourself when you are ill)?
❐	❐	Do you participate regularly in recreational/leisure activities?
❐	❐	Do you drink at least eight glasses of water or other liquid daily?
❐	❐	Do you limit alcoholic beverages to no more than two drinks a day? (One drink is 1.5 oz. of hard liquor, 12 oz. of beer, or 4 oz. of wine.)
❐	❐	Do you avoid using alcohol, medications/drugs, or cigarettes to calm your nerves?
❐	❐	Do you maintain a healthy weight?

If you answered "yes" to all of these questions, congratulate yourself. A "no" response reflects areas to work on for better health.

Proper diet, adequate sleep, and regular exercise are necessary for all of us, and even more so when we are caregivers. These lifestyle factors increase our resistance to illness and our ability to cope with stressful situations.

Exercise promotes better sleep, reduces tension and depression, and increases energy and alertness. If finding time to exercise is a problem, try to incorporate it into your usual day. Perhaps the person receiving care can walk or do stretching exercises with you. If necessary, do frequent short exercises instead of using large blocks of time. Find activities you enjoy.

Walking is considered one of the best and easiest exercises. It helps to reduce psychological tension as well as having physical benefits. Walking 20 minutes a day, three times a week, is very beneficial. If you can't be away 20 minutes, 10-minute walks twice a day or even a five-minute walk are beneficial.

Work walking into your life. Walk whenever and wherever you can. Perhaps it is easiest to walk around your block, at the mall, or a nearby park. The next time a friend or family member comes to visit, take time for a short walk. When the care receiver is getting therapy, take a walk around the medical facility.

Breathing for relaxation. Stressful situations or memories of those situations can cause changes in our breathing. Often the more tense we feel, the more shallow our breathing becomes.

Stress management tools usually include a focus on breathing. The following breathing exercise takes only one or two minutes and you can easily do it anywhere. Use it often to lower stress.

> **BREATHING FOR RELAXATION**
> Follow these steps:
> 1. Close your eyes. If that isn't possible, quietly become aware of your breathing.
> 2. Inhale to the count of seven, slowly and deeply. Exhale to the count of seven, slowly and deeply. Exhaling is "letting go."
> 3. Repeat—without forcing your breathing in any way. If your mind becomes distracted, refocus on your breathing.
> 4. Continue for one to two minutes or longer if you want. Notice how relaxed you feel overall.

Meditation. The word "meditation" comes from the Sanskrit word *medha* which, when taken literally, means "doing the wisdom." Meditation aids in relaxation and in achieving physical and mental wellbeing. Meditation is keeping your attention focused in the moment to quiet the mind and hear your body's inner wisdom. You, too, can learn to meditate. See the "Process of Meditation" box on the next page.

> **Meditation**
> *The more faithfully you listen to the voice within you, the better you will hear what is sounding outside.*
> Dag Hammarskjold

Music. Music is another tool for reducing stress. It can alter the body and the mind. It can induce deep relaxation, act as a stimulant, and take you into other states of consciousness. Music is often used specifically for healing and decreasing stress and tension. Use the following steps as a guideline.

1. Choose soothing music you like.
2. Relax and close your eyes.
3. Breathe deeply and easily.
4. Lose yourself in the music, listening with your body, not your mind.
5. After the music is finished, open your eyes and notice how you feel.

Music is a universal language. Listening to music can be healing for both you and the care receiver, either together or alone. People with dementia, especially, respond to music when they may respond to little else.

Humor. Caregivers who maintain and foster their sense of humor do better. It is often hard to find much that is humorous in caregiving, but the secret to succeeding as a caregiver is to find humor in your daily routine. Finding humor does not deny the fact that, at times, your heart is heavy with the pain and sadness of caregiving. Those times will exist, but they can coexist with laughter and humor.

Tears and laughter are closely related. They each offer a release of tension and are often intermingled. Humor does not minimize the seriousness of a situation; rather, it helps you embrace it.

Humor can be a helpful tool in many ways, from making us laugh at our shortcomings and impossible situations, to reducing anxiety and stress. Laughter relaxes and helps calm emotions, allowing us to regain emotional balance and think more clearly. If you want to laugh, or want someone else to laugh, you may have to find a reason, as George and Alma do.

George and Alma watch their favorite comedy show on television every week-night at 7 P.M. They look forward to it and anticipate laughing together. In addition, Alma and George look for humorous car-toons and jokes to share with each other. The fact that Alma has a disabling medical condition doesn't mean they can't appreci-ate laughter.

In his book *Anatomy of an Illness*, Norman Cousins wrote of his fight against a crippling disease. He credited his recovery to the use of laughter. He intentionally sought healing through watching videotapes of comedies, reading joke books, and listening to people tell jokes. He had read about the effects of stress and emotions on illness. He understood that disease was caused by chemical changes in the body, due to the stress of strong emotions such as fear and anger. He concluded that perhaps love, laughter, hope, and the will to live would counteract those effects. He was right in his

PROCESS OF MEDITATION

1. Choose a quiet spot where you will not be disturbed. Ten to 20 minutes should suffice.

2. Sit in a comfortable position.

3. Close your eyes to better concentrate.

4. Relax your body by tightening, then relaxing, each of your major muscles from head to toe. This need not take long, only a minute or two.

5. Be aware of your breathing without trying to change it. Your breathing may get slower as meditation proceeds, because of relaxation and your body's metabolism slowing down. Breathe naturally in and out.

6. If you like, choose a word for focus. This is sometimes called a mantra. It can be any word or words that mean something to you. Many people find that words like "love," "let go," and "peace" work well. Others may use a phrase from a favorite prayer. Repeat the chosen word or phrase silently with your breathing, on the in and out breaths. One

caregiver's focus words are "I," on the in breath and "AM," on the out breath, "I AM." Together the breathing and words anchor the mind.

7. Don't judge your performance or wonder how you are doing. You will have distracting thoughts which you can let go of by return-ing to awareness of your breathing and focus. With repetition, awareness will continue to develop and carry over into the rest of your life, inducing a peaceful state of mind.

8. Practice a minimum of once a day for 10 to 20 minutes. Twice a day is even better. The best times to meditate are often in the early morning, after exercise and a shower but before breakfast, or before dinner. Since meditation is an exercise in concentration, avoid meditating when you're tired or you might fall asleep. However, if you have difficulty falling asleep at night, meditate while lying down to facilitate relaxation and sleep.

belief. Recent studies show that laughter helps to stimulate breathing, muscular activity, and heart rate. This serves to reduce stress and strengthen the immune system.

Humor is important to health. It lifts the spirit and provides a way to connect with others. The following suggestions can help you make laughter and humor a larger part of your life:

◆ Seek out humor. Humorous tapes and books can be found at video stores and libraries. Spend time with friends or family members you enjoy and can laugh with.

◆ Surround yourself with humor. Put jokes, cartoons, funny pictures, and humorous sayings on the refrigerator or bulletin board where others can enjoy them with you.

◆ Laugh at yourself. Don't take yourself too seriously. Poke fun at yourself by making light of your shortcomings (which we all have).

Developing action plans

Action plans are tools for change. They can be a useful way to identify and plan specific activities for reducing stress and making change. Feelings of accomplishment are necessary for thriving as a caregiver. Action plans can help you achieve these feelings. Even the smallest action can make a big difference. This was true for Evelyn.

Evelyn needed more time for herself during the day. She made a plan to take a leisurely, warm tub bath four times a week instead of the always-hurried shower. Evelyn settled her father to watch the 5 o'clock news on television on the days she took her baths. This worked well for both of them and became an accepted part of their routine. Accomplishing the action plan encouraged Evelyn to make other action plans that made a big difference to her.

See pages 7–9 for more information on action plans.

Feelings of mastery and confidence are usually the result of developing new ways of coping. Use the information presented in this chapter to help you identify your stressors, and improve coping skills. The activity in the box on the next page can be a useful tool for managing stress.

This activity can be useful on a regular basis. It will help you assess and cope with current stressors. Since your caregiving situation and stressors continually change, it is important to be aware of when you feel stress and to use stress-reducing tools that work for you. Most important, build stress reduction and nurturing activities into your daily life to prevent distress. Be proactive. And remember, what is good for you is good for the person receiving care!

Finding hope and meaning

The ability to find hope and meaning in the caregiving situation enables you not only to survive, but to thrive. Finding meaning and hope are what keeps us going. It is a way to make sense of our circumstances.

In his book *Man's Search For Meaning,* Dr. Viktor Frankl, author-psychiatrist, tells of his experience as a long-time prisoner in a prisoner of war camp during World War II. Many of his family members died in the camps. In spite of the fact that he faced death constantly and suffered severe

---

REFRAMING YOUR STRESS

Make a list of those things that you find most difficult or stressful. Be specific. Write at least two (more if you can).
1.

2.

Answer the following questions in relation to each item on your list.
Can I ignore this? Or can I let it go?
1.

2.

Can I change anything about this? If so, how can I change it?
1.

2.

If it can't be changed, can I change my perception of it? If so, how? What is a more helpful perception?
1.

2.

Select one stressor from your list to work on first. The stressor is:

Develop an action plan for addressing this stressor. Be specific and realistic. (See pages 7–9 for more information.)

punishment, Dr. Frankl was able to find meaning and hope in his life. He noted that the prisoners who were able to sustain even a flicker of hope were better able to survive the terrible circumstances than those who felt hopeless. He concluded that what did remain, when all else was taken away, was "the last of the human freedoms," the ability to "choose one's attitude in a given set of circumstances." Out of that experience, Frankl's guiding philosophy was born: "To live is to suffer, to survive is to find meaning in the suffering." He also believed that man's need for meaning is universal.

The need to find hope and meaning is also important when you are a caregiver for a person with a chronic illness. Uncertainty, loss, and suffering may shake your foundation. After all, you have much at stake. Your world, as you have known it, has changed drastically and you may be left with questions such as, "Why me?" and perhaps, "Where is God?" Questioning often leads to a search for meaning. No one else can tell you what the meaning is for you. It can be a lonely journey.

> A sense of hope is knowing that your present moment has meaning.
>
> Robert Randall

A search for meaning can be a conscious choice. There are ways to stimulate your search. The following can be helpful:

1. **Ask yourself questions like, what am I to learn from this?** What good can come from this? Am I a better person now? These types of questions can help you open up to possibilities for finding meaning.

2. **Reflect.** Periods of quiet reflection, especially after a difficult time, are important and offer opportunities to learn from the experience.

3. **Talk with a trusted person.** Whether this person is a counselor, religious advisor, or friend, sharing can help clarify your thoughts and feelings. As you tell your story, it often takes on meaning.

4. **Write.** This is also a way to clarify your thinking. Writing is a way to bring out your thoughts and feelings. Write freely and spontaneously. Don't concern yourself with proper sentence structure or punctuation. Writing is a way to talk to yourself.

   Re-reading your journal over time provides an understanding of where you were when you started and where you are now. You will probably see changes and find new understanding and meaning.

5. **Seek spiritual renewal.** This is especially important when you are facing difficult times. Many caregivers report that faith and prayer help them find comfort, purpose, and meaning. It may be that even when you feel anger because of suffering and sorrow, your need for meaning is greatest.

Like Frankl, it is hopeful to believe that meaning can be found in difficult and painful experiences. Hope and meaning play a large part in the following story of Margaret and Tim.

Tim's frequent visits to his elderly mother, Margaret, in the nursing home, were meaningful to him. Years ago, when Margaret was healthy, she shared some of her beliefs with Tim. She had told him, "If there comes a time when I am not able to recognize you because of Alzheimer's disease, or for any other reason, I want you

to know what I believe to be true. I believe that my true essence, my spirit, will always be present, even though my physical body and mind may not be the person you remember. Please know that I am with you. We may not be able to talk with each other as we did in the past, but if you play my favorite music, read poetry, hold my hand, or just be with me, I will feel your love and you will feel mine for you."

In sharing her beliefs, Margaret gave Tim the gift of finding meaning in what can be a most difficult and challenging situation. Meaning is all around us. It is the "stuff" of life. Meaning is personal. It is up to each person to find his or her own meaning.

SUMMARY

Are you better acquainted with your stress? Have you identified what you can do to reduce at least one stressor? Do you realize the potential strength in considering your needs and in practicing self-care? Can you find meaning in difficult experiences? Have you learned that often the compassion and care you give to another comes back to you as a gift of meaning?

Remember that your response to a situation will affect the situation itself. As much as possible, make it be what you want it to be. Reflect again on the words of Virginia Satir:

> *Life is not the way it's supposed to be.*
> *It's the way it is. The way you cope*
> *with it is what makes the difference…*
> *I think if I have one message, one thing*
> *before I die that most of the world*
> *would know, it would be that the event does*
> *not determine how to respond to the event.*
> *That is a purely personal matter.*
> *The way in which we respond will*
> *direct and influence the event more*
> *than the event itself.*

Overview

Chapter Three

Listening: the Heart of Communication
Barriers to Being a Good Listener
Setting the Stage to Listen
How the Best Listeners Listen

Expressing Yourself Effectively
How to Best Express Yourself
"I" Messages: The Backbone of
Expressing Yourself Effectively

Assertive Style of Communication
"I" Statements and Assertiveness
The Four Steps of Assertiveness
Limits to Assertiveness
Timing and Letting Go

Aikido Style of Communication
Getting Started
Other Purposes for Alignment
Reaching People Who Are Hard to Reach

Communicating Effectively with Others

Many caregivers say that a lack of communication is the underlying problem in misunderstandings and poor relationships with family members, friends, and health care professionals. It doesn't have to be this way. Although we cannot cure chronic illness, we can do something about how effectively we communicate with others.

> *The greatest problem in communication is the illusion that it has been accomplished.*
>
> George Bernard Shaw

Good communication skills are critical in caregiving. Over the course of long-term illness we must rely on our communication skills to obtain and share information, to adapt to change, to ask for what we need, and to stay connected to others. Our effectiveness as communicators depends on:

- ◆ how well we listen and what we think and feel.
- ◆ how we come across to others.
- ◆ what we choose not to say.
- ◆ whether others feel we respect their rights and feelings.

This chapter will review tools to enhance the communication process. It will discuss listening skills, positive ways to express yourself using "I" statements, and two communication styles—assertiveness and Aikido.

LISTENING: THE HEART OF COMMUNICATION

Effective listening skills are more important than many of us realize. In her book *Communicate With Confidence* Dianna Booher claims that mindful listening is important because it keeps us "informed, up-to-date, and out of trouble." Also, how well we listen is an important sign we care.

> *One of the best ways to persuade others is with your ears— by listening to them.*
>
> Dean Rusk

To be good listeners we need more than just ears. If ears were all that we needed, then we would only need feet to run the Boston Marathon. Good listeners also have an open mind—they respect differences of opinion, and they try to understand the perspectives and feelings of the other person.

The challenge of being a good listener is greater if you provide care. Fatigue may be a problem. Worry is another. At times your worries might completely occupy your thoughts; you may hear people speaking to you without actually listening to a word they say. This unintentionally sends the message that you don't care enough to listen.

Barriers to Being a Good Listener

Marge stood in front of us and introduced herself and her husband. We were all part of a tour group. We were gathered at a meeting to get acquainted. In a kind but serious manner, she gave us a short lesson about listening. She said:

My name is Marge and this is my husband, Norm. I have his permission to talk to you tonight. My husband had a stroke a year ago and because of it he has some trouble communicating. He understands what you say to him but he has difficulty speaking. Because of this, I would like to ask two very special favors of you.

Please give Norm an extra ounce of attention when he talks to you. You may be able to pick up clues from his gestures and the expressions on his face that will help you understand. It is so much less stressful for him when he doesn't have to struggle to be heard. Also, if he feels listening to him is too difficult for you, he won't join in the fun. Norm needs extra time to respond to you because it takes him a while to put his thoughts into words. If you would give him a little extra attention and time, it will mean more to both of us than I can say. Thank you for listening.

We were touched and we were educated. Without her words, we wouldn't have realized that we, not Norm's stroke, would be his biggest barrier to being heard, to taking part, to feeling important enough for people to listen to him.

A good place to start working on listening skills is to figure out why we may not listen sometimes. Our preconceived ideas about strokes might have been our reason for not listening to Norm. In addition to preconceived ideas, fatigue, and worry, other personal and environmental barriers can interfere with listening.

Personal listening barriers

We all have personal listening barriers we bring to every conversation with another person. These barriers change depending on the situation and the people involved. They include:

◆ personal needs

◆ emotions and moods

◆ attitudes

Personal needs. Our personal needs play a huge role in how well we listen. Anything we need at a given time (food, rest, peace of mind) can reduce our ability to listen. For instance, to meet our need for peace of mind, many of us develop ways to tune out whatever is bothersome to us and unwelcome news.

Tuning out allows us to hear only what we want to hear; it saves mental energy, helps us concentrate, and protects us from problems we can't face yet. Tuning out may help us ignore the repetitive questions of a family member who is memory-impaired. In other words, it works. After a while we may tune out even when listening is important. We have to make an effort to catch ourselves *tuning out* and to concentrate on paying attention.

Emotions and moods. Living with chronic illness means you sometimes feel strong emotions. These may include feelings of anger, sadness, or "down in the dumps." You may be in no mood to listen. If you can't listen because of your mood, postpone your conversation to a time when you're in a better frame of mind.

Attitudes. Your attitudes and beliefs about a person's behavior, motives, age, race, religion, appearance, education, and lifestyle play a large role in whether you listen with an open or a closed mind. You can change an unfavorable attitude by changing the way you look at a person or situation. In the following story, think about how a different view of a care receiver's behavior would affect a caregiver's attitude.

Sally was convinced Roger was eating his mashed potatoes with his hands just to get on her nerves. Then she remembered what Lena said at an Alzheimer's support group meeting:

"When my husband starts annoying me, I try to change the way I think about him. Instead of thinking he's just trying to 'get my goat,' I look at him and say to myself, 'He has forgotten his memory of good manners and he's doing the best he can.' My whole attitude toward him changes when I do this."

Being a good listener does not mean abandoning your values and beliefs. Rather, it means being aware of how they affect how well you listen.

Identify someone you have trouble listening to. Check the statement below that most closely describes your personal listening barrier or add your own barriers.

I find it difficult to listen because this person:

❒ has a different education level than me.

❒ smokes or drinks.

❒ is offensive to me because of his or her appearance.

❒ has different religious beliefs than mine.

❒ always seems to say the same thing.

❒ is like _____, whom I don't respect.

❒ _____

❒ _____

Sensory barriers

We need to be aware of and correct changes in our own vision and hearing that interfere with our ability to listen. Adequate lighting and quieter surroundings, perhaps a hearing aid or glasses, can make it easier for others to communicate with us.

Environmental barriers

Activities and noise can disrupt our ability to listen and the speaker's ability to focus. Remember, the other person may be bothered by noise and activity you don't notice anymore. As you read the list in the box below, check off the distractions that apply to your surroundings. Add your ideas to the list.

You may have no control over some distracting noises and activities. However, reducing the ones you can control will improve your effectiveness as a listener.

Environmental distractions that affect my ability to listen:

❒ Outside noise, ranging from barking dogs to power mowers, trains, cars, and wind chimes

❒ Background music, radio, or TV that is either too loud or barely audible

❒ Household noises, from electrical appliances to ticking clocks

❒ Interruptions from ringing telephones or people coming and going or needing attention

❒ Poorly lighted rooms

❒ A room that is too warm or too cold

❒ Uncomfortable or overly comfortable seating

❒ Mouth-watering cooking smells or unpleasant odors

❒ Pets and small children in the room

❒ _____

❒ _____

Setting the Stage to Listen

With listening barriers noted, there are still some listening challenges to overcome. One challenge is listening with an open mind to opposing opinions about emotional issues. The following suggestions will help you meet this challenge.

Prepare yourself

In a highly emotional situation, it can seem impossible to listen objectively. However, you can prepare yourself by asking, "What if…?" and thinking about how you would respond. For example, "What if Dad refuses to give up the car keys?" Feeling prepared reduces anxiety and increases your ability to listen. It also helps to be at your physical best, rested and fed.

Help others prepare for an exchange with you

Prepare people in advance for a discussion with you. For example, tell them, "I want to hear your point of view about…." Advance notice gives people time to think things over. It's crucial to planning and decision-making. People who feel prepared and who believe they will be heard are more likely to participate in making caregiving plans and decisions.

Create an atmosphere of trust and confidentiality

Some people won't speak openly until they are assured, in advance, that you won't reject them or get angry over differences of opinion. They must hear you say something like, "I won't get mad, and I will keep our discussion just between us."

Building trusting relationships is a gradual process. People need time to confirm that it's safe to speak openly, especially if this hasn't been true in the past. Ruth will vouch for this.

> When they were children, Ruth, being the oldest, bullied her younger sister, Cynthia. Even as adults Ruth let little secrets "slip out" that embarrassed her sister. Now their mother is ill and Ruth needs her sister's help. She knows she has to earn her sister's trust if they are going to work together to provide care for their mother.
>
> Ruth called Cynthia to arrange a time to discuss their mother's memory problems. She said, "I would like to hear your ideas about Mom and what you think we should be doing to help. I'll come to your place if it's okay. When would be a good time for you?" Cynthia agreed to meet. However, she suspected her sister had already reached a decision and the meeting was simply to divide up the tasks.

Ruth set the stage. She knew Cynthia felt intimidated by her so she arranged to meet where Cynthia felt strongest, in her own home. She told Cynthia her intentions in advance so Cynthia could prepare her thoughts. Ruth said, "I want to hear your ideas…" to reassure Cynthia that she was coming to listen. Ruth recognized it would take time for Cynthia to trust her.

If people feel apprehensive about speaking honestly, chances are they won't reveal why they feel that way. We have to assume their trust must be won by listening to them with an open mind. If you wanted to reassure someone they could speak openly with you, what would you say?

How the Best Listeners Listen

Ellen considered herself a good listener. She said proudly, "People just seem to open up to me." She considered her listening skills a matter of being polite. Actually, people talked to Ellen about their personal matters because she listened without judging, interrupting, or arguing, and she never betrayed a confidence.

Ellen was a skillful listener because she knew how to make people comfortable. People talked to her because they felt she cared and they trusted her. Ellen also knew how to end a conversation without "cutting people off." She knew if they felt "cut off" they wouldn't reach out to her again.

Although each situation varies, you will be a better listener if you do the following:

◆ Give the speaker your full attention

◆ Encourage people to speak

◆ Confirm what the person said

◆ Acknowledge spoken and unspoken feelings

◆ Fit your voice, tone, and mood to that of the person speaking

- Use the words the speaker uses
- Make certain all concerns have been heard
- Be aware of disclaimers

Give the speaker your full attention

Attentive listeners act interested. They stop what they are doing and reduce distractions. They use good eye contact. They don't read the paper or walk away with the comment, "Go on, I'm listening."

Encourage people to speak

Sometimes people are reluctant to speak, especially about sensitive issues. Signals like nodding, maintaining gentle eye contact, and making short comments like "I see," "really," "um-hum," or "how interesting," are cues that encourage people to share with you. Comments like these are especially helpful during telephone conversations.

Confirm what the person said

Confirming what you heard eliminates guessing, making incorrect assumptions, and jumping to conclusions. Two ways to make certain you understand the speaker's meaning are (1) asking open-ended questions and (2) paraphrasing.

Open-ended questions. The purpose of the open-ended question is to check out your understanding of the speaker's feelings or to request more information to improve your understanding. The other person is not limited to a one-word answer such as "yes" or "no." The open-ended question encourages people to talk about their thoughts, feelings, fears, and concerns and it gives them control over how much they want to say. The following are examples of open-ended questions:

- "I am not sure I understand. Could you tell me more about your situation to make it clearer to me?"
- "Would you give me an example?"
- "Could you tell me more about how you feel about this?"

Paraphrasing. If you feel you have missed the point, you can check whether you have understood by paraphrasing. To paraphrase, you restate what the speaker said using your own words. Paraphrasing shows the speaker you are listening and lets the speaker know if you need further explanation. It also helps you focus on the important parts of a conversation, particularly when the speaker tends to ramble.

You can paraphrase on different levels: words, feelings, and hinted words and hinted feelings. The following are suggested ways to paraphrase (reflect) on these levels:

- "So, as you see it…."
- "Let me make sure I understand. Are you saying that…?"
- "So, to sum this up, is it that you feel…?"
- "Do you mean that…?"

Acknowledge spoken and unspoken feelings

Problems related to changing care needs are usually emotionally laden. Tone of voice and how loudly, softly, quickly, or slowly a person speaks often reveal his true feelings. If you reflect the person's feelings with statements like, "Are you feeling…," you communicate understanding, acknowledgment, and acceptance. Once you deal with a person's emotions it is then easier to discuss the facts and details of a problem.

Fit your voice, tone, and mood to that of the person speaking

This sends an indirect message that you are "in sync" with him. For instance, if the person is sad and talking in hushed tones, reflect his mood by being serious and quiet-spoken.

Fitting the mood doesn't mean matching it. Fitting means using an appropriate response to convey understanding. This means you wouldn't match anger with anger nor would you laugh at an angry person. Because anger is a serious emotion, your mood should be serious. There are times when you can use humor to lighten a conversation, but be careful that it doesn't demean the person, situation or someone's feelings.

Use words the speaker uses

Using the same language as the speaker tells the person you hear, understand, and respect his words. If the person uses "down in the dumps" to describe feeling sad or depressed, you should do so to.

Make certain all concerns have been heard

The sensitive nature of many caregiving problems may prevent them from being raised and resolved. You can try to bring these issues out in the open by asking, "What troubles you that we haven't touched on?"

Be aware of disclaimers

Listen for words such as "may," "might," "perhaps," "maybe," "probably," "ordinarily," "usually," and "I'll try." These words are disclaimers, and are like the "small print" of a contract. Be sure you understand them. When you hear disclaimers, especially during discussions with health care professionals, ask for explanations. For example, ask: "What do you mean by 'the treatment may help'?"

Listen for other qualifiers that imply that the word "but" belongs at the end of the sentence. Notice how the implied word "but" changes the meaning of the following sentence. "For the most part, the diagnosis is correct, (but)...." When someone uses qualifiers, politely repeat the important words in a question: "What do you mean by 'for the most part'?" Other "qualified" sentences begin with "of course," "essentially," "basically," "all in all," and "most."

Good listening tools include keeping an open mind, reducing listening barriers, creating a safe haven for openness, using appropriate eye contact, confirming what you hear, and giving your undivided attention. Listening well is at the heart of good communication and it takes conscious effort.

To become a more effective listener, apply "The Golden Rule of Listening." It says, "Listen to others as you would have them listen to you." If you do this, your listening effectiveness will take a giant leap forward.

> **Listening in a nutshell**
> Listen as you want others to listen to you.

EXPRESSING YOURSELF EFFECTIVELY

Communication is a two-way street. It involves both listening carefully and expressing yourself clearly. Caregiving offers enough challenges without having to struggle to be heard and understood. Often the words we choose to say—or choose not to say—can have a major impact on our relationships.

> *Please fill my mouth with worthwhile stuff and nudge me when I've said enough.*
>
> H. H. Brackenridge

For many caregivers, a big hurdle is getting needed information from health care providers and help from family members. Some caregivers are afraid they may lose valuable support from friends and family if they ask for help or set limits. They don't want to risk upsetting and losing the people they love and need. As you read the following statements, check the box that reflects how you feel at times.

Yes	No	
❐	❐	I hesitate to ask for help for fear of being a burden and risk losing the help I do receive.
❐	❐	I shouldn't have to ask for help. People should see what I need and offer to help.
❐	❐	I rarely set limits because I feel guilty saying no.
❐	❐	I feel like I'm letting people down and disappointing them.
❐	❐	I rarely express feelings such as anger or frustration because I don't want people to think less of me.

If you answered "yes" to any of these statements, you have plenty of company. Speaking up is a daunting task for many of us; sometimes it may seem easier or safer to say nothing. But eventually issues need attention and decisions must be made.

How to Best Express Yourself

Learning to express ourselves more effectively takes time and practice. Sometimes we have to unlearn old habits. The best way to begin is by practicing the following tools for expressing yourself.

1. Use "I" messages.
2. Respect the rights or feelings of other people by what you say or do.
3. Be clear and specific.
4. Speak directly to the person(s) involved.
5. Be a good listener.

If you keep these tools in mind and use a positive speaking style, people are more likely to listen to you. They will better understand what you are saying, how you are feeling, and what you need. Next we will discuss the importance of using "I" statements and positive styles of communication.

"I" Messages: The Backbone of Expressing Yourself Effectively

Bill is 75 years old. He has been a caregiver to his wife, Mary, since she was diagnosed with Parkinson's disease years ago. Several weeks ago Mary fell and broke her hip. In addition to the in-home nursing services Mary receives, Bill hired a housekeeper to help him with housework and cooking. Ellen, his daughter, has dropped by for a visit, but Bill doesn't have much to say to her.

Ellen: "What's wrong Dad? Why are you so quiet?"

Bill: "Nothing's wrong. Everything is just fine."

Ellen: "From your tone of voice, I have a feeling you're upset about something? Is it something I did?"

Bill: "No, it's something you didn't do."

Ellen: "What didn't I do? "

Bill: "If you really cared you would know. You didn't bother to look around here and see what you could do to lend a hand when your mother came home from the hospital. I had to hire a stranger to help me with the housework. Apparently, you can't even pick up a few groceries for us."

Ellen: "Not that it matters to you, Dad, but I have a family and a job. I barely have time to clean my own house."

You can see where this conversation is headed. Upset and tired, Bill indirectly accused Ellen of not caring. He also expected her to read his mind. His words put his daughter on the defensive because they contained "you" messages: "If you really cared you would know…," "You didn't bother…."

When people hear "you" statements they feel attacked; they either fight back or withdraw in silence from the situation. "You" messages also tend to increase anger and frustration in a situation. Ellen felt attacked and fought back with her own "you" messages.

Relationships face many tests during the course of chronic illness. Knowing this, some caregivers hesitate to ask for help or express their feelings. They fear getting too emotional and "opening the flood gates." Others feel that when they speak up, their frankness creates hard feelings. What they said was heard as blaming and they aren't sure why. If they had voiced their concerns by using "I" statements, they would have greatly increased their chances of being heard.

"I" statements: A powerful communication tool

Speaking for yourself from the "I" position is one of your most effective communication tools. With "I" statements, you take ownership for your feelings, thoughts, and concerns. By saying "I feel…," "I need…," "I am frustrated…," or "I am worried about…" you are expressing your own feelings, motives, and needs. You are not blaming someone else for the way you feel.

How might you feel about or respond to the following "you" messages versus the "I" messages?

"You" message: "Apparently, you can't even pick up a few groceries for us."

"I" message: "I have a short list of groceries we need. I wonder if you could pick them up the next time you go grocery shopping?"

"You" message: "You didn't call back yesterday. You made me wait all day to hear from you."

"I" message: "I was hoping to hear from you yesterday, Doctor."

Like any new skill, "I" messages take practice. The trick is to catch a "you" statement before you say it. You can begin by simply taking the "OOPS challenge."

Every time you are about to say "you," think OOPs, and take a moment to change the "you" to "I." Then, in a matter-of-fact manner, say what is on your mind. Take the "OOPS challenge" for a week or so and you'll notice a difference in how people respond.

Watch out for hidden "you" statements

Sometimes "I" statements carry a blaming tone because they contain hidden "you" messages. They are not true "I" statements because they are subtle accusations. "I" is usually followed by the words "when you" in a sentence. You can sense the implied blame in the following statement:

Hidden "you" message: "I feel badly when you treat Mother like a child."

"You" message: "You treat Mother like a child."

"I" message: "I feel badly because I think Mother feels like she's being treated like a child."

Other uses for "I" statements

Besides expressing feelings and needs, "I" statements can be used to raise concerns, return problems to the person who raised them, and to state your intentions. They also are an effective way to express positive feelings and compliments. For instance:

◆ Raise a concern: "I am concerned about your living alone."

◆ Return a problem to the person who raised it: "I need to know how you will deal with this."

◆ State your intentions: "I want to work this out with you. I'm here to learn, not to criticize."

◆ Express praise and appreciation: "I really like the way you fixed Mom's hair."

Changing "You" to "I" statements

Consider the following examples. How would you change them into "I" statements?

Stating feelings: "I know it doesn't matter to you, but I get depressed."

_____

_____

Stating needs and desires: "You always give me advice, but you never help me take care of Mom."

_____

_____

Stating expectations: "You're always late picking up Dad, and you worry him. You should be on time."

_____

_____

Take a moment to re-read the statements. Do you feel any different with the "I" messages you have written versus the "you" messages? Look over your "I" messages. Are there any hidden "you" messages in them?

Speaking for yourself from the "I" position increases the chances people will hear you out. When done correctly, "I" messages come across as "speaking from the heart." They make it more difficult for people to argue with your feelings and perceptions, and they leave room for others to express their point of view and to use their own "I" statements.

If your "I" messages don't seem to work at first, keep trying. People who are used to

hearing "you" messages may automatically hear them for awhile. Eventually, your "I" messages will make a positive difference and you will be heard.

Remember: The purpose of "I" messages is to express your personal needs, feelings, and concerns in a positive way. It is not to get others to do what you want them to do. When "I" messages are used as a means to manipulate another person, problems can get worse.

The ability to communicate effectively is a powerful caregiving tool. It helps you build and maintain supportive networks of family, friends, and health care professionals. Positive communication skills also allow others, such as the care receiver, to express needs and wishes that differ from your own. This give-and-take philosophy strengthens caregiving relationships and reduces stress caused by unresolved misunderstandings. Two effective communication styles are assertiveness and Aikido.

ASSERTIVE STYLE OF COMMUNICATION

Some caregivers hope and hint rather than ask for help or set limits. They hope that people will anticipate what they want and need. It is unrealistic to expect others to know how we feel or what we want. To avoid feeling hurt and to be fair to others, we have to communicate directly.

Assertiveness is a specific, direct communication tool for expressing ourselves. The goal of assertiveness is honest, open communication. Being assertive means that you:

◆ express your thoughts and feelings honestly and fairly.

◆ respect the rights and feelings of others, including their right to be assertive.

◆ listen attentively and validate what you are hearing.

Assertive communication is used to settle problems, not to win contests.

Assertiveness is not a form of aggression. People who are aggressive do express their feelings, wishes, and thoughts, but they do so at the expense of another person's rights and feelings. They often verbally attack, intimidate, raise their voice, use sarcasm, or put down someone else to get what they want. Statements often begin with "you" and contain absolutes such as "always" and "never."

To use assertiveness effectively, you may have to erase a few lessons you learned as a child, such as "children are seen and not heard." Or perhaps you were told that standing up for yourself was rude and asking for things was selfish. As an adult you have to speak up or lose control by default. Your responses to the following statements can help you decide if you need to work on being more assertive.

Yes	No	
☐	☐	I sometimes look back and wished I'd expressed myself more strongly.
☐	☐	I tend to brood about something a person said rather than talk about it.
☐	☐	I sometimes blame others for my feelings.
☐	☐	I have trouble setting limits.
☐	☐	I can't prevent situations in which people take advantage of me.
☐	☐	I rarely get all the information I need from the doctor.
☐	☐	I tend to accuse others when I criticize.
☐	☐	I sometimes regret something I said.
☐	☐	I often find it difficult to disagree without getting upset.
☐	☐	I have trouble asking for help.

Your responses to these statements will help you decide if you need to work on being more assertive. If you answered "yes" to any of these questions, assertiveness will help you express yourself more effectively.

"I" statements and assertiveness

"I" statements are the foundation of assertiveness. Using "I" says, "These are my feelings, needs, and motives; I own them." "I am…," "I feel…," "I need…," "I will…," and "I expect…" clarify where you stand

and what you want. At the same time you respect the rights of others to disagree and to express themselves. Being assertive means:

◆ you are clear, direct, and fair.

◆ there is no mind-reading or second-guessing.

◆ you do not blame or accuse others.

The Four Steps of Assertiveness

In her book *Assert Yourself*, Sharon Bower breaks down assertiveness into four manageable steps. She calls them DESC for describe, express, specify, and consequences. It's important to do them in the following order.

1. DESCRIBE: Use "I" statements to describe an observable behavior or problem. Describe what happened or what is bothering you without emotion, evaluation, or exaggeration (as if you were giving a report).

Example: "I received a call from Dad's doctor yesterday. He missed his appointment. I'm wondering what happened."

2. EXPRESS: Using an "I" statement, express how you feel. Identify your feelings without blaming the other person for making you feel that way. ("I feel _____ about what happened.")

Example: "I am concerned Dad won't make the appointment that has been rescheduled for next Thursday."

3. SPECIFY: Using an "I" statement, tell the other person specifically what needs to happen or what needs to be done.

"I want/need _____."

Example: "I need to know if you can pick Dad up and take him to the doctor next Thursday morning. He has to be there by 10 a.m."

4. CONSEQUENCES: Close with an "I" statement explaining the consequences of the behavior. The consequences include what you will do or what will happen if the person doesn't follow through. Avoid blaming, bluffing, or threatening. The consequences also can include what you will do or what will happen if the person does follow through.

The use of the word "consequence" may seem negative. But consequences are the result of an action or condition and can be positive and rewarding. ("Because of _____, this happened or will happen.")

Example: "I'll be glad to take Dad to his appointment next time if I can count on you to take Dad to his appointment this week."

Example: "If you cannot take Dad to his appointment, he will have to pay for a cab. This will put a strain on his budget."

Example: "If you can't take Dad, please make other arrangements for his transportation."

Give it a try. How would you change the following statements to assertive responses?

Describe: "Everybody says they'll help but nobody does."

Describe: _____

_____

_____

Example: "I would like the family to meet so we can divide up the housekeeping and transportation responsibilities."

Express: "Nobody knows what it's like to be the only one responsible for the folks."

Express: _____

_____

_____

Example: "I feel totally responsible for the folks being able to live at home."

Specify: "Any help is better than nothing."

Specify: _____

_____

_____

Example: "I'm concerned about the handrail on the porch at the folks' place. I'm afraid it will give way. Will you help me see that it gets fixed?"

Consequences: "The folks may have to move into a care facility because nobody else helps them and I can't do it all anymore."

Consequences: _____

_____

_____

Example: "I can't provide all the help the folks need to stay in their own home. I would be able to continue with some help."

Limits to assertiveness

Like all things, assertiveness has its limits. It won't change other people and it doesn't guarantee happiness or fair treatment. There are times when the assertive style is not appropriate, for example, when the other person:

◆ is already trying to do what you want.

◆ is unstable medically or emotionally.

◆ has the power to penalize you or cause you harm.

Timing and letting go

Someone said "timing is everything." Dealing with issues and problems in a "timely" manner means that what we say is appropriate and beneficial. For instance, we correct an in-home helper as soon as we can do so privately, not a month later or when other people are present.

Knowing when to say nothing and let go of an issue is also important. After considering the situation and the consequences, you might decide to drop the matter if:

◆ your personal safety is in jeopardy.

◆ you are wrong.

◆ the issue is much more important to the other person than to you.

◆ the outcome would unnecessarily hurt someone.

◆ maintaining harmony is more important than solving the problem.

◆ the situation is temporary.

◆ you don't have time to deal with the consequences of pursuing the issue.

During times of conflict we can lose sight of what we have in common. Sometimes letting go may be in our best interest because it helps us reach common goals. Being flexible and deciding to let go of an issue, when letting go makes sense, doesn't weaken effectiveness; it strengthens it. Remember, assertiveness is about settling problems, not winning disputes.

You may find situations where you feel uncomfortable being assertive. If so, there is another positive, less direct style you can use to express yourself effectively. It is called the Aikido or alignment style.

Assertiveness in a nutshell

◆ Use "I" statements.

◆ Apply the tools for best expressing yourself.

◆ Follow the DESC steps.

◆ Use assertiveness with the knowledge of its limits.

AIKIDO STYLE OF COMMUNICATION

The Aikido style of communication is patterned after the principles of the Aikido School of Marshal Arts. These principles state that instead of fighting with another person, you try to move with the person's energy. This is called alignment, and it is the key to the practice of Aikido.

The Aikido style of expressing yourself is disarming and somewhat less direct. It is a particularly effective tool when emotions are running high. Many caregiving issues involve strong feelings and differences of opinion. In an emotionally charged situation you may find "you" blaming messages directed at you. These can be very hard to hear.

Your gut response may be to fight back or withdraw from the situation. Neither of these responses will solve the problem. Using the Aikido style of communication helps neutralize the attack so you can redirect the conversation to the problem and look at ways to solve it.

Aikido regards anyone who behaves aggressively as "not balanced." Based on this belief, the Aikido style involves recognizing and understanding the other person's needs or motives. The goal in using Aikido is to help the person regain balance by meeting some of his needs. You use your energy to look at the situation from his perspective, not to fight back or give in. You try to help the other person feel heard so he has no more reason to argue or resist.

Aikido focuses on building harmony. It has two goals:

◆ Maintain your own peace by not giving in to emotion.

◆ Help the other person maintain his equilibrium and peace.

Getting started

To use the Aikido style, follow these steps.
1. Align.
2. Agree; find areas of common ground.
3. Redirect energies.
4. Resolve problems.

Align

To align with a person you "put yourself in his place." It is the same as empathizing with the person to build rapport with him. You have to try to relax and stay physically and emotionally balanced. This is not easy in situations involving strong emotions. However, staying in control is necessary because you need to pay close attention to what is being said and done around you. (The deep breathing and relaxation exercises in Chapter 2 will help you do this.)

When you feel relaxed, put yourself in the Aikido frame of mind by asking these questions:

◆ How would I feel in this person's place?

◆ What does this person need from me to feel better? Does the person need understanding? sympathy? praise? recognition? control?

The following statements are suggestions to help you develop aligning statements that fit your style and situation:

◆ "If I could do one thing to help you feel better, what would that be?"

◆ "I don't know exactly what you need. I need an example of something I can do."

◆ "I want to understand your point of view about_____."

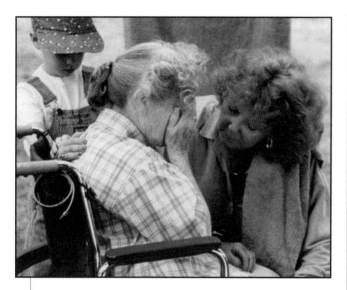

In addition to putting yourself in the other person's place, you align with the person in speaking style and mood. For instance, you are direct with people who are direct with you. You carefully reflect the serious nature of anger and sadness with genuine seriousness. The opposite of Aikido is to be indifferent to the person's feelings or to make light of his problems.

Agree

Find concerns you agree upon. Look for areas of common ground to support alignment. Listen for goals, feelings, needs, and motives that you share with the person. For instance, "I share your concern about Mom's driving." Listen for opinions and suggestions you can agree with such as, "I agree we have to do something before she has an accident." Other statements that foster alignment include:

◆ "If that happened to me, I'd be upset too."

◆ "If I were you I'd feel the same way."

◆ "I share your concerns about_____."

Redirect

Once you discover what concerns or goals you share, you can redirect the exchange and focus your discussion on those areas. You might use statements like:

◆ "We both want to do what is best. Now all we have to do is _____."

◆ "I believe we agree we have a problem. What do we need to begin working on it?"

Resolve

Using "I" messages, try to settle issues and solve the problems you agreed upon. You may do this by working together on the problem or meeting the other person halfway. Or you may "agree to disagree" about this specific issue. An Aikido style statement to start the problem-solving process might be:

◆ "I can learn from your experience. What would you do about_____?"

In the following conversation, Mark heard many "you" messages. Even though he felt under attack, he responded to his mother using the Aikido style.

Marge: "You never talk to Dad since his stroke and he can't talk about sports with you. You ignore him and it hurts him. You should know that. I think you take his crying jags personally and you shouldn't. The doctor said some people cry for no apparent reason after they've had a stroke."

Mark: (Aligning: How would I feel in Mom's shoes? What does Mom need from me to feel less troubled?) "I do take Dad's crying jags personally. I'm sorry that it looked like I was ignoring him. I just don't know how to act when he cries."

Marge: "Your Dad won't be around forever, you know."

Mark: (Agreeing) "You're right. I worry about losing Dad too. (Redirecting.) What do you do when Dad cries? What do other people do? (Resolving.) Maybe we could go to a stroke support group and ask other people how they handle tearfulness.

> **AIKIDO IN A NUTSHELL**
>
> **Align.** As you listen and observe, put yourself in the other person's place and then ask: What does this person need from me to feel better?
>
> **Agree.** Look for areas of agreement or common ground.
>
> **Redirect.** Redirect the exchange to those areas of agreement.
>
> **Resolve.** Seek to resolve by finding a middle ground you can live with, working together on areas of common concern, or agreeing to disagree.

Mark heard many "you" blaming statements: "You never…," "You ignore…," and "You should…." Mark purposefully overlooked the "you" messages. He showed compassion. He found a problem he and his mother shared (common ground) and found ways to work on it.

Other purposes for alignment

You also can use alignment as a tool to encourage people to cooperate with a treatment or to accept help. Aligning tells people you want to understand how they feel and what they need so you can address those needs. Once people feel heard, they are more likely to listen. Take Mary, for example:

Mary doesn't want to try walking since she broke her hip and had hip replacement surgery. Her doctor wants her to exercise. Bob gets frustrated with his wife and tells her she is her "own worst enemy." Finally, he asked Ellen, their daughter, to talk her mother into using the walker.

Ellen: "Walking must seem scary after all you've been through, Mom."

Mary: "It is. What if I fell and broke the other hip? I'd probably end up in a nursing home if that happened."

Ellen: "If I was worried about that I'd be afraid to use the walker too. Keeping up your strength is important though. What would make you feel safe using the walker?"

Mary aligned with her mother by asking herself the following questions:

◆ How would I feel if I was in my mother's place?

◆ What does Mom need from me to feel better?

Reaching people who are hard to reach

The Aikido style works well in emotionally charged situations with people who are verbally aggressive. But how can you align with someone who communicates with sighs, sulking, and silence?

If you believe the person who is sulking feels unable to express his feelings outwardly, you can try to draw the person out with soft-spoken statements like, "I want to understand what is troubling you. I'd like to talk it over." If you don't get a response, give the person space and time to be alone. You might say, "I want to understand your position when you feel like talking about it." This gives him an opening to raise his concerns later. If you believe he uses this style in an indirect way to manipulate you, you might be more effective using the assertive style.

Describe: "I heard you sigh, but you haven't said a word in over an hour."

Express: "I have a feeling something is troubling you."

Specify: "I'd like to talk about it."

Consequence: "I cannot read your mind so I can't talk with you without knowing what is wrong."

SUMMARY

How do the assertive and Aikido styles compare? What do these two styles have in common? How do they differ? When might it be best to use assertiveness? Aikido? The following chart summarizes both styles of communication.

The differences between the assertive and Aikido styles of communication are general ones. You may feel you are more comfortable with one style of communication. In many instances, you can use either style.

ASSERTIVE VS. AIKIDO STYLE

Assertive	Aikido
"Standing tall"	"Standing with"
Positive style	Positive style
Direct, clear, straightforward	Less direct; more gentle and supportive
Especially useful in:	*Useful to:*
◆ setting limits	◆ defuse emotionally charged situations
◆ asking for help	◆ help others feel they are understood
◆ advocating for another	◆ reduce anger
◆ making difficult decisions	◆ balance emotions so can deal with issues
◆ dealing with difficult styles of communication	

CHAPTER FOUR

Communicating Effectively in Challenging Situations

Many caregivers say one of their biggest challenges involves uttering the word no. The feeling is that saying no is somehow not permissible. If you feel this way, ask yourself, "Is there courage and nobility in saying nothing and burning out? Or does true courage and nobility lie in taking care of yourself so you can be a caring helper longer?"

> *A "no" uttered from the deepest conviction is better and greater than a "yes" merely uttered to please or, what is worse, to avoid trouble.*
>
> Mahatma Gandhi

Keep those questions in mind as we discuss in this chapter tools for dealing with these caregiving challenges:

◆ setting limits

◆ asking for help

◆ expressing and responding to criticism

◆ expressing anger

We will also discuss how to communicate more effectively under special circumstances and with people who use the following communication styles:

◆ Passive/peacekeeping

◆ Aggressive/pitbull

◆ Factual/computer

COMMUNICATING TO TAKE CARE OF YOU

Caregivers frequently report they have difficulty setting limits and asking for help. Yet, these are critical tools for avoiding burnout, maintaining your wellbeing, and getting the support you need. It's equally important to express your feelings and give criticism in constructive ways. You want others to hear what you have to say, *not* to focus on how you said something.

Setting Limits

If you have never set limits, it can take time to feel good about doing so and to communicate your limits in positive ways. At first people may not take you seriously and you might back down a few times. But with time and practice, you can do it. You might be surprised at your family's reaction. Many caregivers discovered that their relatives were pleased and relieved when they began setting limits. It seems family members worried less knowing that caregivers were taking care of themselves.

Because only you know what your limits are, setting your limits is up to you. Setting limits is a form of self-respect and honesty. It's realizing that you can't do everything and that's okay. It also shows consideration for family and friends. It helps take the guesswork out of planning and problem solving when you tell others what you are able and unable to do.

Remember, your limits are not engraved in stone. You can be flexible and change them when your priorities change and when time, place, people, and circumstances demand it.

What happens if you don't set limits

As a caregiver, do you think setting limits is selfish? Do you believe people who set limits are uncaring? If so, think about what can happen if you don't set limits. Not setting limits can lead to:

◆ feelings of resentment on your part.

◆ caregiver burnout, and possibly, the inability to provide the help needed.

◆ concern by family about your health and even your survival.

◆ health problems related to stress and fatigue, or even death.

Limits carry risks

Relationships suffer when they are based on someone doing whatever another person wants or needs. If you lose closeness with a person because you set limits, ask yourself, "Am I better off without a relationship completely defined by what the other person wants?" Then weigh the risks, to yourself and the care receiver, of not setting limits. Think about the serious effects on you and the care receiver if your health fails.

Consider the consequences of setting limits

Before saying or doing anything about setting limits, review possible consequences of what you want to do. Ask yourself:

◆ What would be the worst outcome? How would I handle it?

◆ What are the chances the worst outcome will happen? Could I live with it?

◆ What are the consequences if I do nothing? Can I live with those?

◆ What is the best thing that could happen?

Some limits are not negotiable

Look carefully at limits you cannot exceed. These are your non-negotiable limits. What is the most you can give to others? This has to be clear, "I am able to help two days a week. That is all I can do."

Look at how you set limits now

Evaluate your current style of setting limits, particularly with the care receiver and other family members. Check the boxes that most closely describe how you set limits.

Yes	No	
❒	❒	Do I set limits so seldom that people don't pay attention when I do?
❒	❒	Am I so meek about setting limits that people don't take me seriously?
❒	❒	Do I usually wait too long—until I can't continue—before I set limits?
❒	❒	Do I hint or expect people to read my mind about what I can and can't do?
❒	❒	Do I complain instead of setting clear caregiving limits with those who need to know my limits?
❒	❒	Do I set limits and flip-flop by not sticking to them?
❒	❒	Do I try setting limits once and then quit if people ignore them?

Did you check "yes" in answering any questions? If so, the following suggestions will help you set and communicate your limits.

Start small. If you have trouble setting limits, start with people outside your family and start with small matters, like telling a caller you can visit for only five minutes.

Start with the easy people. This means practicing saying a polite, firm "no" to someone either unrelated to you or that you don't even know, such as telephone sales solicitors, fund-raisers for questionable charities, or pollsters in the local mall. A simple "Thank you for your call, but I cannot donate to your cause" (or whatever the request is) is all you need to say. If the person persists, just keep repeating your statement and soon he will give up.

Start with easy situations. It's a good idea to warm up on situations or tasks that are impersonal or that you don't like. For example, if you enjoy volunteering but you don't care for the schedule or the assignment, try saying, "I enjoy volunteering but I must cut back. I'd be glad to help one Thursday a month at this time with…." Then work up to family situations, such as who will host the holiday dinners.

Communicating your limits

The following tools will help you communicate what you can and cannot do.

Be clear about your limits

Use "I" statements and be as specific about your limits as possible. "I am happy to stop by after work tonight but I have to leave by 6:30." (The formula is: "Up to this point I can do _____ . Beyond this point I will do_____," or "_____ happens.")

Offer choices within your limits

This is a way to replace what you can't do with a choice of what you can and are willing to do. "I can't take you shopping today, but I can do it either on Thursday afternoon or Saturday morning. Which is best for you?" (The formula is: "I am unable to do _____, but I can do _____ or _____. Which do you prefer?"). Sharon said to her son:

> I've enjoyed having the grandchildren stay at the house over the holidays every year. Because Grandpa needs more help these days, I can't ask them to stay with us this year. I would like to have them over to sing carols and decorate Christmas cookies with Grandpa. Let's talk during Thanksgiving.

Make no excuses

Giving factual reasons for setting limits aids understanding and is different from making excuses. Offering excuses sounds apologetic. Notice that the following statements contain no excuses or self-criticism:

- "I'd like to do that, but for now I can only handle these three things." (You are being factual and specific, and suggesting the limits are not permanent ones.)

- "I appreciate your suggestions. Right now I can't fit them into my day." (This is a good response to unsolicited advice.)

- "I need some time to think about it. I'll let you know tomorrow." (This gives you time if you feel like making excuses or if flattery or "guilt trips" undermine your resolve.)

If you want to make it easier, you can prepare people over the phone or in writing that you have to rethink how much you can do. You also can mention that your doctor advises you to cut down.

Some people may respond negatively to your limits. This doesn't mean you are wrong. It usually means things are changing that other people wish would stay the same.

Asking for Help

Some caregivers feel that by asking for help they are somehow falling short. But asking for help may be the only way they can continue to provide care at home. They are not falling short; they are adapting to changing care needs that cannot be met without help. It is a caregiver's responsibility to ask for help. If you feel uncomfortable asking for it, consider the following questions about asking for salt.

Yes	No	
☐	☐	Do you expect people to pass the salt before you ask for it?
☐	☐	Do you blame people for not knowing you want salt?
☐	☐	Would you plead, hint, or whine to get the salt?

You probably answered "no" to the salt questions. Just as we expect to ask for salt in order to receive it, we also need to ask for the help we need in caregiving. As you ask for help, remember to use the tone of voice you use when asking for salt. It's probably pleasant and matter-of-fact, without blaming and hinting.

Prepare yourself to ask for help

Before you ask for help, consider the following suggestions.

Consider the person's special abilities and interests. Before approaching someone with a request, consider their likes, dislikes, areas of interest, experience, abilities, and knowledge. For instance, if someone enjoys cooking but dislikes driving, your chances improve if you ask for help with cooking.

Your chances for success also improve if you ask the person to help you with tasks he feels comfortable with and knows how to do. Tasks unrelated to caregiving are easier for some people.

Note: When one family member has a medical or nursing background, it is natural to expect that he is the best one to help with caregiving. Take care that other relatives are not automatically excused from responsibility because there is a health professional in the family.

Resist asking the same person repeatedly. Ask yourself if you are requesting help from a certain person because he or she has difficulty saying no. It is important to capitalize on your stronger speaking skills rather than on someone else's inability to set limits.

Consider the person's special needs. Personal, private time is hard to come by. As a caregiver, no one knows this better than you. Other obligations in people's lives may limit the time and energy they have to give. Consider these matters before asking for help and talk them over. "I need more help with the _____. I know you are very busy and I'm concerned about asking too much of you. Would helping me a few hours during the week be more than you can do comfortably?" Out of concern for everyone's needs, you may decide it's time to inquire about hiring in-home help.

Decide the best time to make a request. Timing is important. A person who is tired, hungry, stressed, or busy is not a good candidate for a request.

Prepare a list of things that need doing. If you are unsure what people prefer to do, and relatives say they don't know how to help, make a list of tasks you need help with (cooking, errands, yard work, someone to visit with the care receiver) and let them choose.

Some caregivers turn providing help into gifts given. The idea is that when people give their time and energy to help, they are giving the caregiver a valuable gift. They may call their list "Gifts of Help" or "Gifts You Can Share/Give."

Be prepared for hesitance or refusal. Your request might be answered with a simple no or silence. The person may be unable or unwilling to help and is setting personal limits. Sometimes refusals upset caregivers. Realizing the refusal has hurt the caregiver's feelings, the person may change his mind and decide to help, but the relationship will suffer. If the person hesitates, ask, "Would you like time to think about it?"

Suggestions for asking for help

The following communication tools may help if you feel uncomfortable putting your request into words.

Use your please-pass-the-salt style to make requests. This is the tone you want to use when you ask someone for help. Practice making a request: "I would like to go to church on Sunday. Would you mind staying with Grandma?" in the same tone you would use to ask for the salt.

Use "I" statements to make clear, specific requests. A statement like "I need more help" is vague. A specific request sounds like, "I would like to go to church this Sunday. Would you stay with Grandma from 9:00 a.m. to noon?"

Avoid weakening your request. If you say "Could you think about staying with Grandma?" you weaken your request. Saying, "It's only a thought, but I'd like to go to church," sounds like your request isn't very important to you. Notice the strength of the statement, "Would you stay with Grandma from 9:00 a.m. to noon?"

Use an "I" statement to express appreciation for any help even if it is given reluctantly. "I want to thank you for staying with Grandma so I could go to church today."

If your request is turned down

If your request is turned down, try not to take it personally and give yourself credit for asking. Most likely the person is turning down the task, not you. Or he may worry about doing the task the way you want it done. Consider asking, "Do you have any concerns about what I have asked?" Then express appreciation for the person's willingness to hear your request. "Thank you for taking the time to listen."

Try not to let a refusal prevent you from asking for help again. The person who refused today may be glad to help another time.

Expressing Criticism

If setting limits and asking for help seems risky to caregiving relationships, expressing criticism may seem even more risky. But sometimes you must speak up whether you want to or not. This is especially true when health or safety are involved. Because the person may not like what he hears doesn't mean you shouldn't

> *I never give them hell. I just tell the truth and they think it is hell.*
>
> Harry S. Truman

speak up. Usually, how criticism is given affects people more than the criticism itself. Consider Grace's approach:

> Don't load the dishwasher that way. Always put the glasses on the upper rack and the cups in rows behind the saucers. You're wasting detergent. I never use that much.

How would you feel about loading Grace's dishwasher? Was the way you were doing it wrong or simply different? Grace could use some advice on constructive ways to correct people.

Before offering criticism

Constructive criticism helps people learn. It focuses on problems, not personalities. It shows you care enough to level with the person. A courteous, respectful tone makes your words, not your behavior, worth remembering.

Before you say anything, reflect on why you are criticizing. Use the following checklist to be certain you are criticizing for the right reasons.

Yes	No	
☐	☐	Are you in a bad mood?
☐	☐	Do you want to appear wiser, more knowledgeable or more experienced?
☐	☐	Do you want to punish someone?
☐	☐	Are you criticizing because something is done differently (not wrong or worse) than you do it?

Re-evaluate your "yes" responses because all are invalid reasons for criticizing. Valid reasons include unsafe activities and behavior that violates the rights and feelings of others. Once you decide your motives are valid, think about the timing and possible pitfalls before you offer criticism.

Address problems promptly. Timing is important. If you ignore a problem or delay addressing it, you give someone the message that he is doing fine. Then when you do speak up, the person wonders why you didn't say something earlier. Delays in addressing the problem may also allow it to grow worse and your feelings about it to build. This often leads to blaming "you" statements like, "Why don't you ever…?" "You always…," or "You never…."

Avoid the pitfalls. Before you say anything, mentally review pitfalls you want to avoid. It's important to:

◆ resist offering an opinion about the person's motives for doing what he did.

◆ avoid mind-reading and judging the other person's motives for doing what he did.

◆ avoid making comparisons with other people.

◆ avoid raising questions about the person's loyalty or commitment.

Ways to deliver constructive criticism

Bringing up a problem can be the hardest part of communicating effectively. If the person has seen you (or others in the family) do what you will be discussing, mention that you are also working on this problem. This makes you partners against the problem.

Grace has done this in the following scenario. Compare this with her statements earlier about loading the dishwasher. Do you feel differently about the way the criticism was given?

I'd like to talk about the way the bathroom is left after Grandpa has his shower. I know he throws his damp towels on the floor; I would like them put in the laundry. I step in puddles of water when I go in the bathroom and I worry about slipping and falling. You can use the mop in the kitchen closet or the damp towels to soak up the puddles. I would appreciate it if you would make sure the floor is dry. Thanks.

Grace's criticism was constructive because she applied the following suggestions. She used an "I" statement when she said, "I step in puddles." She focused on the problem, not the person, by saying, "I'd like to talk about the way the bathroom is left." She was specific when she said, "You can use the damp towel to soak up the puddles." She focused on the issue of concern—the bathroom. She didn't mention the dishwasher.

The following are additional tools for giving constructive criticism:

Phrase questions carefully. Your questions and comments can help or hurt. Asking why the person did something sounds accusatory. Frequently people don't know why they did something. Questions beginning with "how," "what," and "when" sound like you are gathering information, not blaming.

◆ "How do you usually do this?"

◆ "What do you think went wrong?"

◆ "When does the problem arise?

Offer face-saving comments. Your intent is to protect the person's pride and feelings by offering valid, impersonal reasons for what has happened. Ask yourself the Aikido question when a criticism must be given, "What does this person need from me to feel better or to save face? Protection from embarrassment? A chance to improve without having to apologize?" Some examples of face-savers are:

◆ "I can see how a mistake could be made. The directions are confusing."

◆ "This is easy to forget, especially when it's a busy time."

◆ "I hope we can continue to talk things over at a later time."

End on a positive note. You can end on an upbeat note by mentioning positive, helpful contributions the person has made and expressing your belief that things will work out. For example, Gerald said to an in-home worker:

> I notice how patient you are when talking to Dad, especially when he keeps asking who you are. One thing I've become more sensitive to when talking to Dad is to say 'you' instead of 'we.' It sounds more respectful to say 'How are you today?' instead of 'How are we today?' With a little forethought, this can be an easy change to make. And it's a change I will appreciate very much.

Remember the tools for how to best express yourself:

1. Use "I" messages.
2. Respect the rights and feelings of other people with what you say and do.
3. Be clear and specific.
4. Speak directly to the person(s) involved.
5. Be a good listener.

Responding to criticism

Although you may do your best to offer criticism in a constructive manner, you may not always be treated in the same way. This can be infuriating even when you sense a criticism has merit. Being open to criticism isn't easy, but it's important. As a caregiver you may be offended by criticism you feel is neither deserved nor wanted. How does one deal with criticism? The Boy Scouts say it best: "Be prepared." Here are some other tools that will help:

Think about the merits of the criticism, not just how it makes you feel. Does the criticism have merit? Did the person truly criticize or was he expressing a concern that you viewed as a criticism? For example, if you were told you needed help to provide care, would you see it as a criticism of your ability? Are there times when you could be wrong? If so, it shows true grit to admit a mistake and apologize. Just be sure your apology doesn't have the word "if" in it. Saying "I'm sorry *if* I was wrong" suggests you don't really believe you were wrong. A genuine apology has no "ifs" and says, "I was wrong and I'm sorry."

Use your Aikido skills if the criticism is valid. Step into the other person's shoes and try to see things from his point of view. Ask what needs to change for him to feel better: "I need to understand what you want done differently." Perhaps you can't make the changes he wants, but you can listen with respect and concern. That might be all he wanted. (See Chapter 3 for information about Aikido.)

Don't take unjust criticism to heart. Another part of readiness is the ability to disregard unfair criticism. You can ignore the criticism by simply saying, "I find your remarks interesting" and dropping the subject. If ignoring the criticism isn't the answer, you can calmly assert yourself by returning the problem to the critic with a statement like, "It would help me if you would share how you would have done ____." Or, to deflect criticism, try a remark like, "That is another way of looking at this…." If you need time to collect your thoughts, tell the person, "I will think about what you've said."

Responding to criticism from the care receiver

Taking criticism from the person receiving your help can be particularly difficult. This is especially true if you are the brunt of all the criticism and you are doing the most.

If the criticism is undeserved or invalid, try using Aikido to respond and try not to take the criticism personally. Aikido is a very useful tool to use in these situations. It tends to disarm the person because he has no opponent and is not given "fuel" for an argument.

Some caregivers have also found it helps to calmly interrupt when the care receiver takes a breath and suggest talking later. Other caregivers quietly state that they can't listen any longer: "I need to excuse myself for a while," and leave the room. Offering a snack or something to drink gives you a reason to leave the room and may reduce the stress of the moment.

Another option is to suggest the person put his criticisms in writing because you can't remember everything. (The idea here is that people who criticize for the sake of criticizing often will not take the time to

put their criticisms in writing.) This also may help to focus you and the care receiver on legitimate issues that need to be addressed.

Remember, you do not have to listen to a barrage of unfair and hurtful criticism. Regardless of the criticism or its source, how you react to it affects how you will feel about yourself later. It's gratifying to look back on a challenging situation and say to yourself, "I handled that very well."

Expressing Anger

Like most of us, you can probably relate to this quote. Being able to express anger in ways that are positive and not hurtful is critical. This can be especially true when you find yourself facing emotionally charged problems and decisions. This happened to Betty when she least expected it.

> *Speak when you are angry and you will make the best speech you will ever regret.*
>
> Ambrose Bierce

Betty is 50 years old. She is the youngest of three children in the family and the only one who lives near their parents, who are both in their nineties. Her sister, Catherine, lives on the East Coast and her brother, Allen, lives in France. Betty thought the family should get together at least once while both the parents were alive. After much planning, a family reunion was held.

Betty still gets a knot in her stomach when she thinks about what happened that weekend. Catherine had said she felt the folks should move in with Betty because they "shouldn't live at home alone at their age." Allen agreed with Catherine. Betty became upset and angry.

Betty: "You're both fine ones to give me advice. You do none of the work. You never offer to send a dime to help me with the folks' expenses. I end up doing all the work and paying for everything. Now, you have the nerve to suggest that they move in with me so I can sacrifice what little free time I have left to take care of them!"

Catherine: "I didn't realize you would be so touchy about my idea."

Allen: "You never asked for any help or money. How was I to know you needed it?"

Betty: "Just forget I said anything. You're obviously too busy with your own lives to care about your own parents and me."

Silence descended on the group. The rest of the time was spent avoiding each other while trying to be polite in front of their parents. The family reunion ended with polite good-byes. Nothing had changed, except Betty wishes she had handled her anger in a better way.

The goal of expressing anger effectively is to share your feelings in a positive way so that people hear what you say versus hearing only your anger. Reaching this goal requires taking the time to regain perspective and to prepare.

Begin preparing by taking a look at what triggers your anger. Is it advice from people who don't help? Is it repetitive questions or behavior? Is it a request for help just when you have a moment to yourself? Once you identify the triggers, think of ways to cool off before you say anything. Deep-breathing and stress reduction activities might help you regroup. Counting to ten remains an effective way to calm down and think about what to say. Once you feel composed it helps to apply the following communication tools:

Use "I" messages in a non-threatening manner. Be aware of your body language. For example, don't tower over people when you talk to them. Place yourself at or below eye level when you say, "I get upset when I get advice instead of help taking care of Mother."

Avoid "you" messages. Blaming, accusing, and mind-reading are huge pitfalls. They usually lead to strong feelings of remorse later.

Speak in a normal tone of voice. Talking fast with a raised voice implies anger, regardless of what you actually say. Maintaining a moderate tone, volume, and rate of speaking suggests you are in control of your anger.

Getting angry is only human and saying so is not a bad thing as long as you follow the tools for how to best express yourself.

Responding to anger

When we respond to anger, our goal is to defuse the anger and calm the situation. Applying the Aikido style of communication is an effective way to do this. If Catherine and Allen would have responded this way, the family reunion might have turned out differently.

> *Catherine:* "If I believed that my brother and sister didn't care about me or the folks, I'd feel the same way you do."

> *Allen:* "I don't know exactly what you need from us. Give us an example of what we can do from such long distances."

> *Betty:* "I figure I spend about $200 a month on the folks. I would really like some help in covering my out-of-pocket expenses."

> *Catherine:* "I can see we have a problem. What would you like me to do to help? I don't have much money."

> *Betty:* "If you could come out once a year and keep an eye on the folks so I could take a vacation, it would be a big help."

In this example, Catherine and Allen aligned with Betty. They empathized with her feelings and asked for more information. This told Betty they cared. Meanwhile, they received information from Betty to redirect the conversation and move toward resolving the problem.

Other possible tools for responding to anger

Be careful with the following tools because they can backfire and make people angrier. Your knowledge and experience with the person will help you decide if these responses are appropriate in your situation.

Excuse yourself and leave the person alone. Sometimes anger builds as it is being expressed. You may decide to say, "I have to excuse myself. Let's talk when we both feel less emotional," and calmly leave the room. This is an option if your presence is making the person angry, if your safety is at risk, or anger is building and the person usually calms down when alone. Be careful about using this response. There are times when even politely leaving the room will increase someone's anger.

Use humor to ease tensions. Humor, used wisely, can recast unfairness into nonsense. It can help people rethink a problem. The difficulty is that not taking someone seriously is a powerful act of defiance. Using humor can come across as insulting or arrogant when it isn't meant that way.

Either way, there is a risk of increasing anger if the person feels you are making fun of him or light of an issue.

Refer to yourself, *not* the other person, in using humor. "So, I guess I'm not 'person of the week'" or "Here we are madder than hatters at each other and Dad is the one with the driving problem."

Change the subject. This is risky, too, because the person may think you don't understand or don't care. He needs to feel you have heard him before you change the subject. A remark like "You have a good reason to be upset. I have news I hope will help you feel better…." may work to lighten the atmosphere.

Expressing anger with blaming and accusations or responding to anger with anger doesn't promote family unity or help to solve problems. The assertiveness and Aikido communication tools will help you accomplish more.

EXPRESSING YOURSELF UNDER SPECIAL CIRCUMSTANCES

Talking On The Telephone

Bob lived several hundred miles from his father. He called his father weekly, but was increasingly concerned about his father's wellbeing after the calls. He said:

> My dad is 85 years old and very frail. He is hard of hearing and has poor vision. Lately he seems more forgetful. I learned from a neighbor that my dad had a blood test at the hospital the previous day. Dad didn't remember anything about it. Every time I call, he tells me "Everything is just fine." But his voice sounds weaker when he says it. I have a feeling something just isn't right, so I'm going down for a visit.

Although telephone conversations can reveal clues about potential problems, they also can lead you astray. Miscommunication can occur because you don't have "the messages" that body language and facial expression provide. If you want to understand what the person means or feels, you might have to check with the person to make certain you both understand each other. For instance:

◆ "From the sound of your voice, I have the feeling you are worried. Is there something that is worrying you?"

◆ "I'm having trouble understanding what you mean. Can you explain a little more?"

◆ "It sounds like you mean (want, need, feel) _____. Am I right?"

Some people feel safer talking on the telephone than they do face to face. It's possible to capture honest thoughts, concerns, and feelings that would not be disclosed in person. If you discover this, try to schedule your calls when you won't be interrupted and you have time to talk. You don't want to cut off someone who finally trusts you and opens up to you. If your time is short when the person calls, mention in advance how long you can visit.

Telephone skills

A skilled, considerate telephone listener will:

◆ listen for clues in the tone of voice or manner of speaking that are different from earlier conversations.

◆ ask open-ended questions to get more information about those clues, like "How did you feel?", "What do you mean?", or "What do you think about…?"

◆ confirm what was meant: "Are you saying Dad won't agree to stop driving?"

◆ stop other activities such as housework or driving while on the phone.

◆ take notes. Details of telephone conversations are easy to forget, perhaps because there is no visual information to support what has been said. Taking notes helps you remember key concerns and to refer to them during future calls.

◆ summarize the conversation at the end to clarify what you both said.

Communicating With The Doctor

As you provide care over the years, you wear various hats. You are an expert in the care of your relative, a consumer of health care services, and the person who works with the doctors. You may also be a patient occasionally. In any case, you want to build a partnership with the physician and other

health care providers. You, as well as the physician and his or her staff, have a role in forming and maintaining this relationship.

What to consider before going to the doctor

Think about the main reasons for your visit and what you expect from the doctor as you prepare for your visit. Consider the following tools.

Prepare your questions. Make a list in advance of your most important concerns and questions. This increases the likelihood your office visits will meet your needs.

Consider other reliable sources of information. Before you decide what questions you want to ask the doctor, consider other reliable sources of information. Your pharmacist can answer questions about medications and the office nurse may have answers to your caregiving questions. Most caregiving issues relate more closely to nursing than to medicine. Also, the nurse usually has extensive knowledge about the doctor's patients, their illnesses, and the treatments prescribed.

Don't worry about asking the nurse questions the doctor should or prefers to answer. The nurse will refer you to the doctor for those questions. Depending on her background and the doctor's wishes, you can usually ask a nurse questions regarding:

◆ what you can learn from various tests and examinations.

◆ scheduling tests and what you have to do to prepare for tests or surgical procedures.

◆ providing personal care and measures to prevent problems such as pressure sores.

◆ managing medications at home.

You also can obtain information from support groups, specialty clinics, your local health department, and organizations dealing with certain health problems such as Parkinson's and Alzheimer's diseases, and stroke. These organizations offer free or inexpensive educational materials or can tell you where to get them. Sharing this information with non-caregiving relatives gives them an objective overview of the illness and related caregiving issues.

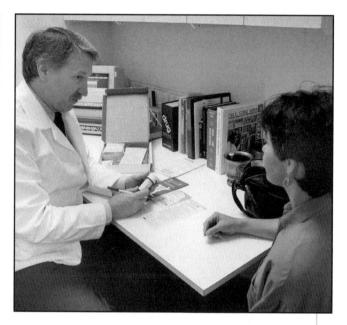

Make sure appointments meet your needs. When you call for an appointment, be clear about the reasons for the visit so the receptionist schedules enough time for you or your relative. Experience has shown that the first appointment in the morning and after lunch, and the last appointment of the day, are the best scheduling times.

Call ahead. Office staff suggest calling before you leave for the appointment to see if the doctor is seeing patients on time. If the appointment is for a memory-impaired relative, mention problems the person might have if kept waiting. Remind the receptionist of these special needs when you check in at the desk.

Take someone with you. Take a friend or relative along if you feel uncomfortable asking questions. They can ask questions you don't want to ask and help you remember what the doctor said.

Build a relationship with the office staff. Introduce yourself to the doctor's office staff. After you get acquainted, consider sending a card during the holidays or dropping a note to a staff member who provided exceptional service. Getting to know the staff often means better service.

Talking with the doctor

The following tools can help you get the most out of your time with the doctor.

Discuss your main concerns first. This is important because if you wait until the end of your appointment there may not be time to properly deal with the main reasons for your visit. You can say something like:

◆ "I have something important I want to talk about."

◆ "There are three things I need to understand better."

◆ "I have three important questions to ask."

Be concise. Clearly, briefly, and frankly discuss your concerns. The doctor will ask questions to get the necessary details. Lengthy, detailed descriptions of past experiences and old health problems are usually a waste of your time.

Refer to a second party. If you want a second opinion but you hesitate to ask for it, tell your doctor. "My _____ and I have discussed the importance of getting a second opinion." (Remember, there is a better chance of getting a second opinion if you ask for it than if you don't ask.)

Get your questions answered. Ask about tests and treatments and the reasons for them.

◆ What do you expect to learn from the test?

◆ When can I expect to hear the results of the test?

◆ How will I (or my relative) feel afterward?

◆ Are there other options to having this test?

Ask about treatment plans. Ask about medications and treatments that don't seem to work. Ask about alternatives for any treatment you find burdensome, such as a medication that must be taken in the middle of the night. Ask for clarification about the diagnosis and treatment plan and the reasons the doctor recommends it, what the treatment will accomplish, and restrictions on activities, food, or driving and the reasons for the restrictions. Find out about recovery and how long it will take to get back to normal, not just to feel better.

Telephone calls to the doctor

Most of us have called the doctor and waited for a call back. Because a doctor may not be able to return a call right away, caregivers and health care providers recommend that you briefly describe the reason for your call and ask when you can expect the doctor to return your call. Be prepared to answer some questions. If you're calling about a new symptom, the doctor will probably want to know what the symptom is, when it appeared, what you think causes it, and if it is getting worse. Be prepared to answer such questions.

When Getting Needed Information Is a Problem

Some caregivers find they can't get the information they need about their family member's condition and functioning because their relative won't tell them. It is important to understand the reasons a person may not want to disclose health matters. Some people fear losing privacy or control.

This lack of trust on the part of the care receiver can hurt and frustrate caregivers. If you have this problem, you face some difficult choices.

◆ Do you ask your relative if you can talk to the doctor?

◆ Do you politely tell him you will be talking to his physician?

◆ Do you contact the doctor even though you were told not to?

◆ Do you just talk to the doctor without telling your relative at all?

Everyone's situation is unique, but it's better to ask your relative about talking to the doctor. Would you agree or disagree with Judy's response in the following conversation?

Judy: "Dad, I need a better understanding of how you are doing. I realize you don't want to talk to me about it so I'd like to talk to your doctor."

Dad: "No, I don't want you to. No."

Judy: "What is it about my talking to your doctor that bothers you?"

Dad: "Frankly, I don't think my health is anybody's business but mine."

Judy: "I agree that your health is a private matter. Privacy is important to me too. I will keep what the doctor says in strict confidence. But I can't help you if I don't know what to do. I have questions that need answering."

Judy called the doctor. She briefly explained the caregiving situation and told the doctor she did not have her dad's permission to call, but he knew she was calling. She asked for the information she needed and the doctor gave it to her. Leona's story is a little different.

Today, Leona's doctor told her she had Parkinson's disease. Leona told her doctor that under no circumstances did she want her daughter Elaine to know her diagnosis. Leona fears the diagnosis will be the last straw because Elaine already helps Leona manage her diabetes, take care of the house, and run errands. She strongly believes Elaine would pressure her into moving to an assisted living facility.

Leona's demand places the doctor in an awkward position. While he respects her right to confidentiality, he also needs assurances his prescribed treatment can be carried out. Leona clearly needs Elaine's help to do this. Faced with dilemmas like this one, some doctors may decline to provide further care. The prospect of losing the doctor usually changes the patient's mind.

If you suspect that, medically, more is going on than your relative will tell you, talk to the doctor about it. If possible, mention specific problems your relative is having that worry you: "I'm helping my mother get along at home and manage her diabetes. I've noticed she has a tremor and seems unsteady when she walks. I need to know if she has other health problems besides her diabetes because I am responsible for her care."

The following tools may also help to deal with this difficult situation.

Tell your family member you cannot help without certain information from his doctor. Mention that health care professionals require similar information to provide the best care possible. If your relative still refuses to share information, you could say:

◆ "I'd like your permission to talk to your doctor about…."

◆ "I can't help you without talking to your doctor."

◆ "I will have to tell your doctor I can't help carry out his treatment orders without knowing what's wrong."

Get the doctor involved. Talk with the doctor. Ask for information on a "need to know" basis. Tell the doctor about the care receiver's objections. Be clear that you are requesting only information you need to help your relative. If the doctor reassures your relative that only information about his current illness will be shared, your relative may agree.

Talk to a trusted friend, relative, or religious advisor. Without betraying confidences, explain that you cannot provide the best possible care without knowing your relative's medical problems. If they agree to get involved, it is best to tell the care receiver up front that you talked to them because you were concerned.

Respect your relative's need for confidentiality. Build trust by sharing only caregiving problems that do not undermine the person's dignity and privacy. Ask, "If I had this problem would I want it discussed with others?" If you still aren't sure, ask permission from your relative before you discuss a concern with someone else.

Communicating with Older Adults

The communication tools discussed so far also apply when communicating with chronically ill, frail, older people. However, it's important to consider how health-related problems may affect communication. Age-related changes in vision and hearing affect 50 percent of people over age 75. Approximately 10 percent of people over age 65 experience memory loss as a result of Alzheimer's disease or a related disorder. You will be able to communicate more effectively if you try some of the following tools.

The hearing-impaired

To communicate more effectively with the person who is hearing-impaired, try these tools:

◆ Approach the person so he can see you to avoid startling him.

◆ Stand or sit between three and six feet away from him.

◆ Get the person's attention before speaking.

◆ Place yourself so the light is on your face for better visibility of lip movements, facial expressions, and gestures.

◆ Speak at a normal rate using normal lip movements.

◆ Do not shout. Yelling distorts sound, making it even more difficult for the person to hear.

◆ Use one-sentence explanations.

◆ Use gestures (nod, point, beckon) and demonstrate what you mean.

◆ Avoid eating, chewing gum, smoking, and turning away from the person while you are speaking.

◆ Do not speak directly into his ear. He will hear you more loudly but not more clearly.

◆ Reduce background noise and activity.

◆ Remember that hearing aids make all sounds louder, not just your voice.

◆ Be aware of false impressions. Head nodding doesn't necessarily mean "I understand."

◆ Give time for the person to respond.

◆ Explore adaptive and assistive listening devices. These include pocket size amplifiers and speakers.

The visually-impaired

Use these tools with the person who has limited vision.

◆ Announce your presence. Speak as you enter the room to avoid startling him.

◆ Ask if the lighting in the room is adequate.

◆ Speak normally and directly to him. Remember, because a person is sight-impaired, doesn't mean he can't hear or talk.

◆ Use a gentle touch, if appropriate. It may help him focus on you.

◆ Tell him when you are leaving the room.

◆ Obtain low vision aids. These devices help a person make the best possible use of remaining vision.

The memory-impaired

Figuring out how much a person with memory problems understands takes some detective work. It can get confusing because some people can read aloud without understanding a word they read. Others may respond with smiles and nods to your words without understanding a word you said. Still others understand what they see and hear but cannot find the words to respond.

Once you realize what aids the person in understanding, you can take measures to communicate in those ways. For example, if your relative cannot understand writing, pictures may be helpful. If he can't find the bathroom, a picture of a toilet on the bathroom door may solve the problem. If your spoken word is not understood, try using gestures and demonstrate what you mean. For example, pat the seat of the chair while saying, "Please sit down," or demonstrate a task one step at a time, allowing time for the person to imitate what you do. These tasks may range from getting dressed to making a sandwich or setting the table.

There are many special tools for communicating with people who have memory loss. Organizations dealing with such problems as stroke, Parkinson's disease, and Alzheimer's disease, have materials written specifically for families. Look in the telephone directory under the name of the disease or call the social services department of your local hospital. Chapter 14, Helping Memory-Impaired People, in the Special Concerns section of this book addresses this topic in greater detail and is another resource for you.

Additional information about hearing and visual impairment is available through local hearing and speech specialists or specialty clinics.

Setting the stage for effective communication

Choose a time to talk that is best for the person. Select a day when little else is going on. Select a time when the person feels rested and medication levels are at their most effective levels. Try to fit your visit in his routine so he doesn't have to delay or skip a daily activity or miss a favorite television or radio program. Make sure he has eaten and doesn't need to use the toilet. Adjust the room temperature and lighting to his liking.

Remove as many distractions as possible. As we grow older, we are more easily distracted by noise and activity in the surroundings. See the list of potential distractions discussed in Chapter 3.

Speak directly and clearly. Older people respond better to clear messages. "I noticed some meat has spoiled in the refrigerator. May I throw it away?" or "Your doctor wants to see you this month. I'll be glad to take you." They may not take a subtle hint like "Hasn't it been a long time since you saw your doctor?"

If the Care Receiver Mistreats You

Bill, a 48-year-old son, said:

When my mother died, my wife and I decided to turn the daylight basement into an apartment for my dad, Joe. At 78, he was lonely and becoming more forgetful. He moved in six months ago. My wife, Marie, provides most of his care. It is just not working. Our teenage sons avoid him because he constantly criticizes them. Lately they've been spending a lot of time at their friends' homes. When he wants something, he yells at us. The stress of putting up with this is too great. Last night we decided Dad will have to move into an assisted living facility.

Charlotte, a retired nurse, said:

Robert's cold, angry look stopped me in my tracks and he wasn't even looking at

me. He was looking at his wife. Even though it was years ago, I still remember how he silenced his wife without saying a word. I was attending a stroke support group meeting. The man I'm talking about actively participated in the group discussion while his wife sat quietly behind his wheelchair. I wondered how long the woman could continue caring for someone who treated her so unkindly.

What do you do if the care receiver trespasses on your rights or hurts your feelings? Do you feel you must suspend your rights because of the person's age or health problems? If the person speaks or, like the men in the stories, communicates in such a way that you feel hurt or "put down," do you just "grin and bear it"?

If a care receiver mistreats you or uses helplessness to control you, you will likely become resentful. Your feelings of resentment will eventually affect your ability to provide care. Letting resentment build and saying nothing is a disservice both to you and to the care receiver. If he sees no consequences to mistreating you, the behavior will continue.

The reality is that a price is paid for mistreating the caregiver. The cost comes as the caregiver's physical and mental health suffers and talk of placement surfaces. Another consequence of mistreatment may come in the use of medications to control aggressive behavior. Often these medications are powerful and may have unwanted side effects.

Caregiver burnout, placement, and the use of potent medications are high prices to pay for not dealing with mistreatment. If you need a refresher, refer to assertiveness (in Chapter 3) and dealing with anger and criticism sections of this chapter. You may also find support groups and professional counseling helpful. Your effectiveness as a caregiver and your relative's ability to remain at home may lie in your ability to communicate limits and consequences in a clear, kind, but firm manner.

CHALLENGING COMMUNICATION STYLES

The challenges of providing care are increased when communication breaks down. This often happens with certain communication styles. These styles frequently emerge when people must make difficult decisions and stress is at peak levels. Also, sometimes people use these styles because they have always worked for them. This section will briefly discuss tools for communicating more effectively with three such styles: passive/peacekeeping, aggressive/pitbull, and factual/computer styles.

Passive/Peacekeeping Style

"Peace at any price" is a motto for people who use the passive/peacekeeping style to communicate. However, when honest concerns and feelings are not raised, it can potentially undermine important relation- ships and decision making. Making sound decisions is difficult because the true nature of problems may remain hidden and cannot be clearly identified and resolved.

Sharon: "Usually I say nothing when my father-in-law ridicules my family and me because I'm afraid of making him mad. Or, I end up saying 'I don't mean to sound disrespectful' and apologizing to him, even though I've done nothing wrong."

Judy: "When our family gets together to decide how to help Grandma, my sister Christy won't tell us what she wants to do. She always wants the rest of us to choose what we want to do first. When we ask her to tell us what she wants, she says, 'Anything is fine with me.'

Yesterday, Ken told me Christy gets tired of doing what nobody else wants to do."

We have called the passive style Sharon and Christy used a peacekeeping style. This is the style where people hope and hint rather than speak directly. They use apologetic, self-defeating language such as "I don't mean to sound…." Their personal needs nearly always take second place to the needs of others. Christy did this when she said, "Anything is fine with me."

It's also easy to fall into this peacekeeping style when providing care because often caregivers don't feel they can speak openly to someone who is elderly or sick. Some people who receive care may feel the same way for a different reason. They might feel uncomfortable speaking up because they are dependent on the goodwill of the caregiver to meet their needs.

Sometimes people use a passive style because they fear speaking honestly to a person who comes across as judgmental or controlling. Perhaps Sharon felt that way when she said "I don't mean to sound…." Sometimes people are passive because they are afraid of rejection or they don't want to jeopardize an important relationship by being open. The peacekeeper's intent is to please, not to deceive. People seeking to please may also:

- seek approval and want to stay in another's good graces.

- avoid confrontation; they might even go so far as to agree with their own critics.

- feel they are accountable for everything that goes wrong.

◆ feel they are responsible for other people's happiness.

◆ be unable to ask for things and therefore use compliments or guilt to manipulate others.

Tools for communicating with peacekeepers

You want to be clear that it is safe to speak openly to you. You may have to say directly that you won't get upset or think less of the person. A gentle, assertive style may be effective. The Aikido style may not be direct enough to ferret out hidden information. However, the Aikido style may work to encourage the person to share his feelings with you (see Chapter 3 for a review of Aikido). In either case, you encourage peacekeepers to speak openly if you apply the following tools:

Recognize how you come across. If a person uses the peacekeeping style to relate to you, ask yourself if you may be the reason. For example, are you coming across as judgmental or controlling? Being aware of your role allows you to act on it by reassuring the person he can say "No" or express his feelings without fear of criticism, retaliation, or judgment. For instance, you might say:

◆ "Please tell me more. I didn't realize…."

◆ "I won't get upset if you tell me how you feel about what happened."

◆ "I want to understand. I'm not here to criticize."

Use a direct, calm, unhurried speaking style. This relaxing manner encourages openness. You can see the Aikido style in the following openers:

◆ "I can only imagine how hard this is for you."

◆ "I understand how (sad, annoying, worrisome) that would be."

◆ "I'm interested in what's important to you."

Give the person your undivided attention. This shows you respect him and what he has to say.

What happens if you use this style?

If you communicate in a passive manner you voluntarily give up your right to:

◆ have a role in making decisions.

◆ advise others of your limits and needs.

◆ get the information and help you want and need from professionals and family members.

Aggressive/Pitbull Style

Joe is a 78-year-old widower. Alone and becoming forgetful, he agreed to move into the basement apartment his son constructed for him. Joe's wife was the quiet type, so Joe is used to "wearing the pants in the family." Living with his son and two teenagers isn't easy. Marie, his daughter-in-law, is easygoing, but must cope with Joe's speaking style.

Joe shouted to his grandsons: "Turn down that terrible music! You never stop to think someone else might not want to hear that junk. And, look at you! You are wearing jeans with holes in them. Why don't you ever wear clothes that look decent? (Turning to Marie) Why don't you put your foot down, Marie?"

Marie: "Boys, turn down the music, it's upsetting your grandfather. I wish you three could get along."

The person who uses the aggressive/pitbull style of communicating is focused on getting his way and ignores the feelings and the rights of others. Joe's "you" statements accuse his grandsons of being thoughtless and slovenly. Joe, and others like him, use this style to maintain power and to control other people. At times, people who need assistance use this style to regain some control over their lives. People using an aggressive style may:

◆ use anger and temper tantrums to intimidate.

◆ use criticism and ridicule to discourage the efforts of others.

◆ make jokes at other people's expense to undermine their self-esteem.

◆ list failings for the other person's "own good," injuring their self-confidence.

◆ blame others by using red flag phrases such as "even you," "don't you even (care)," "you should," "you always," "you never," and "why don't you ever?"

Tools for dealing with aggressiveness

The intent is to stop the aggression. If you reply in a pitbull mode, a shouting match develops. But if you wait without interrupting, the aggressor eventually runs out of things to say.

You can also reduce the need to be aggressive. If the person is angry, deal with his anger. (Re-read the dealing with anger section in this chapter.) If the person wants more control over his or her life, find ways he can regain it by offering choices whenever possible and encouraging independence.

Some tools for dealing with aggressiveness include:

Try the Aikido-aligning style. Agreeing can have a disarming effect on people who are communicating in an aggressive manner. It is the last thing they expect and it surprises them. When a person's emotions get out of control, agreeing seems to initiate some calmness. Marie might have said, "Yes, the boys do wear jeans with holes in them. I know it's hard to believe, but it's the style these days."

Concentrate on areas of common concern or agreement. Asking the individual to elaborate on areas of common concern is pure diplomacy. For example, Marie could have said, "Sometimes I have trouble accepting how the boys dress, too. When I went to school, wearing clothes with holes in them was embarrassing. Was it that way for you?"

Ask about feelings. Sometimes agreement doesn't work. Asking about feelings is usually the next best step. Marie might say, "I need to know what has upset you."

Express appreciation. Sometimes people attack indirectly. They may offer criticism about the way you provide care "for your own good" or for the good of the ill person. It is difficult, but often effective, to respond to this type of aggression with, "Thank you for sharing that. I'm always open to new ideas."

Deal with indirect put-downs directly. Jokes made at another person's expense in the name of "good fun" are a form of aggression. The aggressor acts surprised when the person expresses indignation and may say, "Just kidding." Consider the following situation in which Bert put a stop to Betty's little jokes and he did it with class.

Bert: "Betty, I felt insulted at your remark that I couldn't balance a checkbook if my life depended on it."

Betty: "Can't you take a joke?"

Bert: "I know the joke wasn't meant to insult me but I don't think jokes made at my expense are funny."

Betty: "You are really getting thin-skinned."

Bert: "I don't want it to happen again. If it does, I will call you on it. It won't be funny when I say, 'I don't think jokes made at my expense are funny, Betty.'"

Bert did a lot of things right. He prepared himself ahead of time. He privately practiced what he would say and how he would say it. He gave Betty a face-saving excuse for her remarks: "I know the joke wasn't meant to insult me." He used "I" statements and he used the DESC method.

Describe: He described what Betty said by using quotes.

Express: He expressed his feelings: "I don't think jokes made at my expense are funny."

Specify: He told her he didn't want it to happen again. (He also ignored Betty's "thin-skinned" remark and kept his focus on the "joke.")

Consequence: He told her what would happen if she did it again: "I will call you on it."

What happens if you use this style?

Aggressive behavior creates a vicious cycle for those dealing with chronic conditions because the mere threat of an angry outburst can keep friends and family away. It distances people. This distancing reinforces the aggressor's belief that no one really cares. If the aggressor is the care receiver, the stress caused by aggressive behavior may hasten moving the person into a professional care setting.

There are times when all of us use the pit-bull style to get what we want or to express our frustration or anger. The hardest, shortest, and best way to get back on track is to acknowledge our misstep and, using an "I" statement, apologize for it.

Factual/Computer Style

Some people seek to prevent closeness by using a factual manner to relate to others. The belief is that people use this style of communication to avoid showing their true feelings. Not only do they wish to remain emotionally anonymous, they usually show little or no interest in how other people feel.

Ed is an example of the factual style. Ed and his sister, Nan, were meeting at a local cafe to discuss their mother's driving. Nan saw it as a problem and Ed didn't.

Ed: "Some older people drive until they are well into their 90s. One wouldn't think driving to the grocery store would be such a problem. Most elderly need the independence driving gives them."

Nan: "You're right, many older people do continue to drive. Many older people also voluntarily quit driving and remain independent by using local transportation services. Mom's driving worries me. Did she tell you about the parking meter she totaled last week? Did you know that she got a ticket for passing a school bus unloading children, and that Tuesday she got lost on her way to my house?"

Ed: "Actually, not driving would save on insurance and car maintenance. The money saved could go for cab fare. There are definitely advantages to consider."

Nan gave Ed the telephone numbers of the city bus service and the closest senior center to contact. They discussed contacting businesses that offer delivery services. She knew Ed would be comfortable doing the research and she would help her mother deal with her feelings and concerns.

"Calm, cool, and collected" describes the factual style of communicating. Unwilling or unable to share feelings, the person speaks in impersonal terms, such as "some," "most," "one," and "everyone" instead of "I" and "we." "Some" and "most" are also commonly used words. A factual-style sentence sounds like "Some older people drive well into their 90s," or "Most older people need the independence driving gives them."

Tools for relating to the factual style

The goal in responding to people who use the factual style to communicate is to adapt to it. The goal is not to make these people express their feelings. Using assertiveness or mirroring the factual style works well. The following suggestions may help you communicate more effectively.

Imitate the person's style. If you try to solicit the person's feelings with a question like "How do you feel about that?" the person may retreat further. Use the same impersonal language he uses. For example, change your question to "What do you think about that?" When responding, replace "feeling" words such as "concerned" or "happy" with the word "interesting" to describe what was said. Nan might have said "It's interesting that some older people drive until they are well into their ninetieth year."

Give the person credit for being right. We all like to be told we are right. Once you have agreed on the person's "rightness," he will generally become more receptive to different options and your ideas. Nan did this when she agreed that "many older people do continue to drive."

Give the person intellectual tasks. People who relate to others in this way often prefer dealing with caregiving problems that involve facts or research, rather than emotions. They might do well and enjoy helping in areas of researching resources and dealing with finances and taxes.

What happens if you use this style?

There is good news and bad news. The good news is, you can use this style. Because it is a neutral response, it is effective in emotional, guilt-laden, no-win situations. For instance:

> *Non-caregiving expert:* "Your mother seems lonely. I'm sure she would love to live with you."

> *You (in factual style):* "Many people think older people want to live with their children. Research shows they actually prefer living in their own homes even when they live alone."

The bad news is, if you are like most caregivers, you occasionally want praise or approval. If you want praise or approval from a factual/computer-style communicator, you have to ask for it.

SETTING YOUR GOALS AND MAKING ACTION PLANS

Perhaps as you read the information on communication you found some areas to work on. Improving your effectiveness as a listener or a speaker is easier if you decide on specific goals. Setting goals provides focus and direction.

The next step is making an action plan. An action plan is like a short-term contract to meet a goal. An action plan should include with whom, what, and when you will apply a communication tool. The activity in the box on the next page can help you with your action plan.

Finally, write down how confident you are that you will do it (1 = not confident; 10 = fully confident).

Write one goal for listening:

_____

_____

_____

_____

Write one goal for expressing yourself:

_____

_____

_____

_____

Check the goal you want to work on first.

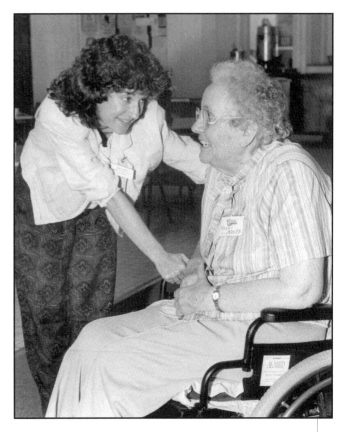

Caregiving is not easy, and enhancing your "box of communication tools" is extra work and does take practice. However, improved communication skills results in better relationships. And being able to communicate your limits and ask for help in positive ways will decrease feelings of frustration and resentment.

You deserve rewards for your efforts. Think of some way to congratulate yourself for applying the communication tools discussed in this chapter.

SUMMARY

Common themes reappear throughout the communication chapters. Here are some qualities and principles to strive for as caregivers:

◆ Listen carefully in an accepting and nonjudgmental way to show you care.

◆ Stand up for yourself without stepping on the rights and feelings of others.

◆ Create an environment in which people feel safe sharing with you.

◆ Respect your needs by setting limits and asking for help in a clear, direct, positive way.

◆ Find a mutual benefit in redefining common goals.

◆ Focus on issues as problems and not on people as problems.

◆ Avoid blaming others.

◆ Prepare ahead of time for contacts with health care professionals so you and the care receiver obtain the best care and advice possible.

◆ Continue to refine your communication tools to enhance your effectiveness in dealing with daily concerns.

IMPROVING MY COMMUNICATION SKILLS
Action Plan

This week I will_____ (what)

_____ (with whom)

_____ (when)

On a scale of 1 to 10, with 1 being "not confident" and 10 being "highly confident," how confident are you that you will reach your goal? _____

**Check the day you
reached goal.**   **Comments**

Monday   _____   _____

Tuesday   _____   _____

Wednesday   _____   _____

Thursday   _____   _____

Friday   _____   _____

Saturday   _____   _____

Sunday   _____   _____

CHAPTER FIVE

Learning From Our Emotions

As you and the person receiving your care adjust to the reality of living with chronic illness, you may be struggling to find the strength just to survive. You may find yourself "within a dark wood." But with time, as you gain knowledge and understanding, your goal may change from seeking survival to finding ways to rebuild your lives and recapture broken dreams.

> *In the middle of the journey of our life I came to myself within a dark wood Where the straight way was lost.*
>
> Dante
> *The Divine Comedy*

Whether you are seeking to survive or to rebuild your life, at times you probably feel painful and complex emotions. You are not alone. Most care-givers experience difficult emotions at one time or another. However troublesome, your feelings are a natural response to whatever is happening in your life.

Your feelings, whether positive or negative, directly affect your situation, and your situation directly affects your feelings. One feeds the other. Negative feelings can affect your situation adversely, which, in turn, may generate feelings of helplessness and depression. But the cycle can be broken. You can learn to manage your emotions and make changes that affect your situation.

This chapter explores the difficult emotions connected with caregiving—to help you understand and learn from them—and offers tools to help you manage your feelings.

ABOUT EMOTIONS

Emotions serve a purpose. They are messages, telling us to stop, look, and listen, to pay attention to what is going on. They can indicate that change is needed. Listening to our feelings prompts questions like: "What is wrong?" "Why do I feel this way?" "What can I do about these feelings?" "What will help?" Asking these questions is the first step toward finding answers.

Remember these characteristics of feelings:

◆ Feelings exist.

◆ Feelings are real.

◆ Feelings are neither good nor bad.

It is how we respond to our feelings that makes the difference in how they affect us and our lives. What will your response be? To simply survive or to find a better way? Do you respond to difficult situations and suffering in a way that allows you to rebuild your life?

Anne Morrow-Lindbergh, a well-known writer and the wife of Charles Lindbergh, famous aviator, offers wisdom gleaned from the nightmare experience of having their 18-month-old son kidnapped from their home and later found dead. She writes:

I do not believe that sheer suffering teaches. If suffering alone taught, all the world would be wise, since everyone suffers. To suffering must be added mourning, understanding, patience, love, openness, and the willingness to remain vulnerable.

Anne Morrow-Lindbergh's words are hopeful. They are a reminder that we can learn from hard times and difficult feelings. We can make a choice about how to respond to life's challenges. And we can grow in wisdom.

It's also important to consider the feelings of the person for whom you are providing care. His feelings are an undeniable part of the caregiving situation and affect you, just as yours affect him.

Mixed Feelings

Caregiving often involves a range of feelings. Some feel comfortable. Others feel uncomfortable. Feelings are referred to as positive and negative, not because they are good or bad, but based on how they often feel. For example, guilt and anger feel uncomfortable to most of us and are often referred to as "negative." Love feels good and is referred to as "positive."

Compassion, caring, and commitment are feelings for many caregivers. However, they seldom stand alone. Often positive feelings are accompanied by those we find less acceptable—like anger, resentment, and guilt. This mixture of contradictory feelings, more often referred to as ambivalence, is natural and human. Accepting ambivalence is crucial in coping with emotions involved in caregiving.

Identifying and accepting all emotions becomes the challenge.

◆ Do you have positive feelings as well as strong and difficult feelings?

◆ Is your caring and compassion mixed with anger, hostility, and frustration?

◆ Do you feel guilty about having "negative" emotions like anger or resentment?

Acceptance is the first step in moving forward. When we accept ambivalent feelings we come to recognize and accept loss.

Kinds of Losses

You and the care receiver may be experiencing many different losses. Losses may be large or small. They may include loss of companionship, financial stability, healthy partner or friend, sexual relationship, dreams for the future, independence, lifestyle as you've known it, weekly lunches with a friend, walks with your spouse, and more. Only you know your losses since your situation is unique and what you perceive as a loss is based on how you view your situation. Another person may perceive the same situation differently. It is important to understand and accept the losses you and the care receiver have experienced.

The care receiver may also be struggling with strong feelings, some of them like yours. He may be feeling sad, depressed, or angry due to the effects of the illness and loss of independence and control. He may experience fear and frustration about loss of his ability to function, or be fearful of the ultimate loss, death. If at all possible, it is helpful to share your feelings and thoughts, as a way to better understand each other's experience.

In certain situations people are unable to share their experiences. For example, those who suffer from dementia or the disabling effects of a stroke may be unable to put their thoughts and feelings into words. This reality limits your ability to communicate, and is perhaps your greatest loss. If the care receiver is unable to talk about his feelings and fears, then you must find other ways to communicate. Observing his behavior and emotions can give you insight into what he is feeling. It is possible to gain an increased awareness of, and an ability to "read" body language, tone of voice, and facial expressions. Many caregivers have found that much can be said with touch. And, touch can be meaningful to both of you.

Marlene, caregiver to her husband who has Alzheimer's disease, made a choice to communicate in a positive way.

As Paul gradually became increasingly helpless, Marlene became frustrated by their inability to talk to each other. She felt at her wits end much of the time. She had loved Paul for more than 40 years and wanted that love to be part of the way she communicated with him, not frustration and anger. A counselor suggested she try "self-talk," which is the repetition of positive statements to yourself as a way to counteract negative thoughts. She repeatedly said the phrase "I choose love" to herself.

Gradually Marlene became adept at replacing negative, frustrated thinking with the positive phrase she chose. This gave her a sense of control over her thoughts. Marlene found it easier, even in the most frustrating and stressful times, to use gentleness, touch, humor, and loving actions to communicate with Paul instead of lashing out in anger. When she was able to change her response, Paul appeared more relaxed.

The exercise on page 92 can be helpful if you and the care receiver are able to communicate verbally. Do the exercise individually and then discuss it as a way to understand each other's perception of what is lost.

As you and the care receiver discuss the responses elicited by the exercise, it will help reduce the stress created by illness and loss. Sharing may also help you maintain and build your relationship, a concern of many caregivers and care receivers.

Chapters 3 and 4 offer important help with communication skills, including the use of "I" statements, active listening, and assertive and Aikido styles of communication. These tools can be helpful in what could be a sensitive, difficult conversation.

IDENTIFYING LOSS

This activity is designed to help you identify your losses and what they mean to you. It is important to recognize both major and minor losses. Use extra paper if you need to. Be specific. Identify each loss individually, and follow it with a statement about what the loss means to you. The first one is an example.

1. *I have lost: personal freedom. This means:*
I can no longer choose how to spend my time
without first considering another's needs.

2.

3.

4.

5.

Recommendations for coping with loss are addressed later in this chapter.

THE ESSENCE OF GRIEF

In completing the "Identifying Loss" exercise you may have recognized multiple losses. When you lose precious parts of your life, grief is a natural response. Loss begets grief. If you dare to love and make commitments, grief will be part of your experience. It happens to all of us.

Your grief response is uniquely yours and is determined by what the loss means to you. Was it a large or small loss? How attached were you to what was lost? How will the loss affect your life? How have you coped with change and loss in the past? These are valid questions and the answers will determine, in part, how you respond to loss and how you grieve.

Grief brings with it many strong, complex emotions, which may include loneliness, frustration, anger, anxiety, confusion, fear, guilt, resentment, sadness, and depression. These are legitimate emotions and may be part of your experience. As you give yourself permission to feel these emotions, your hurt will lessen. However, you must first allow yourself to feel the pain of your loss. Denying, avoiding, or minimizing feelings only complicates your grief response.

Grieving can be lonely. It is well recognized that grief follows a death. However, people may not recognize that caregivers and those with chronic illness go through a comparable grieving process, so they may not offer support. It is important to let others know how you feel and what you need. This can be difficult, but support is critical when you are dealing with a loss.

We can learn much from the way Ernie and Jean handled their situation.

Ernie, a physical therapist, had two serious illnesses, a moderate stroke at age 37 and a diagnosis of Alzheimer's disease at age 55. An insightful man, he clearly told those who knew him how important it was that he be allowed to grieve his losses. He sought out people who accepted his feelings and avoided those who were uncomfortable with them. He talked openly about past and present losses and those he anticipated in the future. He spoke with a sense of urgency, sensing his limited time for clear expression of feelings.

Jean, Ernie's wife bravely dealt with both of their losses. She, too, felt grief, as she dealt with their changing relationship and roles. She was a compassionate, committed caregiver. It disturbed her to have feelings of anger and guilt that seemed incompatible with her caring nature. When she realized that ambivalent feelings are a normal part of grief, she was able to be more supportive to Ernie.

Grieving Your Own Way

Grief is an experience that is unique to each of us. There are many different responses to loss. One is not better than another. There is no right or wrong way to grieve, only your own way. It is helpful to honor each person's grief response. That makes it easier to accept the differences rather than let them be a source of conflict. Lillian and Rob had different ways of dealing with their feelings.

Lillian was angry because her son, Rob, seemed distant and withdrawn. Rob and his dad had always been close, but now that his dad was "leaving" because of Alzheimer's disease, Rob stayed away more and more. When Lillian tried to talk to him about this he became angry and tearful. He was grieving and finding the "long goodbye" extremely sad and stressful. Rob had always found it difficult to talk about his feelings. Lillian, meanwhile, openly expressed her feelings of anxiety and sadness.

Lillian's and Rob's responses to the same situation were neither right or wrong, nor were they more or less caring; they were just different. Rob and Lillian talked about the situation, which helped them to respect each other's feelings and become more supportive of each other.

As you and others cope with losses, try to accept that each of you is experiencing grief in your own way. Respect and honor each other's uniqueness.

Anticipatory Grief

Anticipatory grief is a grief response that can be experienced before an actual death. It is a response to loss. We grieve present losses that are caused by the illness, and we grieve those losses anticipated in the future. It is difficult to adjust to these losses because you can't anticipate a happy ending, that is, a return to "the way things used to be."

Jack felt overwhelmed when his mother, Louise, suffered loss upon loss. Louise had Parkinson's disease for many years and her losses gradually rendered her unable to care for herself. The final "insult" occurred when Louise had eye surgery which was unsuccessful, leaving her blind. The loss of sight triggered intense feelings of loss and grief for Louise. She raged at the world and felt very sad and depressed. She expressed a wish to die and could find no reason to go on living. She talked of suicide.

Jack, as his mother's caregiver, felt sad and angry at the injustice of his mother's losses. He also felt the loss of a friend and loving parent. As Jack assumed increasing responsibility for his mother's care, he felt like the parent. He found this change very difficult. In a very real sense, Jack was feeling the loss of his mother while his mother was still alive. He felt lonely, bereaved, and resentful.

Jack is grieving present and anticipated future losses. As caregiving requirements increase, he feels the loss of her independence as well as the loss of a mother-son relationship. In addition, Jack is anticipating the ultimate loss, the death of his mother.

Jack's situation is just one example of an anticipatory grief experience. Caregivers of loved ones who have Alzheimer's disease have said, "It's like a funeral that never ends," "I lost my family member long before his body died," and "I've already watched the death of my husband, due to Alzheimer's disease; now I'm watching the death of the disease."

Caregivers of people with progressive dementia, as in Alzheimer's disease, understand uncertainty, stress, change, and loss all too well. Nancy's husband was a successful accountant and now he cannot add the simplest numbers. Ralph's wife of 35 years no longer recognizes him. These situations are filled with grief.

Caregivers could be consumed by grieving ongoing change and loss. It is helpful to accept the disease and changes yet to come. Acceptance does not eliminate the hope that some new drug, surgery, or treatment will be discovered to change the medical reality of "what is."

Tasks of Grieving

In his book *Grief Counseling and Grief Therapy*, J. William Worden describes four tasks people must complete to reconcile loss and begin healing after a death. These tasks also apply to people who experience loss as a result of chronic illness. The tasks are:

1. Accept the reality of the loss. Identify and acknowledge each loss. Do not deny or minimize them. This is an emotional and intellectual process and takes time.

2. Work through the pain of the loss. Feel your feelings, however painful. If you don't work through your feelings you can compromise your physical and emotional wellbeing, which may result in depression, health problems, and other symptoms. Doing grief "work" is a difficult task. It is made more so when others are uncomfortable with your feelings and give you the subtle message that you "shouldn't feel that way," or that you should "pull yourself together."

3. Adjust to your losses. Adapting to ongoing loss and change requires that you recognize and accept what you can't change. At the same time, efforts to change what you can will help you focus on pleasures that remain. This can give you a much-needed sense of mastery over your environment. If you strive to hold on to what is lost, you lose the precious opportunities that remain, and your frustration and grief will get worse.

4. Reinvest in life. Reinvesting in life empowers you to move forward. Rebuild your life, incorporating change and loss. There is still a life to be lived in which you can find renewed hope and meaning.

These tasks are an ongoing, sometimes slow process. They do not move in orderly stages, but rather in a fluid process that is interwoven with the rest of your life.

A Different Kind of Loss

We have assumed that many caregivers feel compassion and caring, and therefore feel loss and grief. If you are the caregiver for a person with whom you have had a difficult relationship, and are caregiving out of a sense of duty, you may still feel loss. This is not an uncommon occurrence. Your losses no doubt have more to do with what has never been and can never be, as in Gerald's situation.

Gerald's father had never told him he loved him. Gerald became the caregiver for his father, in part because he hoped that he would hear the words "I love you" or receive some expression of love from him. His father did not respond in that way and Gerald grieves his loss.

Gerald's feelings included a mixture of regret, resentment, anger, loneliness, and sadness. As in most difficult relationships, his feelings were ambivalent, complex, and difficult to sort out. He found it helpful to talk to a mental health professional.

Grieving your losses

The following tools may help you grieve your losses:

◆ **Express your feelings in constructive ways.** These may include physical activity, writing, or other stress reduction activities. Do what is helpful to you.

◆ **Talk about your feelings with understanding people.** There is comfort in being heard and supported by those you trust. Professional bereavement counseling can help people cope with feelings of loss.

◆ **Give yourself permission to cry.** Crying is a valid way to release feelings and tension.

◆ **Get support.** Contact with caring friends, support groups, family or others is important. Well-intentioned people may surround you; you may or may not perceive them to be helpful. A disappointment for many caregivers is when friends they thought would be supportive are not. Support groups offer safe gatherings of people with similar problems and concerns. They are helpful to many.

FEELINGS AND CAREGIVING

The feelings you experience as a caregiver are a normal and natural response to your situation. Most of us experience strong, complex feelings when confronted with loss and difficult situations. It's important to realize you are not "going crazy" because you feel intense emotions.

The Caregiver's Feelings

Your feelings are affected by situational factors. Examples include:

◆ Your relationship with the care receiver. Has it been positive for the most part? Or has it been difficult and full of conflict?

◆ The caregiving situation. Are you a 24-hour-a-day caregiver? Do you manage a full-time job and full-time caregiving? Do you find time for yourself?

◆ Your support system. Do other family members share caregiving responsibilities with you? Do friends help out? Or are you "doing it all?"

◆ Your strengths and coping skills when dealing with loss and change. Do you find healthy ways to release stress and feelings? Can you say no when that is best?

◆ Your reasons for entering the caregiving role. Did you feel you had no choice? Did you do so out of love and caring for the person?

◆ The care receiver's personality. What impact has the disease had on him—emotionally, behaviorally, or physically?

What is your situation? How does it affect your feelings?

Feelings can be helpful. They can be a signal to **stop** and:

◆ assess what is going on for you.

◆ determine how you feel about the situation.

◆ make necessary changes.

David's situation with his father illustrates this point.

David found it increasingly difficult to visit his dad in the nursing home. He often felt irritable and lashed out at his dad, after which he felt guilt and sadness. His dad responded with increasing sadness and despair which the staff noted. The nurse talked with David and helped him recognize that anger was his way of handling feelings of grief over his dad's deteriorating health. The way David was expressing those feelings was affecting both of them.

David responded to the nurse's suggestion that he find a safe outlet for his anger. He began to play racquetball three times a week, an activity that provided physical activity and time with friends. David also began writing in a journal. This provided a safe outlet in which to express and sort out thoughts and feelings. Visits to his dad soon began to improve dramatically.

David's feelings and behavior clearly affected his dad and the situation overall, which made him feel worse. To his credit, David took responsibility for his feelings and accepted support from the nurse. She helped him identify healthier ways to let go of his anger.

Like many people, David wasn't comfortable expressing feelings. He didn't realize that underlying his anger were feelings of loss, grief, and hurt. What he expressed outwardly was different from what he felt inwardly. As David found constructive ways to cope with his feelings, the situation with his dad improved. Consequently, when his dad died, David took comfort in how their relationship had healed.

There can be another ingredient in this mix of loss and grief.

Jean, the wife of Ernie, mentioned earlier in the chapter, was surprised to find that she had overwhelming feelings of sadness and loss over the death of her mother. She spoke of this to the social worker who asked Jean when her mother had died. Jean related that her mother had died when she was 16 years old. She was now 54.

Jean was surprised because she thought she had finished mourning her mother's death. In reality, she had not. No one talked about her mother's death after it happened. As a result, she had not dealt with her grief but rather had suppressed feelings all these years. Now, the feelings surfaced and Jean was grieving the loss of her mother.

Jean's experience is common. Current loss often resurrects past losses and feelings. Unresolved feelings of grief surface later in different ways, as evidenced in Jean's case. The feelings don't go away, no matter how good we are at denying or avoiding them. Jean now had to deal with the death of her mother as well as current losses.

Getting in touch with your feelings, which is often difficult, is a very important step to effective caregiving. No matter what the source of your feelings, it is important to identify and express them. This isn't easy when we live in a society that doesn't always accept the expression of feelings. If you have difficulty sorting out your feelings and grieving your losses, a counselor can help. Jean found the support of a grief counselor immensely helpful. Ways to find help are discussed later in this chapter.

Remember, feelings are:

◆ a normal response to your situation.

◆ fluid and changeable.

◆ an aid in self-understanding.

It's important to identify your feelings, accept them, and learn from them.

The Care Receiver's Feelings

A difficult aspect of caring for people with a chronic illness can be dealing with their emotional responses. Anger is a common response to chronic illness and it is often displaced onto others. It may be that the care receiver directs anger and bitterness toward you and you bear the brunt of his hostility. This no doubt seems unfair since you may be doing the most for him. But you may simply be the one who is there; or perhaps you are the one who is most closely associated with the loss. Maybe you are the safest person for the care receiver to express anger toward. Whatever the reason, a person usually shows displaced anger when he isn't aware that he is angry.

Sometimes emotions are caused by the disease, as in the case of Alzheimer's disease or a stroke. In this situation, it's important to understand all you can about the disease to better cope with the care receiver's feelings and not take emotional outbursts and expressions personally. This can be hard to do.

When anger, resentment, and other negative emotions are directed at you, remember these are complicated emotions and the care receiver's anger contains hurt and pain. The care receiver is responding to being chronically ill and dependent. Part of his adjustment, as well as part of yours, is learning to cope with difficult feelings. The better you both are at identifying and managing feelings brought about by the illness, the more your situation will improve. See Chapters 3 and 4 for communication tools that are helpful in handling difficult feelings.

COMMON EMOTIONS OF CAREGIVING

The emotions most often experienced by caregivers (and care receivers as well) are denial, fear, anxiety, anger, resentment, guilt, depression, and hope. Although we discuss them separately, these feelings are often experienced together.

Denial

Denial is the way people protect themselves from reality. There are times when reality is too painful to absorb all at once and denial serves its purpose. For example, when a person is first diagnosed with a chronic illness, it often takes time for everyone to believe it and accept it. Remember, to accept "what is" is often difficult and brings with it painful feelings.

Denial lessens as you tell the story of your situation to someone you trust. The situation becomes real with the telling of the story. Sometimes this requires telling it again and again. This breaks down denial naturally and helps you accept "what is."

Fear and anxiety

Caregivers and care receivers frequently live with fear and anxiety. The ongoing uncertainty and stress of living with chronic illness is a breeding ground for these feelings. It is sometimes difficult to tell them apart.

Fear is directed toward a specific threat that you can identify. For example, a person who is chronically ill may have a fear of becoming dependent or a fear of pain. You, as a caregiver, can have similar fears, such as:

◆ fear of loss of control over your life.

◆ fear of abandonment by others and the loneliness that entails.

◆ fear of expressing strong emotions.

◆ fear of death. Facing chronic illness, debilitation, and loss may raise your awareness of death and the feelings you have about it.

Anxiety is defined as feelings of apprehension in the absence of a specific danger. It occurs when you are trying to control an unpredictable situation. With caregiving, anxiety has many sources, including:

◆ concern about something happening to you—then who would be the caregiver?

◆ anxiety about an uncertain future—will you be able to maintain your mental and physical health?

◆ living with continuous change—emotional, financial, and social.

◆ changing roles and responsibilities.

Often with fear and anxiety, a sense of dread and a vague sense of impending loss accompany a variety of physical symptoms and increased feelings of helplessness. Physical symptoms may include a feeling of uneasiness or agitation, cold hands and feet, and uncontrollable shaking or trembling. Muscles may be tense, especially in the neck and shoulders.

Circumstances alone do not cause fear and anxiety; it is what we think about them that affects our response. The following is a situation in which fear and anxiety are interwoven.

Eve felt anxious when Al first came home from the hospital after suffering a stroke. She was concerned about his ability to resume his place in the family as father and husband. Would she have enough strength to care for him? Now that they were home, would they have enough support? How would anyone know how lonely she felt? Would she ever feel comfortable leaving the house again for fear he would have another stroke and die? Eve was also afraid that her feelings and thoughts meant she was crazy and "cracking under pressure."

Eve felt relief when she was told that what she was experiencing, in the face of major uncertainty and loss, was normal. She gained strength in remembering that she had coped with difficulties successfully in the past, and that she could cope, and feel anxious at the same time. Eve's continual anxiety was making life with Al more tense and troublesome. She recognized this and sought professional help. In fact, Eve continued monthly meetings with the counselor for the remaining six years that Al survived. Just knowing she had an understanding, helpful person to talk to on a regular basis helped to reduce her anxiety.

Eve found the following steps helpful as a way to manage her feelings of fear and anxiety. She took a bold look at the worst thing that could happen. She:

1. Asked herself what was the worst thing that could happen.

2. Prepared herself to accept the worst.

3. Focused on enjoying what she and Al could do, since the worst hadn't happened.

For Eve, the worst thing that could happen would be for Al to die. As a way to prepare for the worst, Eve and Al talked about their wishes for the end of life and did planning which included drawing up a will and making funeral arrangements. This was difficult to do but it was also a relief. Both Al and Eve had been fearful of "the worst." Having accepted the worst thing that could happen, they were able to look forward to opportunities still available to them.

Whatever your anxieties and fears, identifying the worst thing that can happen, accepting the worst, planning for it, and finding the energy to live, even with your fears, is a substantial help. As the Chinese philosopher Lin Yutang said, "True peace of mind comes from accepting the worst. When we have accepted the worst, we have nothing more to lose and everything to gain."

If you are anxious or fearful about a situation, the following tools may help:

◆ **Confront the worst that can happen.**

◆ **Educate yourself.** Learn about the disease of the care receiver, his treatment, and what you can expect. Knowledge and understanding can lessen anxiety.

◆ **Break fear and anxiety down into specific components.** It is easier to cope with specific, identified concerns than with vague general feelings.

◆ **Problem-solve.** Get the facts, analyze the facts, make a decision, and then act.

MANAGING ANXIETY AND FEAR

The following activity in problem solving is designed to help you focus and redirect your thoughts in a way that will help you feel less fearful, anxious, and indecisive. See Chapter 1 on solution-seeking for further information.

Answer the following questions. Be specific. Identify each one of your concerns. Make a specific plan. (You will feel an increased sense of mastery as you make decisions about your anxieties and fears.)

1. What am I anxious (fearful) about?

2. What can I do about it?

3. I will take the following action:

4. I will start doing this on (date and time):

Anger

Anger is a normal response to the loss of something or someone valued. We protest when this happens, sometimes loudly and strongly. At times life hurts and that hurt generates anger. In our society, feelings of anger are often not understood or accepted. Consequently, we often have trouble accepting and expressing anger. It may seem easier to deny these uncomfortable feelings.

Anger is complex. It would be an oversimplification to speak of anger alone; hurt, pain, frustration, and fear often underlie feelings of anger. As a caregiver, it is necessary to recognize anger for what it is.

> Jan was angry at her friend Marge for not visiting or calling. They had been close friends for years. Now that Jan was caregiver for her husband and needed support, it appeared that Marge had withdrawn her friendship.

In the situation above, Jan felt angry at Marge for not being there when she needed her. A large part of her anger consisted of deep hurt and disappointment. Jan also felt the loss of a cherished friendship.

Anger can stem from many facets of caregiving. The constant changes and losses in your life serve as a wellspring of anger. Perhaps your physical and emotional burdens are increasing as a loved one with Alzheimer's disease worsens. As his personality changes, you may become the recipient of his hostility. When a person has a stroke, uncontrollable emotional outbursts can occur. It may be hard to remember that this is the disease "speaking" and not the care receiver. Perhaps your family has not met your expectations and you feel abandoned and alone. What's more, your efforts have not stopped, or even slowed the progress of the disease. The possible sources of anger go on and on.

If you are an older caregiver, you may experience losses unrelated to caregiving—loss of physical ability and health, reduced income, and the deaths of your friends and loved ones. Perhaps you feel overburdened and are called upon to be a caregiver just when you are least able to do so. This can seem unjust and can cause angry feelings.

You might direct your anger at the care receiver, yourself, or others. And, the care receiver may direct anger at you. Undeserved anger, when directed at you, hurts.

> Roger was losing his physical abilities because of Parkinson's disease. He was often angry and lashed out at Ginny. Ginny asked Roger, "How can you treat me like this?" He replied, "If I can't be angry with you, who can I be angry with?"

This is the case more often than not. You may be the one person with whom it feels safe to be angry. Not that it's any easier to be the recipient of anger, but it helps to understand.

When you feel you are the recipient of unjust anger, the following tools may help you handle the situation:

♦ **Set realistic limits.** For example, when listening, look the person in the eye and allow him to vent his feelings. If this feels too uncomfortable, excuse yourself and leave the room with the comment, "I would like to discuss this at another time. Can we talk about this later today?"

♦ **Count to 20.** During this interval, ask yourself: Is this anger really directed at me? Try to reframe the provoking statement. For example, you might view the situation as:
  – He must be having a rough day.
  – This is not a personal attack.
  – I don't have to get angry just because he is.
  – I don't have to feel like a victim.
  – Easy does it, this could be a tough situation.

♦ **Use humor.** Sometimes humor can lighten a situation but it must be appropriate.

♦ **Develop an awareness of your own feelings.** This makes it easier to respond without anger. Here are some self-statements:
  – I feel tense—take deep breaths.
  – I'm clenching my teeth—time to relax.
  – I have a knot in my stomach—let it go, this is not my anger.

♦ **Develop defusing statements.** For example, you might say to the care receiver:
  – "This must be a rough day for you."
  – "I love you," if appropriate.

♦ **Use the Aikido style of communication.** Be an "Aikido friend." Remember, emotional situations are opportunities to use this style of communication.

Your own anger may appear as frustration, impatience, resentment, and perhaps withdrawal. Caregivers often find it difficult to deal directly with anger. How can you admit anger about a spouse having a stroke and totally disrupting your lives? After all, "he's the one who's sick, how can I be angry at him?" Sometimes anger is displaced onto others like the doctor or nurse. People in the medical profession are frequent targets.

Anger is not a "bad" feeling. It just is. However, it is often an uncomfortable feeling, particularly if you believe nice people don't get angry. Anger doesn't mean people do not love each other. Rather, it probably means they care deeply.

It is very important to find healthy ways to manage anger. "Swallowing" your anger may have physical effects on your body. Symptoms such as backaches, headaches, increased blood pressure, ulcers, and colitis can be evidence of holding anger in. Turning anger inward can contribute to feelings of low self-esteem and depression. On the other hand, it is generally self-defeating to release anger in uninhibited outbursts. It usually serves to make matters worse. Striking out in anger at others can destroy relationships.

Use the following tools to manage anger in constructive ways.

◆ **Recognize and accept your anger.** You are less apt to displace your anger onto others.

◆ **Use "I" messages.** Avoid using "you" messages and blaming others (see Chapter 3).

◆ **Structure situations so it feels safe and comfortable to express feelings.** For example:
  – Use a private room or place to talk.
  – Agree that you will allow each other to express honest feelings without blaming the other. Use "I" messages.
  – Set a time limit of 5 to 10 minutes for each of you to speak.
  – Take turns talking. One talks, the other listens. Do not interrupt.

◆ **Select the best time to express anger.** It is not always necessary to express angry feelings immediately. In fact, there is

often good reason for the old adage, "When angry, count to ten."

◆ **Set realistic limits.** For example, when you are the recipient of unjust anger, say, "I will not stay in this room and listen to anger I don't deserve."

Most important, use the energy and fire of anger to make positive changes. Use anger constructively; make it work for you. Martin Luther understood the benefit of anger:

> When I am angry I can write, pray, and preach well, for then my whole temperament is quickened, my understanding sharpened, and all mundane vexations and temptations gone.

Resentment

When you are taking care of someone else, it is important to balance what you give with what you receive in nurturing and support. When you lean too far in the direction of giving and it becomes burdensome, resentment naturally follows. Self-sacrifice and giving "until it hurts" are not helpful to anyone, least of all to the person receiving your help. No one wants to be a burden to others.

An ideal goal is to be able to enjoy the care receiver and still give needed care. This requires that you balance your own needs with those of the person you are helping.

You can't be a good caregiver unless you take care of yourself. Realistically determine your limits and decide just how much you can do. It helps to realize that no matter how much you do or how often you visit, you can't take away the loneliness or change the diagnosis of the care receiver. You can't live their life for them or make it all better.

The following are tools to help you avoid feeling resentful.

◆ **Give yourself permission to take care of yourself.** Find ways to maintain activities you enjoy. Make a pledge to find time for yourself. Self-neglect can lead to a decline in your health, which can include serious illness.

◆ **Get adequate rest.** This is extremely important, and in fact, critical to caring for another person. An exhausted caregiver is of no help to anyone.

◆ **Set limits.** Learn to say no and communicate this honestly: "I'm sorry, Cal, but I'm very busy at work this week and won't be getting home until 7 P.M. tonight. I've left food you can easily prepare for your dinner. We can have coffee together when I get home." In this situation, the caregiver is making a change that will make her feel less burdened. She is setting the expectation that the care receiver fix his own dinner, which she is sure he can do.

◆ **Find small but important ways to help yourself.** This is something only you can do. Saying no is sometimes the only way to assure that the care receiver does not become overly dependent but continues to do the things he can. This is important for promoting his self-esteem and reducing your feelings of resentment.

◆ **Take time for pleasure.** Plan and do activities or projects together that are pleasant for both of you. Don't let the tasks of caregiving dominate your relationship. Set aside a few minutes each day to share some pleasant time. Whether this is having a cup of coffee together at the end of the day, reading aloud, or reminiscing about good times, your choice will be a conscious one and it will be meaningful to both of you.

Guilt

Guilt is natural in the caregiving situation. It is also a difficult and painful emotion. "What ifs" and "if onlys" may be frequent thoughts. "What if I had taken him to the doctor earlier?" "If only I had paid attention when he told me he was feeling dizzy," "If only we hadn't had that argument the morning he had the stroke," "What if we had kept mother at home instead of placing her in the nursing home—perhaps she wouldn't be so depressed and angry."

> *An appropriate sense of guilt makes people try to be better. But an excessive sense of guilt, a tendency to blame ourselves for things which are clearly not our fault, robs us of our self-esteem and perhaps of our capacity to grow and act.*
>
> Rabbi Harold S. Kushner

There are endless reasons for feeling guilt when living with chronic illness. Some guilt feelings are legitimate and realistic but many are not. Guilt is an emotion that can become inflated and take on unrealistic proportions. Whether realistic or not, guilt feels bad.

Caregivers often feel guilty about the complex, difficult emotions they feel. The anxiety, anger, irritability, and frustration that are part of the caregiving experience lead to feelings of guilt. Also, mixed feelings about the care receiver, the role of caregiver, or the increase in responsibility for decisions may create feelings of resentment and guilt.

A less mentioned situation exists when the caregiver suddenly feels the loss of an unlived life. She is forced into focusing on another person whose life is changing, perhaps drastically. As she assumes the burden of caring for another and ignores her own needs and wishes, the possibilities for her own life may seem diminished. She may be filled with a fierce need to live. Imagine the potential for feeling guilt in this situation.

If you plan enjoyable activities in order to have a life somewhat independent of the care receiver, you may feel guilty about the fact that you are able to do that while he cannot. Experiencing pleasure when a loved one is ill can feel like a betrayal of your relationship. It is not. Sharing your experiences can enhance your relationship, giving it a new dimension. For example:

Carol went to a concert with a friend. As a way to share the event with Gil, she brought him a program and tape of the concert.

Carol and Gil shared the concert, in their own way. Balancing their lives in this way takes cooperation and planning. However, they both gain, as Carol feels less resentful and "tied down" and Gil's world is broadened. Also, they continue to do those activities they can still enjoy together.

Moving on with your life while your loved one's life slows down is difficult. However, it is wise for a caregiver to continue on with life, as much as possible, from the onset of the disease. A pattern is then established with the care receiver and he does not expect otherwise.

Perhaps guilt has always been a frequent companion of yours. If so, you are not alone. Early in childhood many people learn to feel responsible for anything bad that happens. This willingness to accept blame seems to be a human tendency.

Do you have unrealistic expectations and take on too much responsibility for things over which you have no control and are really not responsible? If so, guilt may be the result. When things go wrong, it is not unusual to start the "what if" and "if only" dialogue with yourself. Assuming that if you had acted differently things would be better is usually just not so. This kind of thinking leads to unrealistic, excessive guilt. It is more helpful to realize that you did the best you could, under the circumstances. If guilt causes you trouble, talk with a professional counselor.

What about those times when you have caused hurt or pain to another? When you really have been responsible? It is impossible to care about others without hurting them in some way at one time or another. This is the human condition. At those times, it is important to assume responsibility and to make amends.

In the case of Mary and her mother, Bea, it became necessary for Mary to place Bea in a nursing home.

Bea's condition had declined and she needed almost total care. Mary was unable to meet all of her mother's needs and maintain energy for herself and the rest of her family. Her spouse and two daughters were increasingly irritable with each other. They all loved Grandmother but her needs were greater than they could manage.

The family agreed that a nursing home seemed the only alternative. They found one nearby that met their criteria for care. They felt sad about placing Grandmother in a nursing home, but also a sense of relief at not having responsibility for her total care. Mary, especially, felt guilty about placing her mother in a nursing home. She had promised Bea she would always keep her at home. Now she had not kept her word and had broken her promise. Of course, it was a mistake to make the promise in the first place even though Mary's intentions were good.

As Bea became increasingly angry, hostile, and depressed, Mary felt personally responsible and began to feel depressed. Fortunately, Mary talked about the situation with an understanding social worker at the nursing home. Mary came to realize she had done her best for her mother and had no other option.

Friends and family tried to relieve Mary's guilt feelings by telling her that she had done all she could for her mother. But it was not until Mary forgave herself that she could release her guilt. This happened after she told Bea that she deeply regretted placing her in the nursing home after promising not to. Mary explained that her intent had been honest but none of them could have predicted how difficult it would be to care for Bea at home. Mary assured Bea that she would not abandon her and would always see to her needs as much as possible. Mary realized that caregiving for her mother was really continuing, in a different way, as she visited Bea often and played an active role in supporting her. The time they now spent together was more loving and less focused on providing "hands on" care.

Mary and Bea's story is a reminder that guilt is personal. Others can try to reassure you and relieve your guilt but only you are

able to release it, in your own time. Mary caused hurt by making a promise she couldn't keep. For this she felt guilty. She made amends by apologizing to her mother and maintaining her commitment to certain aspects of caregiving even though Bea was in the nursing home. Promising to "be there" for her mother reduced Bea's fears of abandonment. Mary was then able to forgive herself and let go of guilt.

We all make mistakes and feel guilty. When that happens, the following tools might be helpful:

1. Admit your mistake and apologize. Saying "I'm sorry" can be healing.

2. Correct the situation in whatever way possible.

3. Forgive yourself.

4. Ask forgiveness from the injured person(s).

5. Try to learn from the experience.

If you feel guilty without clear cause, ask yourself:

◆ Did I actually do something wrong, or do I just wish I had done something differently?

◆ Am I feeling guilt or regret?

Regret is a sister to guilt and a feeling that is often present in situations involving loss. For example:

Mark had been meaning to call his mother for several days. When she died suddenly, he regretted that he hadn't called.

Certainly, all of us can recall times when we have felt regret. We are sorry that we did something or did not do something. This is a natural reaction in times of stress. **Regret, however, does not qualify as guilt.** Regret is "a feeling of disappointment or distress about something that one wishes could be different." Guilt is "a remorseful awareness of having done something wrong" or "self-reproach for supposed inadequacy or wrong-doing." Healthy regret is easier to live with than guilt.

Mary felt guilty when she placed Bea in the nursing home because she felt she had done wrong in breaking her promise to her mother. When she was able to make amends and forgive herself, she was able to relinquish feelings of guilt. However, regret was often with her as she wished the situation was different.

Guilt is often a complex, familiar, and frequently undeserved feeling. If you are having difficulty with guilt, try these tools:

◆ **Talk with a supportive, understanding person about your feelings.** This can help you clarify and come to terms with your feelings.

◆ **Stop blaming yourself.** Ask yourself, "Is this my fault? Or do I just wish things were different? Am I feeling guilt or regret?"

◆ **Ask yourself, "What did I do that was good and right?"** Identifying the positive things you have done is a counterbalance to feelings of guilt and blame.

◆ **Understand the limits of your responsibility.** Identify unrealistic expectations.

◆ **Accept the fact that no one is perfect.** Remember, "to err is human." Mistakes happen. It's what we do with them that makes the difference.

◆ **Seek professional help.** This is especially important to do if guilt persists.

Depression

Abraham Lincoln suffered from depression most of his adult life. His suffering is embodied in this quote. He knew the full range of emotions associated with depression—overwhelming sadness, despair, hopelessness, and thoughts of death as a release from the pain of depression. Lincoln suffered many losses in his life both personally and publicly. He struggled with difficult feelings. But he achieved great things and grew in wisdom. His life is a clear message of hope and meaning in the midst of suffering.

> *I am now the most miserable man living. If what I feel were equally distributed to the whole human family, there would be not one cheerful face on earth. Whether I shall ever be better, I cannot tell. I awfully forebode I shall not. To remain as I am is impossible. I must die or be better, it appears to me.*
>
> Abraham Lincoln

When you experience loss, it is natural to feel sad and to grieve. With a chronic illness, distressing changes take place for both you and the care receiver. Hopes and dreams are thwarted. You both may feel depressed. For those with a chronic illness, depression can be a response to chronic pain, loss of function, low self-esteem, increasing dependence, and fear of death. You, as a caregiver, may also feel a deep sense of loss as each of these changes happens.

Studies show caregivers have a higher incidence of depression than the general population. Depression is even higher among caregivers of brain-impaired adults. When a care receiver has Alzheimer's disease, a caregiver may experience a long, unfinished goodbye as the person gradually "leaves," and may feel "suspended in grief."

We will discuss two types of depression—grief-related depression and clinical depression. These are most relevant to the feelings experienced in chronic illness and caregiving. There is much more to be said about depression. You can find more information at your local library, hospital medical library and from your personal physician. If you have access to a computer and modem, you can find much information on the Internet. Also, the National Institutes of Health have free pamphlets on depression. Call 1-800-421-4122.

Symptoms of depression

Grief-related depression (the normal depression of grief) and clinical depression (depression that requires treatment) can look very much alike. For example, both grieving and depressed people can experience sadness, tearfulness, sleep problems, and appetite and weight changes. However, there are differences. If you understand these differences, then you can better recognize depression in yourself (and others) and seek professional help. Grief-related depression, while a natural response to loss, can develop into clinical depression.

Compared to grief-related depression, clinical depression tends to be characterized by:

◆ An inability to experience *any* pleasure.

◆ A sense of hopelessness and pessimism about the future.

◆ Low self-esteem, low self-image, and feelings of worthlessness.

◆ Suicidal thoughts or attempts.

Symptoms of clinical depression are more severe, last for an unusual length of time (present most of the day nearly every day for two weeks or longer), and gradually affect a person's ability to function. Clinical depression is diagnosed by a cluster of at least five symptoms, not by any one symptom. Symptoms may include:

◆ Persistent sad or "empty" mood.

◆ Loss of interest or pleasure in previously enjoyed activities, including sex.

◆ Increased fatigue, being "slowed down."

◆ Marked change in sleeping habits (insomnia, early-morning waking, oversleeping).

◆ Marked change in appetite; significant weight gain or loss.

◆ Feelings of guilt or worthlessness.

◆ Difficulty concentrating, remembering, and making decisions.

◆ Thoughts of suicide or death.

Thoughts of suicide must be taken seriously. If you, or someone you know, has thoughts of killing himself, get professional help from your doctor, clergy, or mental health professional. With help, these feelings will pass and you will feel better.

Managing depression

Depression itself is not a tragedy. Rather, the tragedy is when depression is ignored, undiagnosed, or untreated.

Depression is treatable, with good results. According to the National Institutes of Health, "With available treatment, 80 percent of the people with serious depression—even those with the most severe forms—can improve significantly." Modern treatment for depression is a combination of short-term talk therapy and antidepressant medications.

Short-term therapy. Two short term therapies, cognitive therapy and interpersonal therapy, are highly effective in the treatment of depression.

Depression distorts our perceptions. When depressed, we tend to see the glass as half-empty rather than half-full and to view situations negatively. Cognitive therapy helps a person identify distorted, negative thinking and learn how to "reframe" those perceptions in a more accurate way. Cognitive therapy does not attempt to change "what is," but rather to help you perceive your world accurately, both the good and the bad. For more information on cognitive therapy, refer to the book *Feeling Good* by David D. Burns.

Depression affects relationships. It affects how we think, act and feel toward others. Difficult relationships also can be a factor in causing a person to become depressed. Interpersonal therapy is designed to help people in their difficult relationships with others. It emphasizes communication and relationship skills.

Cognitive therapy and interpersonal therapy have many concepts that overlap. They work so well together that many therapists combine both in their work. Both therapies deal with current thoughts, feelings, and behaviors. They emphasize the present, not what happened in childhood. The focus is on current difficulties and patterns that contribute to depression. Therapy lessens depression by helping you learn new skills and ways of looking at and doing things.

Antidepressant medications. There are many antidepressants from which to choose. None are addictive or habit-forming, and are generally safe when taken as prescribed. The overall effect of any antidepressant is the same. They affect the chemical process in the brain by restoring balance to the neurotransmitters, thereby restoring balance to brain function.

Antidepressant medications can take a few weeks to provide full benefits, although some people feel an improvement within a few days. If you are given an antidepressant, it is important to stay with treatment and report any side effects to your doctor. If symptoms are troublesome, call your doctor instead of waiting for an appointment.

Antidepressant medications must be monitored carefully, and it may be that your doctor will prescribe a different one. Or, he may tell you to continue with the present medication as the side effects can be expected to disappear in two or three weeks. You may feel the results are worth the temporary discomfort. At any rate, do not discontinue or change your medication without first consulting your doctor.

Alcohol, drugs, and depression.

Depression is not helped by alcohol or drugs. They do not offer an escape from the pain of your feelings. They only mask them temporarily. Alcohol and tranquilizers are central nervous system depressants and will make depression worse.

If you find yourself having a couple of drinks to calm your nerves or to help you sleep, stop, before it becomes a habit. Stress situations precipitate heavier drinking which can lead to depression and addiction in certain people. This is a complication you do not need.

For more information on depression, see Chapter 13, "Recognizing and Responding to Depression," in the Special Concerns section.

CARING FOR YOURSELF

You are your most valuable resource. Treat yourself as you would anyone you cherish. Be gentle and compassionate with yourself, not demanding or judgmental. Accept your human frailties, but at the same time, see your strengths. Who you are as a person is the single most important thing you bring to your role as a caregiver.

Taking care of yourself includes managing the difficult emotions of caregiving. This, in turn, can give you an increasing sense of control over your situation. The following tools may be helpful.

◆ **Participate in activities you enjoy.** This may include hobbies or activities of special interest. Rediscover those accomplishments that build your self-esteem.

◆ **Treat your body well.** Eat properly. Adequate nutrition is important for overall wellbeing. Set a regular time each day to exercise, whether it is yoga, running, walking, aerobics class, or other activities. This is also a constructive way to release tension.

◆ **Use relaxation techniques.** Learn to relax as a cat does. Develop an awareness of tension in your body by doing frequent body scans. To do this, mentally scan your body for tension, noting areas that are tense. Then "go limp" all over your body, with special attention to the tense areas. This can be done anytime, anyplace.

◆ **Make use of books and tapes.** They can give you information and tools for working with depression, stress, emotions, and relaxation.

◆ **Get a good night's sleep.** Insomnia is very common in people who are under stress. This is often temporary. Try not to worry about it. Worry causes more stress than sleeplessness. The following can help to manage insomnia:

– Give up caffeine.
– Avoid sleeping pills. They may disrupt your normal sleep patterns. Use sleeping pills only as a temporary measure, if at all.
– Try meditating if you are unable to sleep (see Chapter 2). Or, try repeating prayers.
– Get physically tired. Clean the house, garden, exercise; do any activity that will tire you.
– Get up and read or work until you are tired.

◆ **Get social support.** Have at least one friend you can tell your troubles to. Sustain and nurture old friends. Avoid isolating yourself from others.

◆ **Attend a support group.** Again, this can be a safe, supportive environment in which to meet others who share similar experiences. Other benefits are:

– You will find others who are experiencing similar feelings.
– There is opportunity to give and receive support.
– You learn from each other and realize you are not alone.
– You can find encouragement, support, hope, and friendship.

◆ **Write your feelings down on paper.** Writing in a private journal is a way to keep in touch with and examine your feelings, as well as a constructive way to release them. Writing is a private way to talk to yourself about how you feel. It gives you uninterrupted time to express anything you want, without fear of judgment from others.

◆ **Change negative self-talk to positive self-talk.** Your emotions are derived from your thoughts.

Do the following activity frequently, as feelings are ever-changing. Remember, your feelings affect your situation. Take responsibility for them and learn from them. The changes you make help create a situation in which you can rebuild your life and find hope, even in the midst of loss and change.

IDENTIFYING FEELINGS

In earlier activities you identified your losses and anxieties. The following activity is designed to help you to get in touch with the feelings that are most difficult for you, and to plan actions that will help you manage them. Do the following steps:

1. Identify your feelings, one at a time.

   (Example) I feel: afraid.

2. Identify what would help you deal with the feeling. What do you need?

   (Example) I need: to get more information about the disease John has.

3. Plan to do at least one thing that would help.

   (Example) I will: call his nurse and ask her to send me information about his condition, or refer me to where I can find it.

4. Decide when you will carry out the plan.

   (Example) I will do it: today while John is napping.

HOPE

Hope is the beacon of light by which we travel. Without it, we become lost. Hope is as necessary as breathing. Without it life has little meaning or purpose.

Difficult feelings, including depression and suicide, can be the result of hopelessness and despair. An attitude of optimism and hope contributes to your wellbeing and even creates the potential for slowing the progress of an illness.

As a caregiver, you may hope to just make it through one more day, or hope to find respite, to get a break. Whatever your hope, it is crucial. Also, it is important to remember that even if you feel your situation is hopeless, it does not necessarily follow that the care receiver is without hope.

> *A sense of hope is "Knowing that your present moment has meaning."*
> Robert Randall

Hope is necessary and will change in nature throughout an illness, for both of you. Early in the disease process there may be hope for a cure. When you live with a chronic illness, you may hope for remission and relief from pain and symptoms. If your condition worsens you may hope for a better quality of life.

It's important not to take hope away from another nor to instill false hope. Statements like, "You're going to get better," when that isn't the case, will ultimately lead to a sense of resentment and betrayal. In fact, those who are ill are often the first to know when they are not going to get better. Sometimes the only real hope you can give another is to affirm your wish to care for him to the best of your ability.

Hope is entwined with meaning. As we find our way, we make choices that help us find hope and meaning, perhaps even wisdom, in suffering.

As you walk through your "dark wood," hope can help you find your way. There are lights to guide you and people who can help.

> *We need not walk alone...*
>
> *We reach out to each other with love and understanding and with hope. We come together from all walks of life, from many different circumstances...*
>
> *We need not walk alone!*
>
> The Credo of the Compassionate Friends

CHAPTER SIX

Mastering Caregiving Transitions

As a caregiver, you face changes no matter what level of care you provide—whether you are a full-time caregiver providing hands-on care, a part-time caregiver helping an older relative remain in his home, a long-distance caregiver, or you oversee a relative's care in a care facility. Dealing with caregiving changes is seldom easy.

> *Everything changes,*
> *nothing remains*
> *without change.*
>
> The Buddha

In *Managing Transitions*, William Bridges states that it isn't change that does you in—it's the transition. Change is the external situation—the increased needs of the care receiver, the decreased ability of a caregiver to meet the care receiver's needs, or moving the care receiver to a care facility. Transition is the internal emotional process we go through to come to terms with what has changed. It's these feelings that can be particularly difficult.

The ability to cope with change and transition is an important caregiving tool that can affect your health, the quality of care you provide, and how long you can provide care. This chapter will help you to:

◆ gain confidence in your ability to master change and transition.

◆ examine how your attitude affects how you deal with change.

◆ identify ways to reduce pessimism, that is, negative thinking.

CHANGING FAMILY ROLES

Both you and your family member who needs care may face the difficult task of letting go of old roles and accepting new ones. New roles can challenge everyone involved. They often distress caregiving spouses who must take over what was the other person's role before the illness. The person receiving care may resist and express resentment toward the caregiver. Marge, a 67-year-old caregiver, said:

> Norm had his stroke a year ago today. It left him with weakness on his right side and some speech problems. As I read the notes from my journal, I realize how much Norm and I have changed and how far we have come. Before his stroke Norm managed our finances, took care of the yard, and did the driving. Now I do nearly everything Norm did. I also help Norm bathe and dress, and I still do all the work I have always done. It feels uncomfortable taking Norm's place and I sense he resents it too. The stroke hasn't ruined our lives; we still travel and fish, we just do it a little differently than we did before.

If you are an adult child, you may be providing support, caregiving, or making decisions for a parent for the first time. This is particularly difficult if your parent has always made his or her own decisions, if you have tried to maintain distance between you and your parent because of a poor relationship, if you looked to your parent for assistance, or if you viewed him as a "pillar of strength." Pat said:

> It's not the actual caregiving that is difficult for me. It's seeing the disease rob my mother of who she was and all she could do. She was a very bright woman. I miss the mother-daughter relationship we had. Now I feel more like a parent, rather than a daughter, to my Mom. My Mom helped me make decisions in life. I never had helped her make a decision, and now I am forced to make decisions about Mom's life. It's not easy.

Dealing with changes in your family member may be even more difficult because of competing demands from family and work. The situation of Stephen, a 45-year-old son and caregiver is not unusual.

My mother, Pearl, is 85. She has Parkinson's disease. She needs more help than I can provide but she has refused to let anyone but me help her. Increasing pressure from work and lack of time for my wife and children made me realize that something had to change.

Reluctantly, I discussed my problems with my mother. Mother resisted any change. Finally I said, "I worry about you being alone, and yet we can't live together. I'm afraid I'll lose you if you fall and hurt yourself. I have to find help for you when I can't be here." She said, "Go ahead, I probably can't stop you anyway."

After considerable searching I found and hired a student nurse who needed money and a place to stay and wanted the experience. Mother seems to be adjusting to an outsider helping her, but I'm having trouble getting over the feeling that I let her down. Even though I made the best decision I could under the circumstances, I still feel guilty.

Stephen's experience is not unusual. Even when a change needs to occur or "the best decision" has been made, you may experience emotional turmoil. Particularly difficult is when you must make a decision you had hoped you wouldn't have to make.

A LOOK AT CHANGE

A change involves not just a beginning of something, but also an ending of what was. In dealing with chronic illness, this ending of what was (and generally will not be again) is the reason that even when something is done because it is "the best," you (or the care receiver) may not feel good.

For example, some caregivers experience mixed feelings when they decide to hire paid help because it means their role as the sole provider of care has ended. Caregivers who cannot let go of their old role may have trouble keeping paid helpers or working with care facility staff. They may consider workers deficient if everything is not done exactly the way they do it. Caregivers who accept the ending of their old role are more likely to be flexible in the way quality care is provided.

You and your relative face many uncontrollable changes in health and lifestyle. However, whatever a change, you can choose:

◆ whether or not you deal with making a change.

◆ how you deal with a change.

◆ your attitude about the situation.

◆ whether you look ahead and plan for potential changes or ignore them and wait for a crisis.

How other people respond to caregiving changes is beyond your control. You can *influence* peoples' attitudes and actions but you can't control them. Relatives may deny a change in your family member's functioning that worries you. For example, you may be concerned about your father's memory but your brother insists there is no problem, saying, "Dad has always been forgetful." In such a situation, a relative may not support your decisions. In this case, you might ask your brother to spend a couple of days with Dad in hopes of helping him to see your perspective. However, you can only control how you deal with the situation.

What happens if you do not deal with change? Caregivers who deny change, who try to restore the past or maintain the status quo, may unintentionally:

◆ waste time and energy trying to keep things the same.

◆ lose opportunities for a memory-impaired person to take part in planning for his future (because he may not be able to participate later because of the illness).

◆ develop unrealistic expectations because they are more likely to believe that the impaired person can function as he did in the past if he would just try harder.

◆ "burn out" because they can't accept that care needs have grown too great for them to handle.

It is only natural to want to return to earlier and better days; however, if you try to recreate the past, both you and the care receiver will likely experience frustration. Focusing on "the way things were" will make it even more difficult to deal with current circumstances. Trying to resurrect the past also prevents appropriate decision making and moving forward. However, do not confuse "resurrecting the past" with "reminiscing about the past." Reminiscing can be useful and beneficial.

☙

UNDERSTANDING TRANSITIONS

Caregiving changes and decisions are difficult, in part, because they usually lead to some type of loss for the care receiver. And, sometimes for you, the caregiver. They also frequently create powerful feelings of self-doubt and guilt.

A change involves emotions and adjustments for both you and the care receiver. Too often people are told, or even feel themselves, "This is for the best." Then they wonder, "If it's for the best, why do I feel so bad… so sad?" Or "If the change is for the best, why doesn't the care receiver realize this instead of being so upset with me?" Such feelings are a natural reaction to change and to being in transition.

In *Transitions,* William Bridges says that whenever a change occurs, a transition follows. A transition is the internal emotional process we go through in dealing with a change in our lives. Understanding the transition process can help you master caregiving changes and deal better with your feelings. Each transition includes three phases.

Phase one: the ending. Endings are the starting points of transitions. To make a

transition you have to let go of what has ended. Even a positive caregiving change generally involves a loss, that is an ending, of something. It's important to be able to identify and let go of what has ended.

Phase two: the wilderness period (neutral zone or down time). This is the core of the transition. It is the "no man's land" between the old and the new—the old is gone and the new may not feel right yet. Feelings of confusion, emptiness, grief, and anxiety are common.

Phase three: the new beginning. A beginning is only achieved after an ending has been experienced and time has been spent in the wilderness. This can be frightening because it confirms the ending was real and the old ways won't work anymore.

Phase One: The Ending

Bridges reminds us that change is the external situation in which something new has begun. For example, "Grandma cannot remember to throw spoiled food away. So, now I'll have to do it."

Emotionally, the change in Grandma means more than our concern about her eating spoiled food. It is a sign of Grandma's declining abilities and it saddens us. We remember that Grandma was always there for us when we needed her. Now we have to let go of our old image of Grandma and be there for her. It's this internal process of letting go of "what was" that really bothers us, not the spoiled food.

When we speak of an ending we speak of a loss. However, not all endings are serious or sad; some may be positive. For instance, if the care receiver recovers and no longer needs help, there is a loss of dependency and this is a positive change. A caregiver who accepts this positive change is likely to find ways for the care receiver to be independent. A caregiver who is unable to accept such a change may continue to provide unnecessary care and therefore encourage dependency.

> *What we call the beginning is often the end, And to make an end is to make a beginning.*
>
> *The end is where we start from.*
>
> T.S. Eliot
> *Little Gidding*

Signs of an ending

For some caregivers, incontinence may be a sign that their ability to provide care without help is ending. If they accept this ending they are more likely to seek or accept help. The caregiver who can't accept that he has reached his caregiving limits may burn out and the quality of his care may suffer. This affects everyone involved, especially the care receiver.

Some endings never end

Chronic, progressive illness that causes a gradual decline in abilities or a steady worsening of symptoms may force both you and the care receiver to cope with ongoing endings. Caregivers of people with Alzheimer's disease have described their experience as "the funeral that never ends" and "a long goodbye." They deal with a succession of changes and losses due to the progressive nature of the disease. For many families, these losses multiply without the benefit of a "wilderness time" to grieve and come to terms with them.

Many memory-impaired people face endings but cannot understand what has changed and why. For instance, Dad doesn't remember his near misses while driving. He hears news like "Dad, driving isn't safe for you anymore" as if it is the first time. He may react with shock, anger, and disbelief every time he hears the news. His loss of recent memory robs him of the ability to make sense of what changed and why decisions were made about his not driving. Meanwhile, his remaining long-term memory contradicts what others say. He may argue, "I am a safe driver. I've never had an accident, except once when someone else ran a stop light and hit me." It is unrealistic to expect a person who has no memory of recent events to accept not driving, no matter how many times he hears it, because he does not think that his ability to drive has changed.

Dealing with endings

In any ending there must be a letting go. You may have to argue with an inner voice that tells you not to change, to keep on being the "old you," and to do whatever it takes to keep things the same. To silence such an inner voice, tell yourself, "Something has changed (ended) and I must find ways to deal with it."

Accepting a change or ending does not mean you approve of it or that you have given up. It means you are doing what you must in order to move on to whatever is next in your life. Often this involves a period of grieving as you let go of the way things were or something you once had. This is the purpose of the "wilderness period."

Phase Two: The Wilderness Period or Neutral Zone

The second phase of a transition, the wilderness period, is a time to help you come to terms with change and loss. Some people call it their "down time" because they feel "down." You may experience feelings of grief, confusion, emptiness, depression, uncertainty and anxiety as you search for the meaning in a change. This is a difficult phase. It is important to be patient and self-forgiving during this time. This is also the time to ask questions like these:

> *The lowest ebb is the turn of the tide.*
> Henry Wadsworth Longfellow

◆ What has changed? The person? The situation? Me?

◆ What has ended? For my relative? For me? In our lives? In the caregiving situation?

◆ How do I feel about this change? Sad? Angry? Guilty? Relieved?

◆ What do I do now? Try to change things back? Accept change as a challenge? Learn new ways to deal effectively with the change?

In the following story, Stephen spent time in his wilderness period questioning himself and his decision.

Even though I knew I had made the best decision possible, I still felt terrible about employing an outsider to help mother. I questioned my loyalty. Was I such a good son after all, letting a stranger take care of my mother? I wondered about my character. Was I being selfish and lazy by hiring help instead of helping Mom myself? My conscience bothered me too. My mother raised and cared for me. Was this how I repaid her?

After considerable soul-searching I felt better about my decision. I also realized it did not mean I abandoned my mother; it meant my role as caregiver had changed. Now I manage her care. I am her advocate and spokesman.

During the wilderness period, Stephen dealt with his feelings and realized he was still a caring, loyal, unselfish son.

Getting through the wilderness period

Stephen's story reveals how the wilderness period provides an opportunity to think about what has changed and to decide what must be learned and done for the next step. This is why the wilderness period should not be rushed. This is the time to decide if the direction you are headed is the right one. This "down time" is the crux of every transition. The following tools may help you through the wilderness period.

Maintain structure and order to your life. Plan your day's activities and set small goals you can easily achieve. This gives a sense of control and predictability during this unsettling phase. Give yourself credit for seemingly minor victories and accomplishments.

Take care of yourself. Don't add to your losses by giving up more than you need to. It's important to stay in touch with supportive people and continue enjoyable activities. These provide stability and continuity during transitions.

Identify the reasons you feel troubled. Feelings of confusion, anxiety, and tension commonly surface during transitions. Feeling distressed doesn't necessarily mean something is wrong; it usually means things are changing. Talk to a nonjudgmental listener to help you understand what is happening. Simply being able to identify feelings and describing problems can give you deeper insight and a clearer sense of direction.

Look for the positive in the change. If something forced change upon you, such as a spouse's stroke, look for something positive that came from it. Give some thought to "Things I learned about myself from this" or "Things I had no idea I could do." Consider making a list with one of these titles and adding to it. It may reinforce the positive for you during those tough times.

Avoid doing something just for the sake of taking action. Unless you have to take action, avoid making unnecessary changes during this time. If you make decisions and take action just to fill the void, you may regret these changes later.

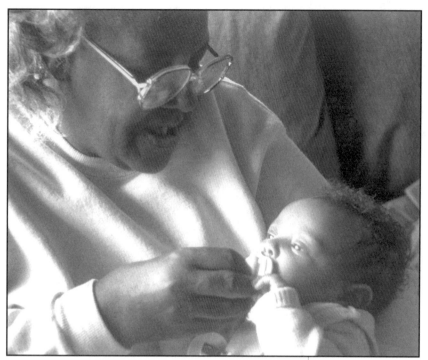

Phase Three:
The New Beginning

Bridges says you come to the new beginning only at the end—that is, only after you have completed the ending and the wilderness phases of a transition. He claims beginnings are vague and "unimpressive."

How do you know you are ready to begin? It would be helpful if you could identify a clear sign. The reality is that you may have only a subtle feeling that you are ready for "a new beginning." You may feel more refreshed and ready to move forward than you have for a while. New ideas and opportunities may surface and you begin looking into these new possibilities. A neighbor mentions she provides companionship services and you hear yourself saying, "I want to learn more about your work." You picture yourself doing things.

Sometimes comments made by other people may repeatedly return to your mind as though prompting you to pay attention. A support group member told Marge: "Your sense of humor about your caregiving mistakes brightened my day and helped me realize I'm not the only one who makes mistakes." For two months Marge kept remembering those words. Finally, one Sunday she talked to the editor of her church newsletter about writing a caregiver's idea and advice column. The editor of the local newspaper asked to print her second column, "Planning to Enjoy the Holidays." This shows the indirect, almost subconscious nature of beginnings. When you start looking for ways to enhance your new and still-changing life, you have begun.

> *When we are ready to make a beginning, we will shortly find an opportunity.*
>
> William Bridges

ↄ

LEARNING FROM PAST TRANSITIONS

Sometimes it helps to look back at earlier transitions (endings, wilderness periods, and beginnings) to see what you learned from them. In the following example, Marge read her journal to reflect on the changes and transitions she experienced after Norm's stroke. She asked questions about how she handled each phase of the transition: What did I learn? How did my attitude help or hinder me? How do I feel about the choices I made? If I had to do it over, what would I do differently?

Using Marge's example, think back to a caregiving event/change that led you through a period of transition, such as accepting your role as caregiver or deciding to relinquish day-to-day care.

◆ What comes to mind as your ending?
  – Accepting a diagnosis?
  – Accepting that changes in your loved one are caused by the illness?
  – Accepting and adjusting to your role as caregiver?

CHANGE AND TRANSITION

Event/Phase	What helped me deal with the event	Things that made it difficult for me
Norm's stroke, right afterward	My friends' support. Confidence in the doctors and nurses. My religion. My relaxation exercises.	Didn't understand the nature of the stroke. Worried about losing Norm, future, money.
2 weeks later	Norm's improvement. Felt encouraged. All would be OK.	Stayed at hospital until exhausted.
2+ months later (still dealing with ending)	Got information about stroke. Learned how to help Norm with his rehabilitation exercises. Realize I did OK at a crisis time and that Norm is getting better but will not be the same as before.	Let Norm's moodiness rub off on me. His progress slowed no matter what I did. Saw friends less. Felt not right to have fun.
6 months later (wilderness)	Went to support group. Learned OK to feel bad. Realize have limits, can only control me. Try to take one day at a time.	Wouldn't accept help from family and friends.
1 year later (new life style)	Try to stay in touch with positive people. Involve Norm in activities with friends and family.	Still worry about future and money.

- ◆ What helped you through the void?
  - – Family?
  - – Friends?
  - – Support group?
  - – Religious beliefs?
- ◆ How did you know when you were ready to begin dealing with what had changed? With caregiving? With your own needs?
  - – Did you take a closer look at the remaining skills of your relative?
  - – Did you begin thinking about favorite activities and considering how you and your relative could still enjoy them?
  - – Was it getting harder to summon the energy to do things in the old ways?
  - – Did you find yourself skimming the classified ads and reading the employment, home help section?
- ◆ What would you do differently in each phase?
  - – Learn more about the illness earlier to help yourself accept it?
  - – Ask for more help?
  - – Attend a support group?

- ◆ What did you learn and do that you can apply to future:
  - – Endings?
  - – Wilderness periods?
  - – Beginnings?
- ◆ What did you learn about yourself?
  - – That you are more patient than you ever imagined?
  - – That you are able to deal with the challenges of change?
  - – That you are more willing to accept help from other people?

Reflecting on how you dealt with past changes and transitions can help you to identify and build on your effective responses to change, and to discard the ineffective ones. As you identify what worked and didn't work for you during past transitions, copy the following form on a separate piece of paper for your notes. Writing down what you learned from your experiences can be a useful tool to help you with future transitions.

CHANGE AND TRANSITION

Event/Phase	What helped me deal with the event	Things that made it difficult for me
Event/Phase	What I plan to use next time	What I plan to do to adjust and begin anew

THE POWER OF A POSITIVE ATTITUDE

Your attitude toward the challenges of caregiving will make it easier or more difficult for you to deal with them. If you have an optimistic attitude, you are more likely to expect that a positive outcome is possible and to focus on what you can do when faced with a change or decision. With a pessimistic attitude, focus is on the negative. Being optimistic doesn't mean you suppress your feelings when dealing with a difficult situation or decision. It's perfectly normal to feel discouraged, angry, fearful, anxious, sad and uncertain. However, people who are optimistic get beyond these feelings to make the most of a situation.

An optimistic attitude helps you avoid depression, helps you focus, and motivates you to move forward. Studies also show that an optimistic attitude may help you avoid getting sick during stressful times. On the other hand, a pessimistic attitude— for example, thinking nothing can be done—will probably keep you from looking for ways to deal with the changes you face and will increase feelings of helplessness. And, it might even put your health at risk.

Optimism creates possibilities and hope; pessimism destroys them. How you view events can either enhance or undermine your ability to master a transition. As Delores said, "It's difficult to remain optimistic when things aren't going well, but a pessimistic attitude makes the job of caregiving even harder."

Learning to Be Optimistic

It has been said that an optimist sees a glass as half full while a pessimist sees the same glass as half empty. The optimist usually sees a favorable outcome and tends to focus on the most hopeful aspects of a situation, whereas the pessimist tends to take the gloomiest possible view of a situation. In his book *Learned Optimism*, Martin Seligman says that if you learned to be pessimistic as a child you can learn to become more optimistic. A pessimistic attitude is not set in stone.

To determine if you tend to be optimistic or pessimistic, complete the following. Check "yes" if you agree with the statement; check "no" if you don't agree.

Yes	No	
❐	❐	Caregiving problems are never-ending.
❐	❐	Good things that happen are only brief moments in time.
❐	❐	Chronic illness casts a dark cloud over every area of my life.
❐	❐	I am responsible for making the care receiver happy.
❐	❐	Nothing can be done to make my situation better.

If you checked "yes" to any of the previous statements, your attitude tends toward pessimism and may be inhibiting your ability to deal with change and to make sound decisions.

Seligman claims your attitude depends on how you explain to yourself things that happen in your life, especially life's negative events and setbacks. You can become more optimistic by applying these tools:

◆ View setbacks as temporary.

◆ View bad things as specific, not universal.

◆ Seek solutions to problems.

◆ Give yourself credit for what you do.

◆ Recognize beliefs are not facts.

◆ Practice positive self-talk.

View setbacks as temporary

An optimist sees good things as permanent or lasting and problems as temporary. For instance, Diane said that she will always feel Alzheimer's disease brought her closer to her mother. Although the effects of this disease are permanent, she found something positive in it. Diane's optimism was evident in her ability to see an increased closeness toward her mother even though her mother's illness was a downhill slide.

A pessimist tends to see good things as temporary or fleeting and problems as permanent. Pessimists frequently use words like "always" and "never." If Diane's opinion had been that her closer relationship with her mother probably wouldn't last, her attitude would have been pessimistic.

View bad things as specific, not universal

An optimist tends to see good things as universal or widespread and bad things as specific. For example, Marge saw the stroke (a bad thing) as affecting only part of her and Norm's daily life, not their whole relationship. They still enjoyed each other and went fishing and on guided tours.

A pessimist tends to see good things as specific and bad things as universal. He may view that unpleasant events will last forever, perhaps even a lifetime. If Marge believed fishing was the only good thing left in their lives and that the stroke ruined their future, it would be a pessimistic attitude.

Seek solutions to problems

Optimistic people generally will look toward hopefulness and at prospects of "what can I do." In other words, when problems develop, they focus on finding solutions. Pessimists tend to feel helpless to change anything.

Give yourself credit for what you do

An optimist is more willing to take credit for the good things that happen and not feel responsible for the bad things over which he has no control. For example, Stephen credited himself with finding and hiring in-home help for his mother.

Pessimists tend to take things personally and blame themselves for the bad things that happen over which they have no control. They credit the good things that happen to outside causes. A pessimistic person might say, "I just make matters worse. If it wasn't for the doctors, my relative wouldn't be getting better."

Recognize beliefs are not facts

Seligman says that many people make the mistake of assuming that the negative things they think about themselves must be true. He suggests we need to challenge self-recriminations in the same way we would challenge someone who accused us of something we believed was not true.

Practice positive self-talk

People who are optimistic practice positive self-talk. Positive self-talk builds confidence and self-esteem; negative self-talk increases pessimism and vice versa.

How do you explain unfortunate events that happen to you? Do you give yourself the credit you deserve for the good things that happen? Are you hopeful about your capacity to deal with changes? As you read the comparisons in the box below, which outlook most closely fits yours?

Optimistic Outlook	**Pessimistic Outlook**
"Things usually work out eventually." *(Sees bad events as temporary that will pass. Shows hopefulness.)*	"Things never seem to work out." *(Sees bad things as permanent and unchangeable. Sees good as fleeting. Believes nothing can be done so does nothing.)*
"Despite the stroke we still enjoy each other and our fishing trips." *(Sees life as generally good with a negative event affecting only a part of life.)*	"The stroke has ruined our retirement years." *(Sees a negative event affecting entire life. Causes feelings of grief and loss for a future now viewed as gone.)*
"Strokes happen. I'm looking at what we can do to prevent another stroke." *(Does not blame self for situations or behavior cannot control. Willing to take credit for good things.)*	"If I had insisted Norm quit smoking and fixed healthier meals, he probably would not have had a stroke." *(Blames self for negative situations over which has no control.)*

When Being Realistic Looks Like Pessimism

Sometimes your outlook may seem pessimistic because you are looking at a situation from a realistic point of view. This doesn't mean you're a pessimist; it means you're a realist. Seligman calls this "flexible optimism" or "optimism with your eyes wide open." You might view the increased care needs of your family member as beyond your capacity. In this instance, your perspective may guide you toward making a decision to seek help. An optimistic but unrealistic expectation of your ability to carry on might lead to "caregiver burnout."

When something does go wrong, an optimist focuses on why it happened, learns from the situation, and considers "what can I do to make it better." An optimist doesn't gloss over a difficult situation, nor does he fall into despair (which is typical of a pessimist).

Realism is healthy and useful. It aids in successful future planning and in learning from misfortune. However, sometimes when under stress, realism can unintentionally slip into pessimism. With pessimism comes an avalanche of negative self-talk. When one is used to frank, realistic self-talk, it can be difficult to recognize, catch and reword the negative self-talk (for example, switching from "hardly anyone helps …." to "I'm fortunate to have the help of….").

How Negative Thinking Undermines Optimism

Negative thinking magnifies problems. Emotions build and problems tend to grow and get worse, fueled by pessimism. Then you usually get what you expect. A situation created solely in your mind can create needless stress and feelings of anger or sadness even though nothing actually happened to change the situation.

Marge was fixing dinner but she was still thinking about breakfast. Since his stroke, Norm had begun pointing instead of trying to ask for things. Over and over, Marge has to guess what Norm wants. When she guesses wrong, Norm gets mad. Marge became furious when Norm did this at breakfast today. All day she thought about what would happen if they were destined to treat each other this way. It would spoil the rest of their years together and ruin what was a wonderful marriage.

A cycle of negative thinking can begin with a minor problem that builds in the mind to a major one. Marge began a cycle of negative thinking in which Norm's pointing lead to thoughts about a breakdown in communication and ultimately, destruction of their marriage. Nothing had changed since breakfast. This depressing outcome was born totally in Marge's mind.

Negative thoughts can become like habits and come to mind automatically. "I can't do anything right" or "Nothing seems to work out" might surface each time you make a mistake or something goes wrong. These automatic negative thoughts undermine optimism, increase stress, and contribute to depression. According to Seligman, "a recipe for severe depression is an existing pessimism encountering failure." Pessimism does not cause depression, but it provides fertile soil in which depression grows.

Negative thinking can be controlled, but it takes conscious effort. Seligman claims that once you are aware of your pessimistic thoughts you can deal with them with two tools. The first is to distract yourself—to shift your attention to something positive. The second is to challenge or dispute negative thoughts. Challenging is the most effective, long-lasting technique.

Distraction

Distraction works because the brain can only think of one subject at a time. Deliberately shifting your attention to something else forces the mind to abandon its original thought. Tasks that require concentration like writing a letter or doing a crossword puzzle work well.

Interrupting habitual thought patterns is another simple distracting technique. Some people put a rubber band around their wrist and snap it every time a negative thought surfaces. Others carry a 3×5 card with the word STOP written on it in large red letters. Clapping hands and yelling *"Stop!"* is another technique. Yelling "Stop" is not the same as saying to yourself, "I'm not going to think about (Norm's pointing) anymore." Telling yourself not to think a negative thought actually focuses your attention on that thought. Saying the word "Stop" simply interrupts the thought process for a short time.

You can strengthen the interrupting technique by combining it with a positive statement. For example, when you think,

"Nothing I do helps," use an interrupting technique, then restate the thought, "This situation is demanding. What I do helps tremendously." Once the positive statement is made, shift your attention elsewhere. It often helps to write down positive statements and place them where you will see them. Mirrors, refrigerator doors, and car visors are ideal places.

When you combine interrupting and shifting attention you will get longer-lasting results. For instance, after you snap the rubber band, direct your attention elsewhere or select a task that requires concentration such as reading or working on a hobby.

You can also stop the cycle of negative thinking by rescheduling it. When a thought nags at you, you can tell yourself, "Stop, I'll think about this after dinner."

Challenging negative thinking

In most cases, negative thoughts are distortions. Therefore, the best method for breaking the cycle of negative thinking is to challenge the truth of it. This works better and lasts longer than distraction and it usually stops the "gathering gloom of depressing thoughts." It also defends you against being victimized by your own self-criticism.

You can effectively challenge negative thinking by playing detective. Ask yourself, "What is the evidence to refute this belief? Is there an alternative way to look at this?" Recall facts and actual situations that contradict negative thoughts.

It was 2:00 a.m. and Stephen was wide awake. He was thinking about how hard he tried to be a productive employee, a good dad, a faithful husband, and a loyal son. His thoughts led him to the conclusion that people only cared about what he could do for them; they really didn't care about him. He began feeling depressed. Then he asked himself: Was his thinking true? Was he being fair? After all, didn't he just get a raise at work? Didn't his boys save their allowance to surprise him with tickets to a Chicago Bulls basketball game? Isn't his wife the one who just spent all day cooking for his Super Bowl party? And weren't there tears in his mother's eyes when she said, "Your dad would have been so proud of you, Stephen."

Stephen challenged the truth of his thoughts. Once he discredited his thoughts with facts he could reject them as false and meaningless. To challenge negative thinking and silence your inner critic, try these steps:

1. **Identify your negative thoughts so they can be evaluated and challenged.**

2. **Make a mental or written note of your negative thoughts. Then ask yourself:**
   - Do I think in terms of "always" and "never"? For example, "No matter what I do it never makes a difference." "Something always goes wrong."
   - Do my thoughts make sweeping claims like, "Nobody ever helps me"?
   - Do my thoughts make me feel guilty? Do I blame myself by using terms like, "I should have…" and "If only I had…"?

3. **Challenge your negative thoughts with facts. Confront your inner critic with evidence that makes your self-talk untrue.**
   - Is it true that I have never made anyone feel better, comfortable, safe, and loved?
   - Is it a fact that no one ever helps? No one ever does anything?
   - Is it really true that I am responsible for things over which I have no control?

   It's a good idea to challenge negative thoughts before expressing them to others. Someone else may be accidentally hurt or offended and may challenge them less kindly. The caregiver who says, "Nobody ever helps me," may be challenged with, "What do you mean? I have helped you."

4. **Identify specific ways to change what you can.**

   If your attitude about a problem tends to be pessimistic, identify something about the problem you can modify. This encourages a positive outlook because it disproves your view of the problem as permanent or unchangeable. If your thoughts say "No one ever helps," asking for help could change these thoughts.

Using the example below, jot down anything negative you say to yourself. Then challenge your claim with a factual statement that makes your negative thoughts or self-criticism untrue.

CHALLENGING NEGATIVE THOUGHTS

Negative Statement

I feel like I never do anything right.

I can't keep anything straight anymore.

Challenge

I found and hired a student nurse to help my mother.

I manage the finances.

SUMMARY

The goal is to achieve a positive attitude based on present reality. Because you have control over your attitude, reaching this goal is up to you. If your current attitude is based on wishful thinking about the past, you can change it by how you deal with change and transition.

If you view a setback as "ruining your entire life forever," you can change your perspective by identifying parts of your life untouched by the setback. If you view mistakes as opportunities to learn instead of signs of personal failure, you can avoid repeating them. If negative thinking and unfair self-criticism undermine your self-confidence, and paralyze your creativity, you can challenge the negativity with facts that make the criticism untrue.

Overview

Chapter Seven

Before Making a Decision
Understand Your Motives, Attitudes, and Feelings
Learn from Past Experiences and Those of Others
Understand Your Relative's Needs and Feelings
Involve Your Relative in Decisions
Investigate Potential Options
Recognize Your Relative's Right to Take Risks

A Model for Making Decisions
1. Identify the Problem
2. Gather Information
3. Generate Options
4. Evaluate Options
5. Create a Plan
6. Act on the Plan
7. Reassess the Plan

Holding a Family Meeting
Include Everyone
Consider a Two-Step Meeting
Plan for Success
Use a Facilitator

Making Decisions Under Tough Circumstances
When Your Relative Covers Up Needs
When You Receive Mixed Messages
When the Care Receiver is Memory Impaired

Plan Ahead If You Can

Summary

Making Tough Caregiving Decisions

The increased care needs of your family member, a decrease in your ability to provide care, or other changing circumstances may require making a difficult decision. This may include hiring in-home help, determining if your family member is still safe driving or living at home, moving your family member into a professional care setting, and making legal or financial decisions.

Making caregiving decisions creates stress, anxiety and worry for many caregivers because such decisions often mean a change in the care receiver's life and there are no guarantees a decision will work. It's a tremendous responsibility to make decisions on behalf of someone who cannot take an active part; you may try your best, but wonder if you are making the right decision or if others will approve.

You may feel guilty if a decision also serves your need for relief from worry and stress. However, it's just as important to consider your needs as those of the care receiver. Decisions based on reality, rather than emotions and past promises, have a better chance of working. This chapter provides you with tools for:

◆ making the best possible caregiving decisions.

◆ conducting a family conference.

◆ planning ahead.

Chapters in the "Special Concerns" section focus on specific major decisions.

BEFORE MAKING A DECISION

Even seemingly minor decisions can be difficult and have significant impact. Consider the decision Diane, a 55-year-old daughter and caregiver, made.

I am a full-time caregiver for my mom, who has Alzheimer's disease. Two weeks ago I decided that both of us should resign from our church choir. Mom loves to sing but during the last few months she has been singing the wrong hymns and getting lost in the music. Her confusion caused problems for the entire choir.

I felt embarrassed for her and for me. Resigning from the choir was one of the most painful decisions I've ever made. Mom still asks me, "When are we going to choir practice?"

Diane decided her mother's memory problems made it impossible for her to continue singing in the church choir. Diane's attitude was that her mother's problems were lasting. She assumed her mother's confusion was so widespread that she couldn't participate at all. In reality, there were certain hymns, especially Christmas carols, her mother knew by heart and could still sing.

Diane would have been better prepared to make this decision if she had explored the basis for it. What was driving the decision—was it embarrassment or the true facts of the situation? Did she investigate ways her mother could participate in the choir in a limited way? Or did she decide her mother simply had to quit? After asking these questions, Diane might have reached the same decision. However, if she had explored possible options and found them unworkable,

her doubts and sad feelings about making the decision would be somewhat relieved by knowing that she tried.

Before making a decision it is important to:

- understand your motives, attitudes, and feelings.
- learn from past experiences and those of others.
- understand your relative's needs and feelings.
- involve your relative in decisions.
- investigate potential options.
- recognize your relative's right to take risks.

Understand Your Motives, Attitudes, and Feelings

Your attitudes, feelings, and motives will influence your ability to be objective and thus, your effectiveness as a decision maker. Ask yourself:

- What are my motives? What do I want? Do I want to open the door for discussing concerns or do I want my relative to do what I believe should be done?
- How would I describe my attitude about the situation? Can I be objective?
- How do my feelings fit into the decision? Would this decision make me feel better, less worried, or less embarrassed? Are my feelings distorting or exaggerating the problem?

Talk to someone you trust if you are uncertain about your feelings or if you suspect you are exaggerating the problem. Another person may give you the needed objectivity.

Learn from Past Experiences and Those of Others

Reflect on past caregiving decisions and consult other caregivers in your circle of family, friends, or support group members who have made similar decisions. Learning from past experience is a valuable way to prevent repeating mistakes and to guide future decisions. Ask yourself:

◆ What about the timing of past caregiving decisions? Were decisions made too hastily? Were they made too soon or too late? Or was the timing about right?

◆ What would I do differently to reach a decision?

◆ What helped me to make a sound decision that can be applied to the current decision?

Ask other caregivers:

◆ How did you decide it was time to make a decision about a similar problem?

◆ What would you do differently next time?

◆ What professional help (social services, private agencies) did you find useful or would you recommend for evaluating the situation or to provide caregiving services?

◆ What would the care receiver do in a similar situation?

Understand Your Relative's Needs and Feelings

An important step is to evaluate your relative's needs and to strive to understand his thoughts and feelings. This can be especially difficult if you are a long-distance caregiver. To get a complete picture, you may need to obtain information from a wide range of people, including your relative, health care providers, family members, neighbors, and local business and delivery people.

Identify areas where help is needed

Before deciding what must be done, you need to know how well your family member functions in daily activities and in performing specific tasks such as driving and managing finances. The more you understand your relative's needs, the better prepared you will be to make a decision.

Some of the areas in which people often need help are:

◆ diet and meal preparation.

◆ home safety and maintenance.

◆ housekeeping.

◆ health care.

◆ personal care.

◆ medication management.

◆ mobility and transportation.

◆ legal and financial issues.

◆ socialization, companionship.

◆ activities and recreation.

Identify your relative's remaining skills

In addition to understanding the ways your family member relies on others for help, consider what he still does independently. Based on your assessment of what activities he performs easily or with some difficulty, you can try to anticipate what help may be needed in the near future. Answering the following questions will help you clarify your family member's needs and remaining skills.

◆ What specific change(s) is my relative experiencing? What problems or needs are these changes creating?

- Are his needs temporary or permanent?
- Does he need occasional or continuous help?
- Does my family member see these changes as problems?
- In what ways does he compensate for these changes?
- Which, if any, of these changes are harmful to him or others?

If you need or want a professional evaluation, contact a care manager, nurse, or social worker who specializes in evaluating the needs and functioning of ill or frail individuals living at home. Your relative's physician, the local senior center, the area agency on aging, or disease-related support groups may be able to refer you to reputable individuals or agencies that provide this service. In addition to providing an objective assessment, a professional evaluation may give you more confidence as you face making a decision.

Be sensitive to your relative's perspective

Try to understand your relative's thoughts and feelings in regard to accepting help, giving up driving, having someone else manage his finances, or moving. Sometimes people welcome a change because they have been worrying about how they will manage. Frequently, however, a change is traumatic and stress-producing.

Involve Your Relative in Decisions

Charlie, age 85, is a widower and a retired commercial fisherman. Once a robust man, he has become frail and hard of hearing. Last week he tripped over his pant leg, fell, and bruised his arms and knees. When his daughter Jennifer asked him about the bruises, he said he couldn't remember what happened. Upon hearing this, Jennifer insisted Charlie let someone stay with him during the day. Charlie resisted. He had other ideas. But Jennifer persisted. She advertised for and hired a home care worker. It seemed perfect, except Charlie decided he didn't like the worker and fired her a week later.

Jennifer's plan didn't have a chance to succeed because she made plans *for* Charlie instead of *with* him. She needed to put herself in her father's shoes. Would she want other people making decisions for her without asking what she wanted? Would she be upset if her dad told her what she should do?

Let's consider how the situation might have been different if Jennifer had actively involved her dad in the decision.

Jennifer asked her dad, if someone helped him around the house, what would he want that person to do? She also asked him if he would prefer the person who did the chores to be a man or a woman. Charlie said, "I'd like a man but men don't do housework." She asked him if he'd consider hiring a woman if a man couldn't be found. He said, "Maybe."

A week later she told her dad she had talked to several qualified men over the telephone who were interested in working for him. She asked if he would like to meet them. She said, "After you meet them you may decide if you want one of them to work for you."

Although there is no guarantee, Jennifer stands a better chance that her dad will accept help this time. The goal is to help your relative meet his needs so he can live the life of his choosing instead of yours. No adult wants decisions made for him no matter how wise those decisions may be. Talk with your family member about his desires and priorities. When he sees his ideas or wishes incorporated into the decision, he has a vested interest in making the decision work. Involving him increases the likelihood he will consider a suggestion and accept a change, even if he prefers a different one.

Including your family member in decision making does not mean decisions are left totally up to him. The tasks within the decision-making process must be within the skill level of your family member. When a person has memory loss or reduced mental capacity, others must take an active role in making and carrying out decisions. Be careful not to leave necessary decisions completely unaddressed because you inappropriately gave the power of the final "yes" or "no" to your family member.

Decisions should not burden others unnecessarily. You can set limits on what you and other family members can do. Then within those limits your family member can make the decision. For example, if your mother can no longer drive, you can make a list of times you would be able to drive her and she could make a list of times she usually runs her errands. Compare the

QUESTIONS TO ASK
The following are important questions to answer when faced with a decision:

Yes No

☐ ☐ Do I know my relative's current and long-term needs?

☐ ☐ Do I understand his capabilities as well as his limitations?

☐ ☐ Have I gathered information on all available options to meet my relative's needs?

☐ ☐ Am I aware of how my relative feels and thinks about his situation and needs?

☐ ☐ Do I know and understand his preferences?

☐ ☐ Do I respect his preferences, even if they conflict with mine?

☐ ☐ Am I willing to allow him to take some risks which may have negative consequences for him alone?

☐ ☐ Do I know how other family members will be affected by my relative's risk-taking?

☐ ☐ Am I fully informed about my relative's financial situation?

☐ ☐ Will he be involved (as much as possible) in making decisions?

☐ ☐ Do I know how other family members (e.g., brothers and sisters) feel about the situation?

☐ ☐ Do I know how others are willing to help?

The more "yes" answers you have, the better prepared you are to make a decision.

lists to see if any of the times match. If no times match, you can seek a compromise that reflects your needs and her needs.

Investigate Potential Options

Try not to have preconceived ideas about what is "the best." It's important to identify all potential options and the benefits and limitations of each—from both your perspective and that of your family member. If possible, your family member should have at least two options from which to choose. Having some choice often helps to give a sense of control and reduce resistance.

Recognize Your Relative's Right to Take Risks

Sally's Aunt Mamie spent the last 60 of her 86 years living on her own in an old three-story house that badly needed repairs. The only bathroom was upstairs and Mamie had trouble climbing stairs. Increasingly concerned about her aunt's safety, Sally tried to talk her into moving to an assisted living facility near Sally's own home. It seemed like a good idea to Sally.

"Nothing doing," said Aunt Mamie firmly. "I've lived here more than 50 years and I'm not moving now!"

Many families worry about a mentally competent elderly relative whose safety is at risk. They may try to work out other alternatives with their relative without success. If an accident occurs, they frequently blame themselves for not stepping in. It's important to remember that mentally competent

adults have the right to make choices regardless of age, as long as they are not putting others at risk. You cannot force change or overrule the decisions of a person who is not mentally incapacitated. However, the person who has the ability and the right to make a decision is also responsible for accepting the consequences of his choices.

If you find yourself in a dilemma like Sally's, communicate your fears and talk about the potential consequences of an injury. Your relative may think that you will provide needed care should an accident occur, or that an accident wouldn't affect his living situation. Unspoken expectations need airing. Saying, "I worry about who will take care of you if you fall and are seriously injured," might open the door to a frank discussion of "what ifs." Faced with reality, the person might reconsider your suggestions about safety. If not, and your fear of an injury comes true, remember the decision was your relative's, not yours—you had no control over it.

A MODEL FOR MAKING DECISIONS

Strong emotions can arise in making decisions. Family members (including the relative you are concerned about) may have different views of a situation, the options, and the decision. They may have different priorities: one may feel the person's safety is most important while another may believe the person remaining at home is more important than safety issues. A decision can become bogged down over emotions and philosophical differences.

Many caregivers find it helpful to have a plan to follow as they make decisions. The figure illustrates a seven-step model for systematically approaching a decision. It can help you to make the most thoughtful and best decision.

1. Identify the Problem

You need to agree on what the problem is before exploring options or trying to reach a decision. Family members may disagree about what the problem is or they may agree on the problem but have different views of it. Present specific facts and situations if one person doesn't see a problem at all. It may help to answer the following questions:

◆ How does the problem present itself? What has been observed?

◆ Why is there a problem?

◆ What makes it a problem?

◆ Who is affected?

◆ What is the current situation? How widespread is the problem?

◆ What are the consequences if a decision is not reached about the problem?

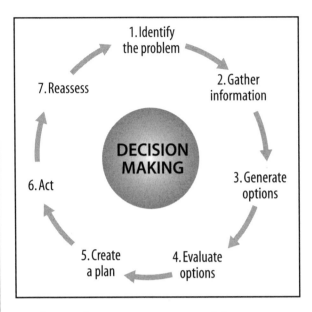

The goal is to pinpoint a problem as specifically as possible. It's important to move from generalizations such as "Dad is a poor driver," to describing specifically what has been observed. For example, "At least twice last week Dad did not stop at stop signs," "A month ago he was cited for running a red light," "He straddles the center line when he drives," and three neighbors have expressed concern about the safety of their young children when Dad is driving in the neighborhood." Without identifying the specific problem(s), a problem can seem too large or vague to tackle. This can lead to feeling overwhelmed and not making a decision or taking action.

2. Gather Information

Your goal is to make an informed decision. Often families are so concerned about solving a difficult situation that pertinent questions, which provide a stronger base for decision making, go unasked and unanswered. It's important to have objective information about the person's health and level of functioning, and to gather information from all relevant sources. This may include information about community and family resources and your family member's finances.

3. Generate Options

Once the problem has been clearly identified, it's time to brainstorm options. This is thinking of as many ideas as you can to address the problem. The likelihood of selecting the best option is increased if all available alternatives are considered in decision making. Keep this step separate from evaluating the options. It's important not to evaluate or censor ideas as they are presented. The purpose of brainstorming is the free exchange of ideas without fear of criticism or rejection. Critical thinking comes later. Health care and social service professionals can help identify options.

4. Evaluate Options

With most decisions there is no one "right" or "perfect" course of action. You are trying to find the best choice among the available alternatives. Remember, any decision you make is likely to have both positive and negative consequences.

The next step in decision making is to figure out which option will have the best outcome for your family. After all options have been identified, think about the positive and negative consequences or benefits and limitations of each one. The following questions may be helpful:

◆ What are the potential benefits of this option for my family member? For myself?

◆ How likely is it that these benefits will occur?

EVALUATING OPTIONS

Options	Benefits	Limitations

◆ What are the limitations or disadvantages of each option for my family member? For myself?

As you evaluate each option, consider both short-term and long-term consequences for you and your family member. Choosing the least restrictive option for your relative is an important goal. This is the option that allows the most freedom of movement and choice. However, an option should not unfairly burden anyone. Therefore, it's critical that everyone involved speak openly and honestly about what they can and cannot do.

Agreeing on standards for evaluating the options—criteria such as financial limits and personal preferences—also can help you select the best option(s). You might also find that combining two or more individual options results in the best decision. It may be helpful to prioritize the options and develop a possible back-up plan. It is possible your first choice may not work.

A good guideline to follow is "Be easy on people; be tough on issues." Good communication is an essential ingredient in making decisions as a family.

Writing identified options on a chart like the one on page 142 helps organize ideas. Recording points made can also help to reduce confusion and misunderstandings. And, it gives a visual model of how you reached the decision.

Another reason for evaluating options may be to streamline them. We often feel "the more choices, the better"; however, for some memory-impaired people too many choices can be overwhelming. Reducing the options to the best two or three may reduce confusion, and yet give the person a sense of control over the decision.

5. Create a Plan

This can be the most difficult part of decision making, especially if there doesn't seem to be a single best choice. At times, you may feel that you must select the "least worst" of the options. But, if your choice meets your relative's needs, if you tried to preserve the greatest control and freedom for him, consider that you made the best decision for now.

Developing a step-by-step strategy for implementing the plan, putting the plan in writing, and indicating who has agreed to do which tasks can reduce disagreements among family members. A written plan can also be useful later when you evaluate it.

6. Act on the Plan

Carry out the plan. Try to establish a trial period, using the perspective of "This seems like the best decision for now. Let's give it a try for _____ weeks/months, then look at our plan again."

7. Reassess the Plan

A plan should not be considered as "final and forever." Because situations change, flexibility is key to quality decision making. Reassessing a plan can be hard to do, especially if you want closure to a difficult situation. You might want to skip this step because it takes you back over old issues you want behind you. However, asking "How well is the plan working?" and making necessary adjustments is decision making at its best. Be prepared to try a different option or go back through the decision-making process.

This decision-making model is a guide. No plan is foolproof, but by following a decision-making process, you increase your chances of making a decision that works.

Decisions are influenced by many factors, including the personalities of family members, the quality of relationships, and communication patterns. Other factors include whether the older person is mentally intact and able to participate, whether a decision is being made in advance or at a time of crisis, and whether family members are living nearby or at a distance. In spite of these differences, quality decision making can occur by following a decision-making process and focusing on issues and options (not personalities or old grievances).

HOLDING A FAMILY MEETING

A family meeting is one tool for deciding how to share caregiving responsibilities and for making caregiving decisions. It gives everyone an opportunity to discuss concerns, identify current or potential problems and solutions, and negotiate the sharing of caregiving tasks. It can also reduce misunderstandings and clarify each person's expectations. The following guidelines can help insure the effectiveness of a family meeting.

Include Everyone

Involve everyone who is concerned and affected by caregiving decisions. This includes siblings, spouses, other relatives, housemates, the person for whom plans are being made, and perhaps close friends or neighbors. If illness prevents the care receiver from being involved directly, get his input and keep him informed.

A family member should not be excluded because of distance, personality, or limited resources. It's just as important to include a family member who is difficult, argumentative, or never visits, as those who are supportive. Telephoning distant relatives to get their input and keeping them informed will help them feel a part of decision making. Involvement of all family members in developing caregiving plans and making decisions ensures greater support, and helps prevent undermining of decisions.

Consider a Two-Step Meeting

Sometimes families find it helpful to hold a two-step meeting. The first meeting is held without the care receiver to air ideas and feelings, identify concerns, look at gaps in information, and discuss responsibilities.

The purpose should not be to make the decision or to "gang up" on the care receiver. A second meeting is then held with the care receiver, who is actively involved in looking at the options and making decisions.

Plan for Success

A family meeting is most successful when you do the following:

◆ Before the conference, ask family members to list their concerns and the tasks they are willing to do.

◆ Hold the meeting in a neutral setting.

◆ Create a feeling of trust, support, and confidentiality.

◆ Keep the meeting focused on the current concern rather than on other issues or past conflicts.

◆ Be certain everyone has an opportunity to express feelings, voice preferences, and offer suggestions without being put down.

◆ Focus on the positive. Identify what each person can do, but encourage everyone to be honest about their limitations.

◆ Prepare a written plan, listing what each person will do and when they will do it. But, keep it flexible. A written plan can prevent later disagreements about who agreed to do what, and can assure that needed tasks will be completed.

Use a Facilitator

A family meeting is not always easy. Decision making is most difficult if family members have never discussed feelings or family issues, or if family conflicts already exist. When family members come together after years of separation, old conflicts can re-emerge with regard to relationships, family roles, expectations, and even inheritance.

If family conflicts or hidden resentments are likely to prevent rational discussion and decision making, seek professional guidance. A counselor, health or social service professional, private care manager, or a member of the clergy trained in family counseling can help you deal with family conflicts. He also may be able to facilitate the family conference and provide objectivity.

MAKING DECISIONS UNDER TOUGH CIRCUMSTANCES

Special circumstances or difficult relationships may hamper decision making. Sometimes people hide problems, send mixed messages about what they want or will do, or cannot participate in decision making. This can place you in a quandary: Do I force a decision or let things ride? Letting things ride ultimately puts you in the position of waiting for a crisis before making a decision or addressing a problem.

When Your Relative Covers Up Needs

Some people cover up problems because they fear they will be forced to move or to accept in-home help. If involving them in the decision and reassuring them of your intentions doesn't help you to get needed information, try these steps.

- **Talk to others in the family.** Ask what they have observed. The information and opinions expressed might give you additional insight and alert you to potential areas of disagreement among family members.

- **Ask friends and neighbors** if they have concerns. You may be surprised by what friends and neighbors know and how much they do to help your relative. This is also an opportunity to strengthen your relative's support system and acknowledge their help by showing your appreciation.

- **Talk to local business people (grocers, druggists, fast food employees).** Individuals who provide services such as mail delivery and garbage pickup—also may have seen or suspected problems. This is also an opportunity to let them know you value their watchfulness and who to call if they suspect a problem.

- **Write down your findings.** Take notes. Use quotes. With permission, include names and telephone numbers of your business and neighborhood contacts. This information provides a broader base for making sound decisions.

- **Seek professional advice.** Ask your family member's health care provider for information about professionals who can evaluate your relative's functioning and needs. Public and private agencies offer care management services that include an assessment of a person's needs.

When You Receive Mixed Messages

How do you make a decision if you receive different messages on different occasions? What do you do if your relative agrees to hiring help, then the next day resists the idea? How do you decide about a move that the person wants to make in the morning and then opposes in the evening?

Often mixed messages indicate that your relative is thinking about the impact of a decision. Try sharing your observation of the mixed messages and talking with him about what they represent. Listen carefully. This allows him to express feelings and may reassure him that you are sensitive to his position, uncertainty and feelings.

When the Care Receiver is Memory Impaired

If a decision must be made and declining memory is an issue, consider the preferences the person has expressed over time and incorporate these into the decision. Advise relatives of the person's wishes and your predicament.

Consult the person's physician. An assessment and "straight talk" may encourage your relative to agree that a particular decision needs to be made. However, if your relative suffers from memory loss, he may agree… then later forget. Even when this happens, you can feel more confident in moving forward with a decision because of the base of information you have. You may also use the doctor's opinion to persuade the person, "The doctor says (this change) is necessary because…."

If memory problems affect your family member's judgment, if he poses a danger to himself or others and cannot make rational decisions, you are justified in making decisions and in taking preventive action on his behalf. However, you don't have to do this alone. The physician and other professionals involved in your family member's care can provide guidance.

PLAN AHEAD IF YOU CAN

One important decision-making tool is to plan ahead. Although we can't always predict change, we can discuss potential future changes and decisions with our family member, unless he is memory impaired or cannot communicate. Advance planning can focus on issues such as declining health and long-term care, living arrangements, financial and legal issues, end-of-life decisions, and death and funeral arrangements.

The advantages of talking about and making plans in advance of need is that it helps to reduce heartache, increases understanding about a person's wishes, makes decisions easier in difficult times, and reduces uncertainty and disagreements. Advance planning also enables care receivers to maintain maximum control over their lives, especially if a time comes when they cannot actively participate in decision making.

One approach is to talk with a family member about "what ifs." For example, ask "What if the doctor said I could no longer provide the care you need, what would you like to have happen?" Talking about future "what ifs" is not always easy, particularly if frank discussions of emotional issues have been avoided in the past. Also, planning ahead requires anticipating situations we consider negative. This can make everyone feel uneasy.

Look for "natural" opportunities to talk. For example, when the care receiver says, "When I die…" or "When I can no longer live here…," be receptive to a discussion. Too often others discourage discussion by saying things such as "Don't be so morbid," or "We've got plenty of time to talk about this. Let's not talk about it now," or "You'll probably outlive all of us." Other natural times for talking may be when a family member of friend experiences a health crisis, has a car accident, makes a change in living arrangement, or develops Alzheimer's disease, or you are preparing your own will or powers of attorney for finances or health care.

When making advance plans, it is important to explore options and to have more than one plan. Circumstances later on may require flexibility.

SUMMARY

Making sound, compassionate decisions is a skill that requires preparation, cooperation, and practice. It also involves the risk that you might make mistakes. But, there is a positive side to mistakes. They provide important information to guide future decisions. A realistic attitude about present and foreseeable caregiving needs is also important to effective decision making.

There are no perfect or easy answers. There are no ready-made solutions. Every caregiving situation is unique. Although it may seem that decision making is risky, remember that not deciding is still a making a decision.

Special Concerns

CHAPTER EIGHT

Hiring In-Home Help

The day may come when you sense that it's time to look for someone to help your family member with personal care, chores or errands. Or you may come to realize that you can't do it all. Karen said:

> Dad has Alzheimer's disease and recently he began wandering away. Mom has a heart condition, and keeping a constant eye on Dad is wearing her out. I suggested she hire someone to give her a break or help around the house. She said no, not until she "really needs help." I worry about both Mom and Dad. I want to help more, but I am busy as a single parent and I work.

Bill stated:

> My wife, Mary, has Parkinson's disease. Last Tuesday she fell and broke her hip. She is coming home from the hospital in a few days. The hospital social worker told me about the limited services Medicare provides. I know I will need more help than that.

This chapter will guide you through the maze of finding, screening, and hiring an in-home worker. You will learn:

◆ when to use in-home help.

◆ how to decide the type of help you need.

◆ effective ways to supervise in-home care workers.

◆ how to end a working arrangement with an in-home care worker.

BENEFITS AND CHALLENGES

There are many benefits of using in-home help. They include:

◆ making living at home possible for longer.

◆ providing caregivers with a break and help with care.

◆ saving money. It may delay costly placement in a care facility.

◆ increasing flexibility. In-home help may be used on a temporary basis and tailored to meet both the needs of the care receiver and the caregiver.

◆ enhancing quality of life.

In-home help has its challenges, too.

◆ Cost is a factor. Although some services are covered by private insurance and Medicare, many are not. Be sure to get clear information about coverage limits.

◆ Resistance may surface. The care receiver may say he doesn't need help or want "strangers" in the house.

◆ The unexpected can happen. In-home workers may not show up or may quit without notice. You may have to juggle schedules and look for a new worker just when you thought everything was arranged.

◆ An employer's role isn't easy. You may be the one who has to interview and check references and orient, supervise, or even fire a worker.

Despite the challenges, in-home help may be the best option even for a short time. However, deciding what help you need and selecting a worker is a sizable task that requires careful thought, planning, and research.

ENTERING THE WORLD OF IN-HOME CARE

You might enter the world of in-home services after a relative's unexpected illness or injury means he needs help upon returning home from the hospital. Or perhaps your relative's care needs have gradually exceeded your physical or emotional ability to meet them. Especially when caregiving responsibilities put *your* health at risk, it's time to consider paid care providers. Remember, everyone is affected if *your* health fails.

Using In-Home Care After Hospitalization

Ideally, planning for in-home care should begin soon after your relative enters the hospital. Many caregivers have said they received very short notice of their relative's discharge and were not prepared for it. The hospital's discharge planning may not begin until your relative is about to be discharged. The doctor decides if certain medical treatments or therapy require in-home care services. The doctor does not decide if your relative needs housekeeping or personal care services (such as bathing and dressing).

If you are concerned about your ability to provide the needed care, talk to the doctor or nurse about in-home care services. Emphasize your concern by saying "I am very worried about providing the care my relative needs after he comes home. Who can I talk with about getting the help I need?" In many cases, you will be directed to a social worker in the hospital's social services department. If you feel your relative needs to recuperate in a professional care setting, say so.

Hospital discharge planners make arrangements, such as transportation and nursing services, that are needed so your relative can go home. Give the discharge planner a clear picture of your caregiving situation and the help you may need. The discharge planner may also advise you about health insurance and Medicare or Medicaid coverage for in-home services.

STEPS TO HIRING IN-HOME HELP

Hiring in-home help is an eight-step process:

1. Learn about home care services.

2. Develop a profile of care needs.

3. Write a job description.

4. Find out about legal, financial, and tax issues.

5. Decide whether to hire privately or through an agency.

6. Screen and interview applicants.

7. Check references and background.

8. Sign an agreement.

Step 1: Learn about In-Home Care Services

In-home care can be divided into two major categories: *Skilled care* and *Home support services*. Skilled care is care provided under the direction of a doctor and by health care professionals such as nurses and therapists. It includes medical procedures such as wound care, home dialysis, and physical therapy. In-home support services include housecleaning, meal preparation, and assistance with grooming and dressing. In-home care can be a combination of these services.

The hospital social worker or local area agency on aging may refer you to reputable sources of in-home help. The patient's physician may be able to give references, but typically physicians are less aware of these resources.

Talk to friends, relatives, and members of your support group who have hired in-home help. They often have valuable insights and advice.

You also need to understand who does what and how much various services cost. Different agencies give different titles to workers providing in-home services. A "homemaker" at one agency may provide personal care while a "homemaker" at a different agency may provide only housekeeping and no personal care. To add to the confusion, self-employed workers often choose their own titles. Ask exactly what a certain worker will and won't do. For a review of available in-home help, see Chapter 9, "Using Community Services."

Step 2: Develop a Profile of Care Needs

Assess your needs

You may already know the specific help you need and how often you need it. However, if the situation is complicated, consider hiring a professional who can help evaluate care needs. The local area agency on aging may offer in-home assessments or direct you to another agency that does assessments. Private home health agencies will provide assessments for a fee without expecting you to hire in-home workers through them. An assessment can help you:

◆ Define your relative's care needs and your caregiving needs.

◆ Determine worker duties and skills needed.

◆ Develop the job description.

◆ Evaluate the job performance of in-home workers.

An assessment should include your relative's needs and any special problems, such as mental confusion or difficult behavior. The assessment should cover personal care,

Profile of Care Receiver's Needs

Name:_____ Age:_____

	Yes	No	Sometimes	Comments
understands own needs	❏	❏	❏	_____
asks for help	❏	❏	❏	_____
gets around independently	❏	❏	❏	_____
needs help to eat	❏	❏	❏	_____
needs help to bathe/shower	❏	❏	❏	_____
needs help to dress/undress	❏	❏	❏	_____
needs help to use toilet	❏	❏	❏	_____
needs help with mobility	❏	❏	❏	_____
is incontinent	❏	❏	❏	_____
is bedridden	❏	❏	❏	_____
needs supervision	❏	❏	❏	_____
needs help fixing meals	❏	❏	❏	_____
needs help with medications	❏	❏	❏	_____

Special concerns:

	Yes	No	Sometimes	Comments
visually impaired	❏	❏	❏	_____
hearing impaired	❏	❏	❏	_____
confused/disoriented	❏	❏	❏	_____
depressed/anxious	❏	❏	❏	_____
Other: _____	❏	❏	❏	_____

Help needed with:

	Yes	No	Sometimes	Comments
laundry	❏	❏	❏	_____
light housework	❏	❏	❏	_____
meal preparation	❏	❏	❏	_____
transportation	❏	❏	❏	_____

Special information about the care recipient:

favorite activities: _____

favorite foods: _____

favorite clothes: _____

exercise needs: _____

emergency safety issues: _____

difficult behavior: _____

Special issues related to personal habits such as smoking; biases toward religious, racial, or ethnic groups; sensitive conversation topics: _____

_____

meals, housekeeping, medication management, and assistance needed with mobility, transportation, transferring and errands.

Your needs as a caregiver are also high priority. An assessment should consider your need for respite, help you need with tasks, and replacement help if you are employed or have other competing responsibilities.

If you do your own assessment, the sample assessment on page 157 may be helpful.

Step 3: Develop a Job Description

Use the "Profile of Care Receiver's Needs" and a list of your needs as a caregiver to develop a job description. The job description lists the tasks you want the worker to do in the home. It may include tasks related to personal care (such as bathing, dressing, and grooming), housekeeping, and leisure activities.

The more specific the job description, the better it is. It should clearly state expectations, duties, and responsibilities. It will help you recruit, interview, and hire workers. It will help applicants understand your expectations of them. It also provides a basis for evaluating a worker or terminating employment. The job description can also be included with the agreement.

The sample job description on page 159 is intended only to give you ideas for yours.

Step 4: Find Out About Legal, Financial, and Tax Issues

Clarify legal and financial issues before you begin looking for in-home help. Review insurance coverage, know your tax responsibilities if you will be employing a worker directly, and understand what is involved in

hiring an independent contractor (see "Responsibilities as an employer" below).

Insurance coverage and limits

You need basic information about insurance coverage. Ask the insurance agent:

◆ Does the automobile protection cover employees driving the family car? What are the exceptions?

◆ Does the homeowner's insurance cover property damage, theft, and personal injury that involves an employee or other person working in the home?

◆ Should liability limits be raised on the homeowner's insurance?

◆ What about bonding an employee? Bonding is an insurance policy that protects both the employee and the employer against financial loss. It does not ensure quality service. For information, check with your local automobile or life insurance agent, or look in the Yellow Pages under "Bonds, Surety, and Fidelity."

Responsibilities as an employer

The nature and extent of your responsibilities as an employer are affected by whether you hire an "independent contractor" or an "employee." These are legal distinctions with important differences.

Some caregivers, seeking to reduce paperwork and taxes, try to hire people as independent contractors rather than as employees. Independent contractors are responsible for reporting their income and paying their own Social Security and Medicare taxes.

Although this sounds great, it isn't easy to qualify as an independent contractor. The IRS insists that independent contractors use their own equipment, set their own hours, be self-supervised, and provide services to other clients. The IRS is strict about this and holds the employer responsible for proving independent contractor status. The IRS rule is: "Anyone who performs services is an employee if you (the employer) can control what will be done and how it will be done—what matters is that you have the legal right to control the method and result of the services."

For information about independent contracting, call 1-800-829-1040 and ask for Publication No. 937. The local number is listed under "U.S. Government, Internal Revenue Service."

The laws and Social Security. Be aware of laws regarding overtime, equal pay and discrimination that may apply to in-home help.

You must have your employee's Social Security number. As an employer, you are responsible for verifying that a prospective employee is eligible to work in the United States. For more information, see the "Handbook for Employers" available from

---

JOB DESCRIPTION

Household Tasks

Household Tasks	Comments/Frequency
Dust, vacuum living room	Wed & Sat, empty vacuum bag 1/mo
Change sheets	Sat
Do laundry	Wed & Sat

Personal Care Tasks

Personal Care Tasks	Comments/Frequency
Assist w/bath/shampoo	2x/wk Use conditioner on hair
Assist w/exercises	Each visit; before lunch walk to mailbox

Leisure Activities

Leisure Activities	Comments/Frequency
Read newspaper to spouse	Each visit; Likes editorial page, sports, Peanuts comic strip
TV programs	Perry Mason (noon)

Other

Provide quiet times after lunch to reduce confusion and tendency to wander

Swears sometimes. Smokes, but needs supervision.

the U.S. Department of Justice, Immigration and Naturalization Service, 425 I Street NW, Washington, DC 20536.

Tax-related responsibilities. If you employ a worker directly (that is, not as an independent contractor), you may be responsible for filing forms and paying taxes at regular times during the year. You will need an Employer Tax Identification Number (EIN). For information, call the IRS toll-free at 1-800-829-1040. Ask for SS-4, "Application for Employer Identification Number."

For information about your state tax-withholding responsibilities, contact your State Employment Division listed in the "State Government" section of your telephone directory.

You do not have to withhold federal income taxes on wages paid to an in-home worker. However, you may be responsible for:

◆ Social Security contributions (FICA)
◆ Federal Unemployment Tax (FUTA)
◆ State Unemployment Tax
◆ State Workman's Compensation

The expense and paperwork needed to comply with the law may seem overwhelming. Actually, the process is simpler than it appears. If it is too burdensome, a payroll service can help. For a fee, the service will process payroll checks, track payroll for tax purposes, and fill out quarterly tax reports.

Deductibility of health care expenses

Federal and state tax laws keep changing. Seek professional advice from an accountant or contact the IRS and your state Department of Revenue for the latest information.

Certain health care costs may be deductible. These include money spent on medications, treatments, transportation to treatment centers, and certain in-home care costs. Nursing care services are most likely to be deductible; housekeeping services less so. However, recent changes in tax law have made some personal care, supervisory and housekeeping services deductible. The IRS may ask for a statement from your family member's doctor that includes the following information:

◆ A diagnosis of the illness, whether it is permanent, the cause (if known), and the date of onset.
◆ A complete list of health care services needed.
◆ A statement of the need for live-in or daily assistance.

If you are working and sharing a household with your relative who needs care, you may be eligible for a dependent-care tax credit on your federal income taxes. This includes the cost of hiring in-home help. You will need the following information:

◆ Accurate records, canceled checks, and receipts. (Keep records for four years.)
◆ Copies of your tax returns
◆ Your employee's Social Security number
◆ Dates and amounts of wages you paid
◆ Your employee's W-4 form
◆ Any W-2 forms that were returned to you as undeliverable

It's also a good idea to save advertisements for help, job interview notes, and documents and communications such as background checks and performance evaluations.

For more information about your special circumstances, call the IRS office at 1-800-829-3676 (write down the name of the person advising you at the IRS) or order IRS Publication No. 503, "Child and Dependent Care Expenses."

Step 5: Decide Whether to Hire Privately or Through an Agency

The two main options for hiring in-home help are to employ the services of a home care agency or hire a worker privately (on your own). Both options have advantages and disadvantages. One advantage to hiring private workers is that they are usually more flexible and charge less than an agency. The advantage to working with an agency is that the agency assumes the employer responsibilities. The following information may help you choose which option is best for you.

Home care agencies

Home care agencies usually charge more than private workers because the agency assumes a wide range of responsibilities:

◆ Assess, plan, match, coordinate, and manage in-home care services.

◆ Coordinate a range of services.

◆ Recruit, screen, interview, hire, train, supervise, evaluate, and pay the worker.

◆ File forms, pay taxes, pay insurance coverage, and bond the worker.

◆ Find a replacement if the worker is ill or for some reason cannot come to work.

◆ Discipline the worker.

◆ May provide nursing back-up for non-licensed staff.

Home health care agencies focus on the medical aspects of care and may be affili-ated with hospitals. Their services usually are limited by insurance and/or Medicare to a certain number of visits. *Homemaker/ home care agencies* provide both short-term or extended non-medical services such as personal care, housekeeping, companionship and supervision.

If you hire a home health agency that provides Medicare-certified services, they will need information from your relative's doctor. The agency will contact the doctor for instructions and approval of services and then will send out a nurse to conduct an assessment. Your input into this assessment is important.

Finding the right agency. Word of mouth is one of the best ways to find a quality agency. Also, a national network of state and area agencies on aging provides infor-mation about community services in any area of the country. Call the Eldercare Locator at 1-800-677-1116.

Before selecting an agency, ask questions such as the following:

◆ Is your agency certified by Medicare?

◆ Is your agency licensed and, if so, by whom?

◆ Do you develop a written care plan that gives details about services to be provided? Do you provide the family with a copy of the plan?

◆ Are services limited to certain times of day? Is there a minimum number of hours that must be paid for?

◆ Are your workers trained to work with memory-impaired or chronically ill older adults?

◆ Is your agency bonded? Are your workers bonded?

- How long have you been in business in this area?

- What are your fees? Do you have a sliding fee scale?

- What do your fees include? Are there additional costs, such as for travel or home evaluation?

- Will you provide a written statement of your costs and billing procedures? If not then…?

- How will I be billed: by the hour, week, or month? Will I receive one bill for all services or separate bills?

- Who supervises the worker? How often does the supervisor visit the home?

- How do you handle complaints?

- Whom do I call if the worker doesn't come to work?

- Will you find a temporary replacement, if needed?

- What is your procedure if there is an emergency in the home and you can't reach me?

- How do you protect client confidentiality?

- How many references do you require before you hire a worker? (Two should be a minimum.)

- Do you do a criminal background check of employees? (Note: Not every state requires agencies to do a criminal background check. Some agencies do this voluntarily. Others do it at the client's request and charge the client a fee.)

If you want references about the agency, ask the agency for the names and telephone numbers of local professionals, such as hospital discharge planners, social workers, or community organizations who have used the agency and can supply references. You also can call the state licensing agency and the Better Business Bureau.

Working with the agency. Be candid and clear about your relative's condition and any special problems such as confusion. Your openness helps the agency to select a worker who will be compatible with you and your relative. Advise the agency about problems such as:

- The possibility that a memory-impaired relative may "fire" a worker or give away, hide, or lose possessions and then believe someone stole those items. This allows the agency to take preventive measures and prepare staff.

- Any religious, racial, ethnic, or other biases (e.g., dislikes men or women or overweight people) your relative has that might create problems for a worker.

- The presence of pets and any habits (e.g., smoking, swearing, drinking) a worker might find troublesome.

Stay in touch. Generally, agencies want you to stay in contact. They want to hear about good care and exceptional staff, and about problems such as:

- personality clashes.

- a worker who misses appointments, calls in sick, or shows up late.

- a worker who does not follow the plan of care or who fails to keep your relative clean and comfortable.

- a worker who fails to leave the home or equipment clean.

◆ a worker who lacks the skill or physical strength to provide proper care.

◆ verbal or physical abuse directed at you or your family member.

◆ suspicions of theft.

Dealing with problems. If a problem isn't serious, talk with the worker first. If this fails, or if the problem *is* serious, talk to the worker's supervisor as soon as possible. If necessary, talk to the agency's director and write a follow-up letter explaining the problem. Be specific and objective in your letter and keep a copy. If nothing is done within a week—or sooner for a grave problem—restate your concerns.

Don't hesitate to call the agency when a problem surfaces. Most agencies want to hear about problems before a situation gets out of hand or you decide to end services. If minor problems can be satisfactorily resolved early, you can avoid starting over again with a new agency.

If a home health care agency does not satisfactorily respond to a problem, contact the state office that licenses home health agencies and the Better Business Bureau. If Medicare and Medicaid funds are involved, contact the appropriate government agency. Contact the police immediately in cases of theft, fraud, or abuse. Be prepared to put your complaint in writing and to give specific examples to support your claim.

Finally, don't put a worker in the uncomfortable position of doing things that the agency does not allow or that the worker is not trained to do. For example, do not ask someone who only does housekeeping chores to help with personal care.

Finding and hiring a private in-home care worker

Hiring someone privately, rather than through an agency, may reduce costs considerably, but it will take more time and effort. You also must assume employer-related responsibilities, including screening applicants, paying taxes, and supervising the worker. It is important to weigh costs, convenience, and legal and tax responsibilities.

If you decide to find in-home help on your own, begin by asking friends and relatives for names and referrals. If you attend support group meetings, ask members for recommendations. Some community agencies have registries and will provide names of in-home workers they have screened. You may also use a private service. Check the Yellow Pages under the listings of "Home Care Registry and Referral" or "Employment Agency." There may be a fee for referral services.

University departments of nursing or social work may have students who have skills and want to work. Local community college and university career centers, especially those with nursing and social work programs, may be willing to inform students about your need for in-home assistance.

Consider advertising in the local newspaper. Weekends are the best days. Also, place your ads in bulletins and newsletters of local churches, synagogues and senior centers.

Make your own flyers and post them in key places. Type or print flyers in bold lettering on brightly colored paper. Design tear-off strips at the bottom with your first name

> **TIRED OF MINIMUM WAGE? $10/Hr.**
> Need non-smoking home-care aide to assist elderly woman with personal care and errands. Weekdays from 9 A.M. to 1 P.M. Driver's license required. Some experience in home care desired. Call Ann at 555-5555 between 4–8 P.M.

and telephone number. Ask permission to post your flyers on the bulletin boards at:

◆ local houses of worship.

◆ libraries, college dormitories, and college career centers.

◆ senior centers and cultural centers.

◆ hospitals and health care clinics.

◆ retirement communities and mobile home parks.

◆ supermarkets.

You will eliminate needless calls if you describe the job, wages, working hours, and any special requirements such as a driver's license. Include only your first name and telephone number or post office box. Emphasize any benefits of the job such as pay being higher than the minimum wage. The sample above will help you develop your ad or flyer.

Step 6: Screen and Interview Applicants

Your goal is to find the best person for the job; that is, the best match in terms of care needs, services, and personalities. A good, comfortable relationship between you, your family member, and the worker is critical. Although you want someone who can do the necessary tasks, the worker also should be sensitive, caring and understanding of your family member's needs and your situation. The relationship between the care receiver and the worker is often what determines the success of in-home services. Take the time to select carefully.

Screening applicants by telephone

Interviewing begins with screening by telephone. Develop a chart (example on page 166) to record the information you get from the applicant. This enables you to ask the same questions each time and to compare the responses.

Interviewing applicants

After reviewing the information on each applicant, select the best qualified and invite them for a personal interview. Conducting an in-person interview is truly the only way to select the best in-home care worker. Many family caregivers conduct two face-to-face interviews, one *with* their family member present and one *without* their family member present. If you decide on one personal interview, try to include your family member. Involvement increases the chances your family member will give in-home help a try rather than sabotage arrangements you make.

Although the interview provides a chance to get acquainted, it is a conversation with a purpose that requires preparation. In addition to writing your questions in advance, ask yourself, "What would I want to know if I was applying for this position?" Remember, the applicant is also interviewing you. Have a sample agreement for the applicant to read during the interview.

If the job calls for running errands or providing transportation, ask to see the applicant's driver's license and insurance to

be sure they are valid. However, a valid driver's license doesn't mean a person is a safe driver. Therefore, you may want to ask the applicant to provide a copy of his driving record from the state Department of Motor Vehicles.

If you worry about interviewing strangers in your home, arrange to meet applicants in a public place where you can talk easily. If you feel uncomfortable interviewing alone, ask a friend or family member to join you. That person also may be helpful later in sorting out the information you obtain and discussing your impressions.

A home visit is essential before you hire anyone. It allows the applicant to meet your relative and see the work setting.

Ending the interview. Close interviews by thanking applicants for their time and interest in the position. Let applicants know when they can expect to hear from you about your decision. "I'm interviewing several people. You will hear from me by (give date)." Call to notify applicants you didn't select. If appropriate, tell them you will keep their names on file.

After the interview. Write down your impressions. It's always helpful to discuss your impressions and "gut feelings" with your relative (if possible), other family members, or friends. Your impressions will help you find the best person for the job. *Avoid hiring the applicant who talks about personal problems during most of the interview.*

Interview questions

Interviews are more productive if you prepare questions in advance. Try to ask questions that cannot be answered with a simple "yes" or "no" to encourage more information sharing. The following are examples of interview questions; however, you will need to tailor questions to your needs and situation.

◆ What are your current and past home-care experiences? What experience have you had caring for frail elderly?

◆ What is your experience in providing care for a person with (describe the illness or impairments of your relative)?

◆ What are the reasons you chose this type of work?

◆ What do you like about home care? Can you give me an example?

◆ What do you find is the most difficult part of working in home care?

◆ What would you do in case of an emergency, such as_____?

TELEPHONE INTERVIEW FORM (EXAMPLE)

Names of Applicants
A _Mary Smith_   B _Tom Brown_   C _Elsa Block_

Telephone numbers
A _255-5656_   B _256-5758_   C _256-0130_

Days/Hours
A _9-5 wkdays_   B _9-1 M, T, F_   C _12-5 Sat_

Costs
A _$7.00/hr_   B _$8.50/hr_   C _$6.40/hr_

Applicant Questions:

1. Tell me about your current and post home-care experiences. What experiences have you had caring for frail elderly?

A	B	C
Took care of mother who had AD. Felt most rewarding experience	Worked in nursing home. 6 mo. Felt didn't have time to give quality care wanted to give	Volunteer—Friendly Visitor. "Likes old people." Age 72. Cannot lift. Voice soft—can spouse hear her?

2. What is your experience in providing care for a person with (describe the illness or impairments of your relative)?

A	B	C
Mother confused, wandered. Provided total care until she died.	Took care of nursing home residents with AD, Parkinson's and stroke.	Some clients slightly confused.

3. What, if anything, in the job description would you not or could you not do?

A	B	C
No driving: won't work with smokers.	No heavy lifting, no pet care.	Cannot do lifting or transfers.

Take notes of the applicants' answers and your "instincts" about the applicant.

◆ Is there anything in the job description you would not or could not do?

◆ What classes and training have you taken to prepare for this work?

◆ What are your expectations of the family?

◆ Do you have concerns about the job description or agreement?

◆ What were the reasons you left your last job?

◆ Do you have references from past employers? (Request at least three references and require at least two.)

◆ How reliable is your transportation?

◆ When would you be available to start work?

It can be insightful to ask applicants how they would handle hypothetical situations that relate to your family member. For example:

◆ Dad has Parkinson's disease and falls sometimes. What would you do if he fell while you were caring for him?

◆ Sometimes my mother doesn't remember where she put her things and she accuses others of stealing. What would you say and do if my mother accused you of stealing her purse?

◆ Sometimes my grandmother "fires" people that come to help her. What would you do or say if she fired you?

◆ What would you do if my wife wandered away from the house?

◆ My husband has been retired for 25 years, but he often talks about "going to work." What would you say to him if he told you, "It's time for me to go to work"?

Be prepared to discuss the following with applicants:

◆ Responsibilities and duties (including whether lifting is needed)

◆ Wages/salary

◆ Work schedule, flexibility, days off

◆ House rules (e.g. no smoking)

◆ Your family member's current health, needs, limitations, and special problems such as mental confusion or incontinence

◆ How your family member feels about someone being in the home

◆ Emergency back-up arrangements

◆ Notice needed in case worker quits

◆ Notice given if the worker's service is no longer needed

◆ When you will notify the applicant of your decision

Step 7: Check References and Backgrounds

It is critical to contact references and conduct a criminal background check regardless of how impressed you are with someone in an interview.

Checking references

Request at least three references. Try to obtain at least one professional reference. If the person has been a family caregiver or for another reason doesn't have three references, ask for the name of a member of the clergy or a physician you can call. Prepare specific questions and make notes of the answers. Some suggested questions are:

◆ How long have you known the applicant?

◆ In what capacity do you know the applicant?

◆ What kind of work did the applicant do for you?

◆ How well do you feel the applicant would work with someone who is (describe your family member)? Can you give an example to illustrate?

◆ How did the applicant get along with the family? With the person receiving care?

◆ What are the applicant's strengths? Weaknesses?

◆ How punctual and dependable is the applicant?

◆ How would you describe the applicant's personality? Personal qualities?

◆ How well does the applicant follow instructions and respond to suggestions? Can you give an example?

◆ How well has the applicant handled emergency situations?

◆ Would you rehire this person?

◆ Would you like to comment about anything else?

You may have more specific questions, such as whether the applicant is a good driver. You may want to give your telephone number to the person in case he remembers something you should know.

Running a criminal background check

The best time to conduct a background check is before the applicant visits your home. Definitely do so before an agreement is signed. Both the state police and the FBI conduct these checks.

The process varies among states; however, you can begin by calling your state police. Ask for the Identification Services Section (or explain what you want). Some states require a written request. They notify the prospective worker of the impending background check. It usually takes about two weeks from the time they receive the required information from you, which may include the prospective employee's name, date of birth and current address.

The fee is usually around $20. Some applicants pay for their own background checks and make them available to potential employers.

Step 8: Sign an Agreement

You have one more hiring task: completing an agreement. An agreement clarifies the responsibilities, obligations, and duties of both parties. A specific agreement can help prevent many problems, disagreements and confusion about tasks, salary, and work hours.

The agreement should contain these basic elements:

◆ Names of employer and employee

◆ Wages and benefits (e.g., mileage and meals)

◆ Hours of work

◆ Employee's Social Security number

◆ When and how wages will be paid

◆ How taxes will be paid

◆ Specific duties to be performed

◆ Rules of the house (e.g., regarding smoking, swearing, television and radio playing, visitors, house temperature)

◆ Termination—How much notice for firing or quitting and reasons for terminating employment without notice. You may want to consider wording such as: "The family (employer) and care provider

In-Home Care Provider Agreement (Sample)

This agreement between _____ (referred to as family)

and _____ (referred to as care provider)

is intended to clarify specific working conditions and terms of employment, and to set guidelines for the care provider to follow at all times.

Salary: $_____ per hour. To be paid by check by the week _____ month _____
The family will withhold and remit to the proper agencies the taxes legally required. The family will provide a W-2 statement by January 31, for the previous calendar year. The care provider has received a job description. If the family seeks additional services the care provider will be paid at a rate to be determined on a job-by-job basis.

Hours: From_____ to _____

On (list days) _____

    Paid vacation   Yes_____ No_____ Number of days _____

    Paid sick time   Yes_____ No_____ Number of days _____

    Paid holidays   Yes_____ No_____ List of holidays_____

Car use: Family agrees to pay gasoline mileage at a rate of $_____ per mile. Care provider agrees to keep an accurate log of these miles and to abide by the laws of the State of _____

Meals: The family will _____ will not _____ pay for care provider's meals during working hours.

Personal local or long distance phone calls are _____ are not _____ permitted.

Visitors: Friends or family of care provider are _____ are not _____ permitted.

Work rules: Grounds for immediate dismissal include abuse, alcohol or drug use, smoking on the job. Coming to work late without due cause is grounds for dismissal. Number of tardy arrivals to result in dismissal _____.

Number of absences to result in dismissal _____.

Gifts: The giving of and taking of gifts or money between the care provider and the family member is not allowed.

Notice required by family or care provider before leaving position
(number of weeks): _____

We agree to these terms of employment.

Care provider (*signature*) _____ Date _____

Social Security # _____

Family/employer (*signature*) _____ Date _____

(employee) agree that the family has the right to terminate the care provider's employment at any time for any reason, or without a reason. Prior notification is not necessary under the terms of this agreement."

◆ Signatures of employee and employer and date agreement signed

Both parties should have a copy of the signed agreement. The sample agreement on page 169 may contain provisions you don't want or need. They have been included for your information. An agreement also can be revised or updated as needed.

DEVELOPING EFFECTIVE WORKING RELATIONSHIPS

Now that you have hired in-home help, it's time to develop a working relationship. Cooperation is vital. Expect a period of transition. It will take time for your family member to be comfortable with an in-home worker. People with dementia often adjust more slowly to changes. Try to be patient. Everyone involved needs a chance to learn, adjust and feel comfortable.

You have adjustments to make, too. Perhaps you have never dealt with employees who need to be oriented to a home, to what is to be done in what way, and how often. Maybe you have limited experience training, supervising, and terminating someone. If so, you're not alone. In *Home Health Aides: How to Manage the People Who Help You*, Alfred DeGraff says that common mistakes creating problems with in-home help include:

◆ Not giving clear instructions

◆ Adding extra tasks at the last minute, or expecting duties that were not agreed upon

◆ Not expressing appreciation for work well done

◆ Making unfavorable comparisons to other in-home workers

◆ Giving feedback that is either too passive or critical

A satisfying, rewarding workplace begins with good orientation and training.

Orientation

If your relative was involved in screening and interviewing the in-home worker, a special get-acquainted meeting is unnecessary. However, if your family member has

not met the person, consider a face-to-face "dress rehearsal" before the first day of work.

Tell your family member a little about the worker before they meet. Refer to the worker by the name he or she wants to be called. Talk about the worker's experience, working hours, and what the worker will and won't do. Discuss any questions or misgivings your relative raises.

Inviting the worker for a cup of coffee may be all you need to do to begin relationship-building. This visit is especially important if the worker will be providing personal care such as bathing and dressing. Consider paying the worker for this visit.

Depending on how many different services the worker will provide, you may want to set aside one day with pay for orientation and training before the worker starts the job. Listen carefully to the worker's concerns and address them during the orientation.

What is a good orientation?

An orientation should show the worker the layout of the home, where essential things are kept, and how to operate needed appliances. Involve your family member in the house tour, if possible.

A thorough orientation also includes:

◆ A step-by-step demonstration of the way you or your family member want tasks to be done.

◆ Information about the care receiver's and household routines.

◆ A review of emergency procedures and whom to contact if an emergency arises.

◆ Information about your family member's preferences. For instance, tell the worker if your relative enjoys being alone or doesn't like friendly touching.

◆ Clear instructions about what is out of bounds (rooms, thermostat settings, etc.).

◆ A clear procedure for keeping track of cash dispersed and spent if the worker does shopping or other activities that require cash.

◆ How to prevent and respond to potential problems such as wandering.

◆ Information about what your family member enjoys doing and can do for himself.

◆ An overview of general caregiving tips. Make a list of things your family member particularly enjoys or strongly dislikes. This can help the worker create pleasure for your family member and avoid doing things that disturb him.

Training or Coaching a New Worker

In training a new worker to do a task, follow this five-step process:

1. **Tell the worker how to do the task.** If you want a task done in a certain way, explain why. For instance, if your relative wants the bathroom towels folded a certain way, tell the worker that this gives him a sense of order and control when so much order and control seems to be gone. If necessary, write down step-by-step instructions.

2. **Show the worker how to do the task.** Demonstrate what you mean. If your relative likes her hair combed a certain way, show the worker.

3. **Have the worker perform the task while you observe.** Tactfully give feedback and coach the worker when it seems needed.

4. **Praise progress.** Notice and acknowledge even modest gains in skills.

5. **Provide the worker an opportunity to ask questions.** A person is more likely to feel comfortable asking questions in an open, non-threatening atmosphere.

For example, Arleta demonstrated a task as she said:

Dad likes two poached eggs for breakfast. He won't eat scrambled or fried eggs. He likes his eggs poached a certain way. When I do it, I start with about two inches of water in this frying pan. Then I turn the heat on high until the water simmers. I add about a tablespoon of white vinegar to the water to help the egg cook without falling apart. Then I break the eggs as close as I can to the surface of the water and poach them for three minutes. I'll fix the first one and you can try the second. Don't worry about forgetting. I've written step-by-step instructions and taped them inside this cupboard door.

Supervising In-Home Help

In-home workers need information from family caregivers about their job performance and ways to improve. Use positive communication skills and remember to Keep It Short and Simple (KISS).

Offer meaningful praise

Frequently, the primary feedback workers receive is on poor performance. It's important to give feedback on tasks well done. Praise and recognition are key motivators. Individuals who feel good about themselves produce good results. Praise immediately and be specific. If appropriate, share your feelings. Workers like hearing what their efforts mean to you and to your family member. For example:

◆ "I appreciate the special effort you made to find mother's favorite sweater instead of substituting the one in the drawer that she doesn't like as well. Thank you."

◆ "My wife told me she felt like a new woman after you shampooed her hair and styled it for her."

◆ "Thank you for staying 30 minutes longer yesterday when I was stranded in traffic. I worried about my husband being alone and I was so relieved to see you waited for me to get home."

Handle problems constructively

Correcting substandard work can be troublesome. To correct a person's work, give feedback as soon as possible. State exactly what was done incorrectly and offer suggestions for improvement. Keep criticism brief, give specific instructions, and demonstrate the way you want a task done.

Use a calm, matter-of-fact tone of voice. Try to be objective and show confidence that the work will improve. One of your goals is to correct the worker in such a way that the person remembers what you said, not how you said it.

The key is to talk about *what* is wrong, not *who* is wrong. "I had trouble combing the tangles out of Mother's hair today. She needs a conditioner applied to her hair after every shampoo to make it easier to comb out the tangles."

Use terms like "more" or "less" instead of "good" or "bad." "I would like the kitchen sink cleaned more thoroughly. The cleanser is under the sink."

Correcting can be very difficult if the in-home worker continually makes the same mistake. Then, you need to be firm. You might have to reprimand a worker you don't want to lose. Before saying anything, be sure the worker has control over the problem. Was the worker late because the bus broke down or because she overslept and missed the bus?

Use "I" statements. Explain exactly what was done wrong, consequences of the worker's action, and what needs to change.

"Millie, I need to talk with you about my mother's 4 o'clock tea. I noticed that she didn't receive tea at all on Tuesday, and that she waited until 5 o'clock on Thursday. Was there is a reason for this? Would

it help if I posted a reminder on the refrigerator? I realize it seems like a small matter, but I feel it shows respect for Mom when we honor her wishes. Would you agree?"

Be specific when correcting a worker. Be sure your criticism focuses on:

◆ The work, not the worker.

◆ Actions, not the person.

◆ Behavior, not personalities.

◆ What is wrong, not who is wrong.

A worker is less likely to accept criticism if you exaggerate or distort the problem to make a point, such as, "Because you were late relieving me, I was late to work and I'll probably be fired." Consider these suggestions for ways to address problems:

◆ Avoid "you" messages and the words "always" and "never." Statements such as "you always" or "you never" set the stage for an argument.

◆ Avoid interpreting motives or making judgments. Change "You probably don't care. . ." to "I may not have made it clear how important it is to. . ."

◆ Respond promptly. The sooner an uncomfortable situation is resolved, the better it is for everyone. Don't let small irritations build into an angry confrontation. Act before the situation gets out of hand but after you have calmed down.

◆ Talk to workers privately. Never correct a worker in front of other people. You want workers to think about their behavior, not yours.

◆ Maintain a friendly, matter-of-fact manner.

◆ Limit discussion to one issue or concern at a time.

◆ Be specific, brief, and to the point.

◆ Be consistent. Consistency in feedback (and behavior) promotes trust and feelings of security.

◆ Provide a face-saving way out. "I know this can be difficult because I've had to deal with this problem myself."

◆ Express support and reassurance if it seems appropriate. "I appreciate your work. I hope we can work this out."

Communication between you and the in-home worker is important. It helps to meet regularly with the worker to discuss concerns and changes, and to make plans.

Listen to the worker

Handling problems constructively includes being willing to listen to the opinions, feelings and suggestions of the in-home worker. Try to understand a worker's perceptions, reasons and feelings. Seeking feedback is a positive, effective way to prevent and reduce problems. Ask questions such as:

◆ "How is the job going for you?"

◆ "How do you feel about the work you are doing here?"

◆ "What concerns do you have?"

◆ "What suggestions do you have?"

◆ "How can I be helpful?"

Then, of course, you must listen to the answers. If a worker's remarks upset you, consider taking a time out. For example, say, "I need time to think about this. Let's talk at noon tomorrow."

ENDING THE WORKING RELATIONSHIP

Perhaps changes in the situation mean you no longer need in-home help. Sometimes, despite your best efforts, the arrangement doesn't work. In either case, letting go a worker can be accomplished in a polite and respectful manner .

Firing

The following suggestions may help you terminate a worker in an appropriate manner.

◆ Act immediately if safety is a concern.

◆ Be prepared. Gather examples of unsatisfactory behavior you observed and document specifically what happened and when. If you are acting on others' reports, be sure their information is reliable. For example, if you believe the worker has violated confidentiality, ask the worker if what you heard is true.

◆ Refer to the contract and job description to support your reasons.

◆ Be direct and brief.

◆ Outline the situation. Briefly review what happened and the outcome.

◆ End on a positive note. If possible, find something to thank the worker for. "Mrs. Jones, I have to let you go. I missed work three times during the past month because no one was here to care for my mother. Because of my job I must be able to rely on people I hire. I appreciate your kindness to my mother and I wish you well."

If you need to terminate a worker who is likely to believe you are doing so unjustly, you may need to take a different approach. Simply state, "We will no longer be needing your services after _____ (give date)." Do not give reasons. You are not legally bound to give them. If you do give reasons and the worker later sues for wrongful termination, you might have to prove the accuracy of your reasons.

Threats of Quitting

Occasionally a worker may threaten to quit unless you meet certain demands. To confront this problem you may ask that the "requests" be put in writing. Then, arrange a meeting to discuss them.

Quitting

Try not to take it personally if a worker quits. Employee turnover is high in all areas of long-term care, even in the most desirable work settings. Do ask the worker about the reason he is quitting. You want to learn if there were things the worker found particularly difficult or uncomfortable. This information may be helpful in hiring the next in-home worker. Decide in advance how you will respond if the worker asks for a reference.

SUMMARY

Although we have discussed possible problems, there are many successful in-home care arrangements. The best arrangements have open communication and clear, realistic expectations.

Expect high quality in-home help. At the same time, be realistic. Do not expect another person to provide care exactly the same way you do. If the worker is providing safe, compassionate, conscientious care—even though it is done differently—that is what counts.

Strong, positive relationships can develop when family caregivers treat in-home help as they would want to be treated. Many in-home care workers say they receive tremendous satisfaction from their work because they know they are making a difference in someone's quality of life. Here are a few of their stories:

Adelle used to work in a nursing home. Back problems forced her to quit. Now she is self-employed as a home-health aide. John is one of her patients. He had a stroke and is confined to a wheelchair. While she helps him bathe and dress, John teaches German songs to Adelle. Their current song is "Stille Nacht," which is "Silent Night" in German. When Adelle leaves she always says, "Auf wiedersehen," the German words for "till we meet again." At first, John didn't want Adelle in the house, let alone to help him take a bath. Now, he looks forward to her visits.

Marge hired a respite care worker, Phil, to stay with her husband while she went to support group meetings. While she's away Phil and Norm talk about fishing and play cards. When Marge comes home, Norm says, "Are you home already?"

June likes to clean house and cook. Whenever she cleans for the Steins, who are both in their 90s, she brings fruits and vegetables from her garden. Last Halloween she carved a pumpkin and put it on their front porch. Even though it was wrinkled and falling apart, they proudly left it there until Thanksgiving.

When you take the steps necessary to hire the right worker and offer a work environment that tactfully teaches and rewards good work, you demonstrate your effectiveness as a caregiver. And, you increase the likelihood that your in-home care arrangements will be successful.

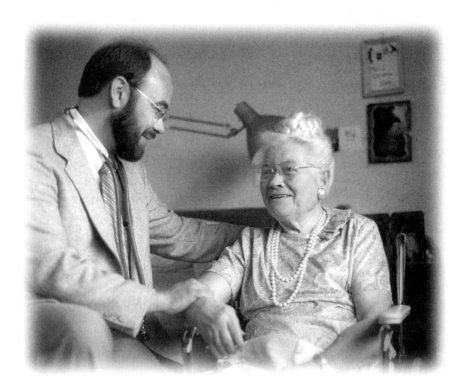

CHAPTER NINE

Using Community Services

Many communities have supportive services that enable frail older people to live longer in their homes. Most older people only need help for a limited time—while recuperating from surgery or an illness, for instance. Others need regular help with shopping, transportation, housecleaning, or yardwork. Some require extensive support and caregiving. Your community may offer assistance in all these areas.

Increasingly there are programs available that address the needs of family caregivers.

The types of services available depend on the community. Do not rule out anything when investigating available services. This is the time to consider all possible sources of help—for now and in the future.

As a caregiver, consider that paying for outside assistance early in caregiving can be less expensive than waiting until you are overwhelmed and exhausted. At that point, the options are likely to be fewer and more expensive, and you may be paying medical bills for yourself, as well as for your older family member.

In this chapter, you will:

◆ Discover available community services and learn how to access them

◆ Identify reasons your relative might refuse non-family help and what you can do

◆ Explore how assistive devices and minor home modifications can increase an older person's independence

BENEFITS OF COMMUNITY RESOURCES

Identifying and accessing community services takes time. And it's not always easy. However, learning about community programs and services is worth the effort. They can make a positive difference for you and for your older family member. Older adults comment about the benefits they received from using community programs:

Esther said:

After my husband died, I just didn't feel like cooking for myself. I started going to the senior center for lunch. It was good for me. I got out of the house, ate one good meal a day, and started going on the senior center's weekly day trips.

Margaret said:

After I returned home from the hospital, I needed a lot of help. The one thing I didn't want my son to do was help me to bathe. A home health aide came to my home twice a week. This made bathing easier and less embarrassing.

Family members comment about the difference a community service made for them.

Tom said:

Mom was determined to remain in her home. However, I constantly worried about her after she fell twice in one week in her home. Mom agreed to use the Lifeline Program offered by the hospital. I still worried about her living alone, but I also felt more at ease because I knew that help would be immediately available if she fell again.

Antonia said:

The volunteer respite program has been a lifesaver for me. Jack, the volunteer, stays with my husband two or three afternoons a month. It's my only time out of the house without having to rush back. One of those afternoons I make needed medical and other appointments for myself, and at least one afternoon a month I enjoy time with friends. I've even gone to two movies. These breaks lift my spirits. I am also more patient with my husband as a result of having "time for me" back in my life.

Daniel said:

Dad never learned to cook, except eggs, sausage and toast for breakfast. At 86 he said he was "too old to start cooking now." For three years after mother died, Dad went to a nearby restaurant for lunch. Then his Parkinson's disease became so bad that he could no longer drive. The senior center now delivers a noon meal daily during the week. Sometimes I think Dad looks forward to seeing Amira, who delivers his food, as much as he does to getting the meal. Dad feels less dependent on us and I feel less burdened. I take turns with my sister and a neighbor preparing Dad's meals for the weekends.

PERSONAL ATTITUDES TO AVOID

As a caregiver, it's important to be aware of personal attitudes that may be barriers to using a community service. Do you ever think:

Yes	No	
❏	❏	No one can care for my family member as well as I can.
❏	❏	Caregiving is entirely *my* responsibility.
❏	❏	I should not have to go outside of the family for help.
❏	❏	Seeking help is a sign of failure.
❏	❏	It's selfish to enjoy myself when my family member is ill.
❏	❏	The care receiver can't get along without me.
❏	❏	The care receiver would never accept help from anyone other than me (or family).
❏	❏	It would never work to use a community service.
❏	❏	I shouldn't spend money on a service that I can do.
❏	❏	I could never have a stranger in my home.

If you answered "yes" to any of these questions, your attitude may be a barrier to your considering community services as a potential resource. A major caregiving pitfall is not being open to help that is available in the community. Avoid the "Yes, but…" syndrome. Consider how Alice undermined all potential help.

Alice's health was deteriorating as a result of around-the-clock caregiving to her husband. She acknowledged being physically and emotionally exhausted. Her daughters offered to care for their father so their mother could have a break. However, Alice always responded, "But what if something happens while I am away" or "But your Dad could never get along without me."

Feeling that their mother did not trust their ability to provide the care their father needed, they decided to pursue hiring professional help to relieve their mother. Still their mother said, "But they won't know your father like I do," or "But I could never let you pay for such expensive help." With every suggestion, Alice came back with a "Yes, but…"

Occasionally caregivers think they must do everything for their ill family member. The reality is that no one person can single-handedly fill all of the many roles involved in being a caregiver. As caregiving becomes more complicated and demanding, eventually most caregivers need help.

Even if you think you will never need a community service, it's still a good idea to know about available resources. Ask yourself: If something happened to me, and family and friends were not available, what community services could I turn to for help? If you find out early about available services and how to access them, you will be better prepared should a crisis or emergency ever arise. As one caregiver said: "A family caregiver should always be prepared for the unexpected. You never know when you might become ill, need surgery or be called out of town unexpectedly. Having contingency plans is no different than being prepared for the occasional power outage and having a flashlight and candles on hand."

COMMUNITY SERVICES FOR OLDER ADULTS

Services differ from community to community, and the name used for a particular service may vary. A wide variety of services are available in urban and suburban areas, while in small towns and rural areas community services are more limited. Services may be provided by public agencies, private businesses, religious organizations, and non-profit organizations for older people.

Before investigating community resources, make a list of the type of help both you and your relative need and how frequently the help is needed.

Cost for services depend on the type and extent of service provided. Some have a set fee based on the services provided and hours of staff time required. Some charge on a sliding scale, and the fee is determined by the ability of the person to pay. Other services may be free or have a voluntary donation because they are provided by volunteers, government, or charitable organizations. Some programs also have age, income, or other eligibility requirements.

The following are examples of community-based programs that have been developed to address specific concerns experienced by older adults.

Emergency alert

In-home medical alert (Personal Emergency Response System; Lifeline). This is an electronic device worn by the older person. If the person falls or needs help, the device sends a signal to a central dispatcher, often located at a hospital. The dispatcher telephones the older person, and summons emergency assistance if the older person does not answer the call. Help is available around-the-clock.

Community alert. In some communities, letter carriers, newspaper deliverers, utility meter readers, and other people who in the course of their jobs have contact with older people are trained to recognize when a person may need help. Where a postal alert program operates, the postal service alerts a designated person when mail accumulates in an older person's mailbox.

Safe Return. *Safe Return,* a program of the Alzheimer's Association, is a nationwide program designed to identify, locate and return to safety individuals who are memory impaired and have wandered away and become lost. Someone who finds the lost person can call the national 800 number on the *Safe Return* identification bracelet or necklace worn by the person. For more information, contact the local Alzheimer's Association or 1-800-272-3900.

End-of-life care

Hospice. Hospice programs offer a range of care and support services to terminally ill patients and their families during the end-stage of disease. Hospices typically offer: medical, nursing, homemaker, and home health services; respite care; and counseling and bereavement services.

Food and nutrition

Congregate meals. Some communities offer nutritious meals in a group setting, often located in senior centers, schools, churches, and housing projects for older adults. Social contact is emphasized. Frequently the mealtime also includes recreational and social activities. Transportation is sometimes provided. Participants contribute what they can to the cost of the meal.

Home-delivered meals/Meals on Wheels. These programs offer meals delivered daily or several times a week, usually around the lunch hour, to homebound people who cannot prepare their own meals. The days for home delivery vary from one area to another. In some communities, an evening meal may be delivered with the noon meal.

Food stamps. Food stamps help low-income people to increase their food purchasing power. The food stamps are treated like cash at grocery stores participating in the food stamp program. Food stamps cannot be used to purchase non-food items. All eligible applicants receive food stamps in amounts determined by the size and income of their households.

Grocery delivery. Some grocery stores will deliver groceries to an older person's home for a small fee. Some communities also have a "Store to Door" program. And in some areas, groceries can now be ordered over the Internet.

Home health care

Home health care agencies. Medical care can be brought into the home, even for people who are seriously ill or dying. Home health care agencies, both public and

private, offer a range of services, from assessing a person's needs to providing the needed care. Services generally include skilled nursing care; physical, occupational, and speech therapy; social work services; and personal care—assistance with bathing, dressing, grooming, and exercising.

Some home health care is reimbursable by Medicare, Medicaid, and some private health insurance policies, but only under very specific conditions.

Home repairs

Handyman and chore service. These services provide workers at reduced cost for minor home repairs, home maintenance (e.g. putting up storm windows, mowing the lawn), heavy household cleaning, and other chores. The service usually does not include major home improvements.

Home improvement/weatherization. Limited home improvement grants or loans are available to older people who meet income eligibility guidelines. Funds can be used for roofing, making ramps, and insulating a home.

Household tasks

Homemaker services. Homemaker services assist with daily living needs, such as grocery shopping, cooking, light housekeeping (e.g. vacuuming, dishwashing, changing linens, and laundry) and errands. Some homemakers may provide some personal care. Homemakers do not provide health care and nursing services.

Legal assistance

Legal aid offices. Legal aid offices provide free or low-cost legal services to people who cannot afford private lawyers and who meet financial eligibility requirements. The types of legal services available vary considerably from office to office.

Elderlaw attorneys. Elderlaw attorneys specialize in the legal needs of older people, including public benefit issues such as Social Security, Medicare and Medicaid; durable powers of attorney for finances and health care; and guardianship and conservatorship for incapacitated older people.

Loneliness

Telephone reassurance. Telephone reassurance programs provide daily or regular telephone contact with homebound or at-risk older people. The older person calls in or a telephone call is made to him at a pre-arranged time. If the telephone is not answered, the caller immediately notifies a designated person or agency (friend, neighbor, police, fire department) who investigates.

Friendly Visitors/Senior Companions. Once or twice a week, these volunteers or paid individuals provide companionship, friendship, support or supervision to older adults who are homebound or living alone. They do things a friend might do: offer companionship and conversation; write letters, read aloud or just sit and listen; assist the person with his or her interests or hobbies; or take the person on walks and other outings. For people living alone, friendly visitors can provide a safety check as well as companionship.

In some areas, paid companions are available to stay through the evening and night. Friendly visitors and companions do not provide housekeeping or personal care services.

Personal care

Home health care agencies. Home health aides, often employed by home health agencies, provide nonmedical services to assist older persons in their homes. They may assist with a variety of activities, including bathing, dressing, grooming, toileting, meal preparation, and reminding and supervising the taking of medications. These workers are also called personal care aides, personal care assistants, nurse's aides, or nurse's assistants. Certified home health aides have successfully completed a state-required training program.

Social activities

Senior center. Most senior centers offer a variety of recreational, educational and social activities. They also serve as a clearinghouse for information. Some provide a range of supportive services—information and referral, meal programs, financial counseling, in-home services, legal assistance, health screenings, grocery delivery, help in applying for Medicare and Medicaid, and transportation.

Bookmobiles/library. Local libraries often offer special programs and services for homebound older adults.

Transportation

Transportation services. Frequently listed in the telephone directory under names such as "Dial A Ride," transportation may be available for specific reasons such as medical appointments and treatments, grocery shopping, nutrition site programs, and other necessary travel. Some programs have buses or vans equipped with lifts or ramps for wheelchairs. In some communities, volunteers use their private vehicles to transport elders to and from their destinations. Transportation services usually must be scheduled in advance.

Taxi service. Some communities offer discounted taxi fares or vouchers for older people.

Utility bill payment

Automatic payment plans. If you are concerned about your family member paying monthly utility bills, contact the utility company about automatic bank payment to the utility company. Some utility companies also offer "third party" notification services and will alert the identified contact person if bills are not paid promptly or at least prior to cutting off service.

Home energy assistance programs. These programs can help low-income households pay heating bills and the costs of home cooling. The amount of assistance varies according to household income, type of fuel, and region. Payments may be made to the household or directly to the energy supplier.

Some major utility companies have programs to help low-income customers pay their utility bills. To determine the availability of a program, contact the community relations or customer service department of the local utility.

SUPPORTIVE SERVICES FOR CAREGIVERS

Although all programs benefit both older adults and caregivers, some programs have been developed to specifically address the needs of caregivers.

Geriatric care managers

Sophia, who was an only child, lived on the West Coast and her parents lived on the East Coast. She said:

My Mom was the caregiver to my father. Then my mother's health started to fail. They were still able to manage in their home, but needed increasing help. When a crisis occurred, I couldn't always be there when Mom and Dad needed me. The best thing I did was to hire Marcia, a local private geriatric care manager. She has been my lifeline. She checks in on my parents regularly, arranges for and oversees any help they need, and is immediately available in an emergency. Living at a distance is difficult, but knowing Marcia is there for my parents, and for me, has increased my peace of mind and made caring from afar less stressful. I feel like Marcia is like a surrogate sister.

If you live at a distance, have competing responsibilities, or simply do not have the time or resources to find needed services, you might want to consider hiring a geriatric care manager (also known as a case manager). Care managers usually are social workers or nurses with training in gerontology or geriatrics. They can offer all kinds of practical assistance—for example, assess a person's situation, locate and coordinate services, oversee a person's care, assist with paperwork, and provide counseling. If you think a care manager would be helpful, contact the local area agency on aging or hospital or find a local care manager through the Internet Web site at **www.caremanager.org**.

Private care management organizations are frequently listed in the yellow pages of the telephone directory under Social Services, Social Workers, Aging Services, and Home Health. Some care managers have private practices.

Interview prospective care managers before hiring. You may want to ask how long the person has worked in the community and how many clients he is currently serving. The longer a person has worked in the community, the more familiar he is likely to be with the services and staff. Client load can affect the time and attention a care manager can give to your family member. Be clear in advance about fees, services, and duties, and set up a system for communication. A care manager's charge will vary depending on the extent of services to be provided.

Lesley said:

A geriatric care manager is not inexpensive. Because of cost, I initially rejected the idea. But when I considered the costs of emergency plane trips, the long-distance telephone calls, and the time and frustration trying to arrange services for Dad from 1200 miles away, a geriatric care manager seemed more reasonable. An added benefit is that my brothers and I found that Dad listened to suggestions made by Barbara, his care manager. He would resist the same suggestions if we made them.

Adult day centers

Adult day centers—also called adult day care or adult day health care programs—are for older people who are either physically or mentally incapable of independent living

and need a supervised environment during the day. Programs are available usually on a weekday or hourly basis. Services range from meals and social and recreational activities to health care—medical monitoring, therapy, assistance with medicine, and personal care. Transportation to and from the center is sometimes provided. Many adult day programs are not able to accommodate individuals with serious cognitive and/or behavior problems.

The program enables some caregivers to continue their employment and care for their relative at the same time. For other caregivers, adult day services provide a break from the demands of caregiving.

After trying an adult day center, Arthur said:

I resisted using the adult day program for my wife. I finally agreed to give it a try for two weeks, primarily so my daughter wouldn't nag me. I found the program was invaluable. It helped me to live a normal life for a few hours a week. And, I also found that my wife enjoyed the activities at the center. The change of routine seemed to be as good for her as it was for me. We used the program for two years before her health declined and she needed the care of a nursing home.

Respite care

Respite care gives family caregivers temporary relief from caregiving. Even a short break from the daily demands of caregiving can help preserve a caregiver's physical and emotional health. While respite care is designed to help the caregiver, care receivers also benefit. For care receivers, respite can mean a break from the routine, isolation, or guilt that comes from being dependent on others. Respite care can be provided in many ways:

- ◆ in a home, community setting, or care facility.
- ◆ for part of a day, evening, overnight, or for an extended time.
- ◆ by paid staff or volunteers.
- ◆ occasionally or on a regular basis.

In the home, respite providers provide companionship, activities, and light assistance to the person. They do not provide hands-on care, but they will assist the person to the bathroom when needed. Some home health agencies may have live-in aides available on a temporary basis, so that the care receiver can remain at home, while the caregiver takes a vacation. Some care facilities and adult foster care homes offer short-term respite care—overnight, for a week, a month or longer.

Caregiver support groups

Support groups offer family caregivers an opportunity to talk and share with others who have similar experiences and problems. Caregivers often find they not only receive emotional support, but they also get practical suggestions for dealing with difficult situations. Some groups are designed for all family caregivers. Others are designed for family caregivers caring for someone who has a specific medical condition such as cancer, stroke, Parkinson's disease, or Alzheimer's disease and related disorders. To find out about caregiver support groups, contact disease-based associations or your local hospital.

A support group isn't for everyone, but

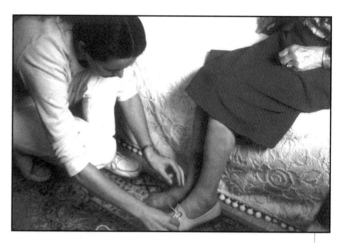

for many caregivers, it does make a positive difference in their lives. Comments by caregivers about the value of a support group include:

- ◆ It was the one place I could say what I felt and others understood.
- ◆ I could talk about my anger, guilt or resentment and people did not say "you shouldn't feel that way."
- ◆ I discovered I was not alone in my feelings and experiences.
- ◆ I learned about the joy of laughter, which had disappeared from my life.
- ◆ I found help on how to deal with a difficult behavior from people who had dealt with the same problem.
- ◆ I learned that it was good to have fun in my life and to take care of me.

Internet web sites

Several web sites offer a wealth of information for caregivers. The following are just two of the many Internet resources.

Caregiver Survival Resources (www.caregiver911.com). This site has one of the most comprehensive lists of quality links about caregiving. It offers general caregiving links and links for specific caregiving needs for 20 different chronic illnesses, including AIDS, Alzheimer's disease, heart problems, Parkinson's disease, and stroke. It includes an e-mail section called "Dr. Caregiver" where users can get answers to their questions. Another section tells caregivers how to compile a personal list of caregiving resources using local directories, telephone books and other resources.

Family Caregiver Alliance (www.caregiver.org). This organization assists family caregivers of adults who have memory loss as a result of a chronic or progressive brain disorder. It includes on-line fact sheets for different diseases and disorders and fact sheets on general caregiving issues such as behavior management strategies and legal planning for incapacity.

Locating community services

Knowing the help that you need is one thing. Knowing where to find it is another matter. Identifying and locating services, especially if you're not familiar with a community, can be a challenge. Fortunately, there are organizations and individuals that can help.

A good place to start is the state or local Area Agency on Aging (AAA). These agencies locate, coordinate, and at times provide direct services. Area agencies on aging sometimes go by other names—for example, senior and disabled services, council on aging, senior services division, council on senior services, commission on the elderly, office of elder affairs.

Many social service agencies, home health agencies, and senior centers can also help you locate services, or may even provide the needed services. Most counties also publish a local resource booklet that

lists what services are available in the area. Resource booklets may be available from the local area agency on aging, chamber of commerce, senior center, or hospital.

Whether your older relative lives nearby or in another state, the Eldercare Locator is another good way to start a search for resources. Funded by the U.S. Administration on Aging, the Eldercare Locator can refer you to information sources for a variety of eldercare services anywhere in the United States and its territories. It is designed to point caregivers in the right direction and to guide family members to local resources. It provides names and telephones numbers of public and nonprofit agencies, not private businesses, such as care facilities, home care agencies, or geriatric care managers.

Anyone—family members, friends, neighbors or older adults themselves— can call the Eldercare Locator toll free number, 1-800-677-1116, Monday through Friday, 9 A.M. to 8 P.M. Eastern Time. Wait times tend to be the shortest during the early evening. Before calling, be prepared to give the city and county or ZIP code in which your older relative lives and to briefly describe the problem or type of assistance you are seeking. The Eldercare Locator does not collect data from callers, so your confidentiality is preserved. You can also retrieve information about local services online at **www.aoa.gov**; then click on "Eldercare Locator" in the box at the bottom of the first page.

Contacting agencies

Most people have a good experience dealing with community service programs. However, navigating your way through the maze of resources can be time consuming, confusing and frustrating. Sometimes caregivers feel as though they are getting the "run-around" when dealing with government agencies.

It's important to be patient and persistent. Plan that it will take time to get the information you seek and be prepared for busy signals, voicemail, and being put on hold. You may reduce frustration by following these guidelines:

Be prepared. It will help if you are as clear as possible about what help you need and your relative's situation, needs and finances. When contacting an agency, have all of the information you might need in front of you.

Write a list of questions. To get the most complete information, write out your questions before calling. Although the appropriate questions will depend upon the assistance needed, you may want to consider the following questions:

- What kinds of help are available from your agency? Or, if you know the specific help you need, ask if the agency provides that assistance.

- During what hours can you provide the service?

- What is the length of time you can provide the service?

- What are the eligibility requirements? What medical or financial documentation, if any, is needed?

- How much does the service cost?

- What are the qualifications, training, and credentials of staff?

- Is your agency bonded?

- Who is liable and responsible if an employee has an accident on the premises of a person's home? if anything is stolen?

- Who do I contact if I have concerns about the services provided?

- What is the application procedure? Is there someone in the agency who can assist with the application process?

Develop a telephone prompter. See example below. This can help you get the best possible information.

TELEPHONE PROMPTER

Place this prompter by your telephone when you call about community services. It will remind you of the questions to ask.

My name is _____

I'm caring for _____

I need _____

Can you help me?

If no:

Can you give me another name to call?

If yes:

What services do you provide?

What are the hours/days of service?

What are the costs? How are they paid?

What are the eligibility requirements?

How long must we wait?

Can you send a brochure or application?

To whom am I speaking?

Do I need to speak to anyone else?

Call first. Get as much information as possible over the telephone. If you are calling long distance, tell the agency representative. Explain your needs as clearly as possible. If you don't understand terms used or something you are told, ask for an explanation. Repeat the information to verify that what you heard is correct. Request that relevant pamphlets and forms be sent to you. If necessary, schedule a face-to-face interview.

Write down the name, title, department, and the direct telephone number of each person you speak with and their comments and recommendations. If you need to call the agency again for additional information, talking with the same person each time may make communication easier and less frustrating.

Ask about documentation needed. If documentation is needed to qualify for a program, find out what papers, documentation, and information you need before you go to the agency's office. Do not leave original documents with the agency; however, allow the agency to make necessary copies. Some agencies also will conduct an in-home interview if your relative is extremely frail.

Ask for a referral. If you are told that the agency is unable to help you, ask if they can direct you to another agency that can help. There may be other options.

Don't give up. If you don't reach the person you need to talk with when you call, leave a brief message about the reason for your call and ask to be called back. Also ask when you can expect a return call. Call again if you do not receive the call when expected.

If an agency representative is not able to answer your questions, avoid becoming irritated and angry. Ask to speak to the supervisor. Say something like, "I appreciate your assistance, but I'd like to ask your supervisor some additional questions." If the supervisor is not available, ask for the best time to call back. In addition, ask if the supervisor has a direct telephone number.

If an agency representative was particularly helpful, consider sending a thank-you note. If a person is rude, discourteous, or not at all helpful, report your dissatisfaction by calling the worker's supervisor and writing a letter of complaint to the director of the agency.

WHEN YOUR RELATIVE REFUSES HELP

It can be frustrating when you know your family member has difficulty functioning independently yet he refuses necessary services. Although you cannot force him to accept help, you need to understand the reasons behind the resistance if you are going to have any success overcoming his reluctance. Ask yourself:

◆ Is my family member concerned about the cost of the service and its impact on his savings?

◆ Does my relative feel he does not have a problem?

◆ Does he view agency assistance as "welfare," "charity," or "going on the dole"?

◆ Is my family member fearful about having a stranger in the house or having possessions stolen?

◆ Does my relative feel the tasks(s) I want to hire someone to do are ones that he can do? Or that family should do?

◆ Does he view accepting outside help as a loss of control and independence, and a sign of increasing dependence?

◆ Are the requirements of community agencies—financial disclosure, application process, interviews—overwhelming to my relative?

It's important to deal with your relative's perceptions and feelings. For example, if your mother feels she does not have any problems, be as objective and specific as you can in describing your observations. Use "I messages." Tell her you know it must be difficult to experience such changes. If your father views government-supported services as "welfare" or "charity," emphasize that he has paid for the service in past years through taxes.

Emphasize independence. Try to approach your family member in such a way that he does not feel helpless. Many of us, regardless of age, do not find it easy to ask for or to accept help. Present the need for assistance in a positive way, emphasizing how it will enable him to live more independently. Try not to emphasize the person's dependence and what he cannot do. Avoid statements such as "you can't do that anymore." Focusing only on limitations often increases resistance.

Start small. If possible, suggest just one change or service at a time and begin with a small change. Most people need time to think about and accept changes. Introducing ideas slowly rather than pushing for immediate action increases the chances for acceptance. The more your relative feels a sense of control in planning and making arrangements, the better it will be for everyone.

Suggest a trial period. Sometimes suggesting a trial period—"try the service for a month"—will help. Some people are more willing to accept a service when they view it as a short-term, rather than a long-term, commitment. A person who feels "forced" into using a service is less likely to be open to its potential benefits.

Give a gift. Some families find it works to give a service as a gift. Examples include giving spring cleaning as a Mother's Day gift, a Christmas gift of hair appointments for the woman who has difficulty brushing her hair because of arthritic shoulders and hands, and home-delivered meals as a get-well gift after surgery.

Hire someone familiar. Some people are more willing to accept help from someone they know than from a "stranger." Could you pay a neighbor to prepare a daily meal for your family member? Is there a responsible teenager in the neighborhood you could hire to do grocery shopping or yard work or provide transportation? Sometimes this person will have more success in getting your relative to accept an "outside service" for a short time when he cannot do it.

Focus on your needs. If your family member insists, "I'm okay," "I don't need help," try focusing on your own needs rather than those of your family member. For example, say, "I would feel better if..." or "I care about you and I worry about..."

Will you consider doing this for me so I will worry less?" This sometimes makes it easier for a person to try a service.

Ask a respected person to suggest a service. Having someone your relative respects, such as a physician, recommend a service may be an effective approach.

A word of caution: Be careful about how much assistance you volunteer to provide. It's important to be realistic about what you can do, and communicate your limits to your relative. For example, if you volunteer to prepare your mother's meals, do your father's laundry and grocery shopping, or clean your grandmother's house weekly, are you really willing and able to do the task for as long as the person needs it? The need that appears to be for only a few weeks may last several months or years. Family members sometime find that once they take on a task they encounter even greater resistance from their relative when they try to hire another person or an agency to do the task.

OTHER RESOURCES TO CONSIDER

Most older people want to live in their homes as long as possible. However, physical needs change, and the home that worked well at age 50 sometimes creates problems at age 80. Fortunately, there are devices that can increase a person's functioning and minor home modifications that can be made to enhance the usability, safety and comfort of a home.

Devices for independent living

Many inexpensive devices are available to make living easier and safer for frail older persons. For example, a long-handled shoehorn, raised toilet seats, adaptive clothing, a reacher to retrieve items from shelves or that drop on the floor, a bathtub stool, medication organizers, color-coded stove dials, and a telephone amplifier can enhance the independence of an increasingly frail older person.

Health-related associations—Arthritis Foundation, Association for the Blind, Parkinson's Disease Association, Stroke Association, Multiple Sclerosis Society, Alzheimer's Association and others—often have booklets available describing such devices and where to purchase them. Occupational therapists, local home health agencies, and medical supply stores are also sources for information. Many adaptive devices also can be found at pharmacies, supermarkets, and specialty stores.

Home Modifications

Many times, relatively simple and inexpensive adaptations can be made in the home to accommodate a person's changing physical needs. For example, installing grab

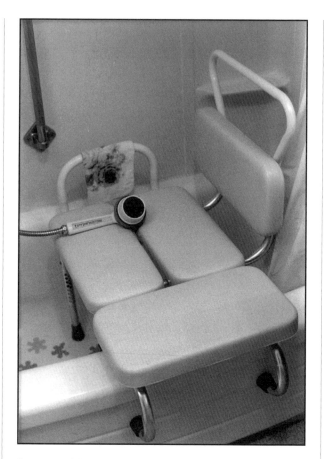

bars and handrails by the bathtub, shower, and toilet can increase safety in the bathroom. A wheelchair-bound person's independence may be increased by enlarging doorways, installing a ramp at the front door, adapting a shower to accommodate a wheelchair, and lowering kitchen and bathroom cabinets.

Changing doorknobs and water faucet controls to levered handles can make it easier for the person with arthritic hands to open doors. With levers, doors can be opened with the palm of a hand or elbow. Many home health agencies have professionals on staff who can help evaluate a home and recommend modifications. Other sources of help are occupational therapists, building contractors, and hardware and home improvement stores.

SUMMARY

Using community services can make a positive difference for both older adults and their families. Whether or not you or your family member currently need assistance, explore community services for potential future needs. Find out about services offered by public and private sectors, and record the information for future use. You never know when you may need a service, and need it in a hurry.

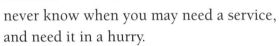

Overview

Chapter Ten

CHAPTER TEN

Making a Decision About a Care Facility

Each year, thousands of families have to decide whether to place a family member in a care facility. About one in four of us will spend some time in a care facility during our lifetime. A large proportion of people who live past age 85—the most rapidly growing age group in the United States—will spend the last few months or years of their life in a care facility. For many people, it will be a short stay for rehabilitation or to recover from an illness, accident, or surgery; for others, it will be an extended stay.

When considering a care facility, families often focus on the negative aspects. However, a care facility can be the most appropriate setting for your family member. Having him in a care facility allows you to be together and enjoy each other without having to devote as much time to caregiving tasks such as bathing, dressing, and 24-hour supervision. Your family member also may become more involved in activities and less isolated.

Whether to place your family member in a care facility is never an easy decision. This chapter will provide you with tools for making a decision, selecting a care facility, and dealing with your feelings and those of your family member. It will also discuss the types of care facilities available, and how to maintain positive contact with a family member who lives in a care facility.

MAKING THE DECISION

The best time to talk about a care facility is when you don't need one. Advance planning makes it easier for everyone involved if you and your family ever face this decision.

This decision is even harder if you are first faced with it during a crisis and have not prepared for it. If your family member is showing signs of deterioration or has received a diagnosis of a degenerative disease like Alzheimer's, or if your own health or relationships are deteriorating as a result of providing care, realize that your family member may someday need to live in a care facility. With preplanning you will be better informed and prepared to make the decision.

When is Placement Appropriate?

When in-home care and community services are no longer adequate, and other living arrangements are not appropriate, it's time to look at residential care options.

Indicators that a care facility may be appropriate for an individual include:

◆ Your family member needs specialized health care services.

◆ A care facility is the only setting where he can receive the amount and type of care he needs.

◆ It has become emotionally or physically impossible for you to continue providing the needed care.

◆ Your family member needs post-hospital rehabilitation following a disabling illness such as a stroke, or an injury such as a hip fracture.

◆ Other alternatives for meeting his needs have been exhausted.

◆ He needs round-the-clock care for an extended time and you, the family, and community agencies cannot provide it.

◆ A care facility is more cost effective than other alternatives.

Who Should Be Involved in the Decision?

A decision about placement is best made with a team approach. There are three vital participants in the decision: the family member who needs care, you and other family members, and health care and social service professionals.

Your family member

As much as possible, involve your family member who needs care in making the decision. It will help give him a feeling of control and reduce his trauma if he moves.

Even people who are very ill or confused should be informed about the alternatives for their care. However, if your family member suffers from a memory impairment, recognize that he may not be able to remember discussions or agreements you made. One son said:

Talking to a parent about a potential move is good advice even if it does not always work out. I talked to my mother many times concerning her condition (in response to her own concerns) and we agreed on the appropriate plan. She could not remember what happened even 30 minutes earlier, however. The day Mom moved went about as smooth as it could, but she did not understand the reason. Realize that even when everything has been done with love and careful consideration, your family member may not understand and may be unhappy. However, it is still a good idea to discuss the plan so the family will have a feeling of doing what is right.

Only in a few extreme cases, such as advanced Alzheimer's disease or a massive stroke, is a person so out of touch that he cannot be consulted.

You may feel that discussing a move with the person needing care will be too complex or too emotionally painful, or you may fear his anger or rejection. Although these feelings may occur, they will be much worse if you don't consult him. You also risk losing his trust.

Remember, a move implies a major transition, and it will involve many losses for him, no matter how desirable a selected facility might be. A move may signify the loss of health, familiar surroundings, personal possessions, privacy, self-esteem, and independence. If you can acknowledge these losses and share your own feelings, both of you will benefit. It's important to spend time discussing the decision with your family member.

A person who is involved in the decision making is better prepared when the time comes to move into a care facility. Therefore, involve your family member as much as possible concerning where, what, when, and how to move. If the choice of a facility is limited, it still may be possible for him to select his room, furniture, and personal items to take, or when to move. Within his capabilities, give him as much choice and decision-making power as possible.

Your family member's feelings may range from acceptance to resignation to anger. He may be fearful—about the future, about being abandoned, about being a burden to you, or because of the "horror stories" he has heard. Or your family member may feel guilt or shame about his inability to be "independent." Encourage him to share his feelings. Try not to take personally any negative feelings that may be directed at you. Negative feelings need to be expressed, and unfortunately they often are directed at the people who are the closest and providing the most care and support.

You and other family members

You and other members of your family are essential in the decision making. You have three basic tasks: sharing information, sharing feelings, and assessing individual resources.

Sharing information. Sharing information is the first step in family decision making. Disagreements about the needs of the older person are more likely if family members do not have a common understanding of the person's medical condition, functional abilities, and changes that have occurred. It is vital to gather accurate information about your older relative and care options.

Sharing feelings. Don't ignore your own feelings or those of other family members. Sadness, anger, grief, guilt, relief, fear, and uncertainty about the future are common. You may feel a great deal of sadness and helplessness, particularly if you have struggled to avoid placement or if the move appears permanent. You may grieve the loss of your family member as he was before, the loss of his companionship, and the loss of your ability to provide direct care.

You may be angry at having to make this decision, especially if you have to do it alone. You and other family members may be frightened or even angry at the prospect of a care facility. However, you also may feel relief that you no longer have to worry about your family member's health and safety.

Some family members may recall promises made such as "We'll never put you in a nursing home." A move to a care facility may be viewed as the worst possible event. The myth that families "dump" their older relatives in care facilities can further contribute to feelings of guilt. Caregivers said:

> When I was faced with the decision about placement, all I could think about was, "My God, what am I doing to Mom?" I wished my mother could just die peacefully in her sleep so I would not have to make this decision.

> My grandmother, who seemed content living in a care facility for over a year, would still say, "No one should live so long that they end up living like this."

The more you and other family members are aware of your own and each other's feelings, the better decision you can make. It's important to acknowledge the feelings of everyone, but it's also important not to base decisions solely on emotions. When family members disagree about this decision, a session with a social worker or therapist might help.

Assessing individual resources. As a family, assess your resources for supporting your family member. Talk about what each person is willing and able to do. Open, honest discussion is vitally important.

If you choose a care facility, your relationship with your family member will not stop at the facility's door. Discuss what each family member is willing and able to do to support the person emotionally, socially, and financially, if this is a concern. The "Staying in Touch" section (page 221) can help you find ways to maintain contact.

Health care and social service professionals. Health and social service professionals can be an important resource in helping you to make placement decisions. Physicians provide critical information about a person's current medical condition as well as educated guesses about what you might expect in the future.

Once you fully understand your family member's medical condition and prognosis, social service workers or hospital discharge planners can help you and your family member make plans.

SELECTING A CARE FACILITY

There are many types of care facilities. The best option for your situation depends on many factors—whether your family member primarily needs supervision, assistance with personal care activities, or nursing care; his current level of functioning and anticipated future needs; financial resources; personal preferences and values; and the options available in the community.

There are two basic services provided by facilities: personal care and skilled nursing care. Personal care (also called assistance with activities of daily living) includes assistance with bathing, dressing, grooming, eating, walking, using the toilet, transferring from bed to chair; meal preparation, including special diets; and medication supervision. Skilled nursing care is a higher level of care provided by trained medical professionals, including doctors, nurses, and physical therapists. It may include injections, catheterization, dressing changes, and rehabilitation.

Your goal is to select a facility that offers the greatest degree of personal independence while meeting your relative's needs for health care, safety, comfort, and convenience. Generally, the more extensive the services, the more costly. Therefore, your relative's resources will be an important factor in choosing a care facility.

Care facility options include adult foster care homes, residential care facilities, assisted living facilities, nursing homes, and multilevel care facilities.

The local Area Agency on Aging is a good resource to contact about options in a particular area. Also, look in the yellow pages of your telephone directory under "Retirement Homes," "Assisted Living Facilities,"

"Residential Care Homes," and "Nursing Homes." For information about care facilities affiliated with a specific religion, call a local church of that faith or denomination.

Adult foster care home

An adult foster care home (also called "adult family home") is a private family or individual's home. The family or individual provides care for an older person(s). The care given varies depending on the provider's background, training, and interests. Care can range from simple room and board with laundry and transportation, to help with bathing, dressing, toileting, and feeding. A provider can remind a resident to take medications, but may not be able to administer it unless he or she is a licensed nurse. A few adult foster care homes, operated by nurses, provide some nursing care.

There are specific requirements for a *licensed* adult foster care home, including maximum number of residents; physical requirements such as zoning, type of construction, and bedroom size; furnishings; meal service; and medicine storage. A provider or manager must live in the home and provide 24-hour supervision.

A potential resident is typically a person who is mentally alert to moderately confused and needs some assistance with personal care and/or 24-hour supervision. Usually, the person must have bowel and bladder control and be able to walk or use a cane, walker, or wheelchair. Adult foster care providers generally will not accept people who wander because they cannot leave other residents to search for the wanderer.

There is a wide range of quality and services offered in adult foster homes. Call your local area agency on aging for information about homes in your area.

Residential care facility

A residential care facility (sometimes called "board and care home," "personal care," "sheltered housing," or "domiciliary care home") may be the answer for a person who needs some assistance with personal care. Meals, social activities, laundry, transportation, and housekeeping services are also provided. Typically, a residential care facility has individual rooms, but no apartments, kitchenettes, private bathrooms, or storage areas. Some facilities have shared rooms.

Residential care facilities are generally licensed (but not in all states) and must meet design and operating standards, including minimum staff requirements. Staff coverage is provided 24 hours a day. Prospective residents generally must be fairly mentally alert; able to dress, feed, and take themselves to the toilet; and able to eat meals in a central dining room. They must need only moderate assistance with personal care or supervision. Some facilities offer specialized care for people with Alzheimer's disease or similar disorders.

In some cases, and depending on the facility, medical assistance programs (for example, Medicaid) may help pay for this type of living.

Assisted living facility

Assisted living facilities are a specific type of residential care facility. They generally feature apartments, often with kitchenettes. Services vary but are generally similar to those offered by residential care facilities.

Regulations and licensure requirements vary from state to state, contributing to a wide range of facilities that are considered assisted living. In some states, financial help may be available through medical assistance programs. However, many assisted living facilities accept only private-pay residents. Some offer specialized care for people with Alzheimer's disease or similar disorders.

Nursing home

A nursing home is an extended care facility that can offer a range of services, including skilled, intermediate, and rehabilitative care. If your family member is seriously ill and needs extensive or continuous nursing care or 24-hour supervision, a nursing home may be the best choice. Usually nursing homes provide two levels of care: intermediate and skilled.

Intermediate care. Intermediate care is designed for people who need assistance with personal care and some health services and nursing supervision, but not round-the-clock nursing care. People who need certain rehabilitation services also may be appropriate for intermediate care. Care is ordered by a physician and supervised by a registered or licensed nurse.

Skilled nursing care. Skilled nursing care is for people who need 24-hour medical supervision, skilled nursing care, or rehabilitation, but do not need hospitalization. This care might be appropriate for a person recovering from a broken hip, recent stroke, or an illness requiring round-the-clock nursing care. Care is provided by a registered nurse under the direction of a doctor.

A physician's order is required for admission. This is the only type of care for which there is partial coverage by Medicare.

Some facilities also have special care units that are specifically designed to meet the needs of people who have Alzheimer's disease or a related dementia.

In some states, preadmission screening is available, or required, for admission. A team of professionals assesses the older person's functioning, the type of care needed, the appropriateness of placement, and possible alternatives. (Some states also require preadmission screening for other types of care facilities.)

Multi-level care facility

Some facilities offer a variety of living arrangements and levels of care under one roof or on the same campus. For example, one section may have independent units (apartments or cottages with kitchens), another section where limited support services such as meals are provided, a residential care section where assistance is provided with personal care, and a section where nursing care is provided.

A major advantage is that residents may be able to move back and forth between areas as their care needs change. A multi-level care facility can be beneficial for couples who have different needs.

Guidelines for Choosing a Care Facility

If you anticipate a care facility may be needed, investigate the possibilities in advance. It will make for a better, less frantic, and less emotional choice. Quality facilities are in demand so you'll want to consider more than one facility as a possibility.

Searching for the right care facility is time consuming but worthwhile. Your goal is to find a facility that you and your family member feel comfortable with and that best meets your family member's needs and financial resources. The guidelines in this chapter are intended to help you meet this goal.

Identify your family member's needs

Before contacting care facilities, make a list of your family member's medical, social, and emotional needs. It might include assistance with incontinence, walking, transferring from bed to chair, eating, and medications; personal care like bathing, grooming, and dressing; and managing challenging behaviors such as wandering or angry outbursts. This list will help you to determine the best facility.

Get recommendations

Talk with people who have firsthand knowledge about local facilities. These may be other families, the physician, clergy, hospital social workers, or placement and referral agencies. Your local area agency on aging is also a good source for information about facilities in your area. Disease-related associations—for example, the Alzheimer's Association, Stroke Association, and Parkinson's Association—and members of local support groups also may have helpful information.

Screen by telephone

Calling first will narrow your choices of facilities to visit. Call during business hours. Talk with the administrator, manager, admissions coordinator, or director of nursing. They should be willing to take the time to answer your questions. Depending on the type of facility you are looking for, you may want to ask the following questions:

◆ Is your facility currently licensed by the state? Also ask if the administrator has a current license. If the answer to either of these questions is "No," then look elsewhere (unless this type of facility is not licensed in the state).

◆ What level of care and range of services does your facility offer? In addition to being sure that the facility can meet your family member's current needs, consider that his needs could change. If they did, would he be able to remain there?

◆ Is your facility Medicare certified? This question is important to ask if you are looking at a nursing home. Although your family member may not be eligible for Medicare now, if he is later hospitalized, would he be eligible for readmission under Medicare coverage? Most people want to return to familiar surroundings.

◆ Is your facility Medicaid certified? If private funds will be used to pay for care initially, but you expect Medicaid will be needed later on, this is an important question to ask. If the facility is certified for Medicaid reimbursement, relocation often is unnecessary if your family member needs to go on Medicaid.
— If a private pay resident eventually must use Medicaid, will he be allowed to remain in the facility?
— If so, is this on a "space available" basis?

◆ Can your facility meet the special needs of my family member? If your family member will require special care for a medical condition, be sure his needs can be met.
— Can the facility meet his special dietary needs?
— If he needs assistance with eating, will it be appropriately provided?
— If he needs therapy, can it be provided as prescribed?
— If he has dementia and wanders, does the facility have a safe area for him to wander?
— If religious services and observances are important to him, how will the facility meet these needs?
— If your family member doesn't speak English, are there staff members who speak his language?
— Conversely, if your family member speaks English, do staff members speak and understand English?
— What happens if additional assistance is needed? Will your family member have to move, or can the facility provide the necessary care?

◆ What are your admission criteria and procedures?

◆ What are your policies and procedures regarding discharge?

◆ What are the facility's charges?
— What is the basic monthly/daily charge? (Services typically covered are those common to all residents.)
— What is included and what are extra charges?
— What are the charges for additional services and supplies? (You may want to ask for a written list of these fees. Typical extra charges are for medications, incontinence pads, therapy, and beautician services.)
— Is an advance deposit required? If so, what is the amount? Is it refundable if not used?
— What are the billing procedures and payment policies?
— How often do fees change?
— What happens with the unused portion of advance payments if a resident leaves or dies? Is it fully refundable?

◆ Is a room (or apartment) available?
— If one is not available, is there a waiting list?
— How long is the waiting list?
— What does it take to get a person's name on the waiting list?
— How long before a room (or apartment) will be available?

Be prepared to answer questions about your family member. Facilities want to meet a prospective resident's needs, and any information you can provide will be useful.

Give an honest and complete picture of your relative's needs—medical, social, emotional, behavioral, and financial. This will help insure selecting the most appropriate living arrangement.

Visit prospective facilities

After you have completed your telephone screening, visit prospective facilities. It's the only way to truly evaluate whether a facility is right for your family member. Talk with the housing manager, administrator, or care provider until all of your questions are answered. Two important questions are:

◆ What is the quality of care provided by the facility?

◆ How well will my family member fit in this facility?

Make an appointment before you visit. Facilities have busy times, especially at meal times and early in the morning, when they are getting residents bathed and dressed for the day. Try to avoid these times.

If at all possible, take your family member with you to visit facilities. Remember, it is he, not you, who will be living in the facility.

If your relative is not able to visit facilities, "step into his shoes." Try to look at the total environment—residents, staff, physical facilities, and activities—through his eyes. Keep your family member informed about what you are doing, and discuss what you learned from your visits. If feasible, encourage your family member to participate in evaluating the options.

Consider asking to take photographs or a video so you can take your family member "on a tour" when he can't tour in person. Take pictures of the group living areas, a resident's room, the dining room, and any special events.

Some places also have brochures filled with photographs or photo albums of facility activities. They often will let you borrow an album to share with your family member.

If your visit will be the first time you have been in a care facility, you may feel uncomfortable. The sights and sounds may disturb you. One family member stated:

> The first time I visited a nursing home, I was upset by the people sitting in wheelchairs along the hall. Now I understand this is a change of scenery and social contact with the staff and visitors going up and down the hall.

Remember, most people are in care facilities because they have significant physical or mental impairments. A confused resident may call out to you "Help, help, help" as you pass by. It doesn't necessarily mean he is in pain. A resident may reach out to you or think you are someone they recognize. Smile and say hello.

Visit a facility more than once. For example, visit at mealtime, during an activity, in the evening, and on the weekend, as well as during the week. This also will give you an opportunity to assess whether the facility is adequately staffed around the clock, seven days a week. Try to visit long enough to assess a normal day.

Observe residents and talk to families. Observing and talking to other residents and their families provides insight and useful information. Are families satisfied with the care their relatives are receiving? Do they have complaints? What problems, if any, have they experienced? How has the facility dealt with their complaints?

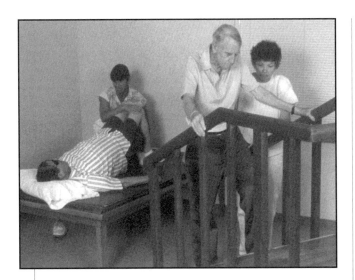

Observe, observe, observe. How do staff interact with the residents? How does the facility appear? How do residents look? Do residents appear happy? What are the residents doing? Does the food look appealing? What sounds do you hear? How does the facility smell? (Note: Many care facilities have incontinent residents, so there will be an occasional odor. However, if you detect a general stale odor or a strong smell of disinfectant, or if on return visits the smell remains, you will want to cross that home off your list.)

Look at residents' rooms. Rooms should have space for personal furnishings and possessions. A resident's room should feel homelike and reflect his personality.

Talk to the ombudsman. Another local/state resource is the long-term care ombudsman office. The ombudsman role is to insure quality care and the rights of residents and to investigate and resolve complaints on behalf of residents and their families. Although ombudsmen cannot recommend one facility over another, they can provide information about the quality of care, the nature of complaints and the results of recent complaint investigations. Almost all state ombudsmen are housed in state agencies on aging.

Read state inspection survey records. You may want to check public records regarding state inspections and consumer complaints. Care facilities that receive funds from Medicare and Medicaid are surveyed annually. These inspection reports provide details about deficiencies and violations involving the health, safety, and quality of life of the residents.

Federal guidelines require nursing homes to make their latest inspection reports available and readily accessible to the public. When you read a report, don't expect perfection. Even the best facilities have deficiencies from time to time. Keep in mind that a complaint or the results of a survey made a year ago may not be valid today. However, citations for consistent understaffing or poor care are "red flags." Another "red flag" is if a care facility is reluctant to share the report. Staff also should be willing to discuss with you any deficiencies found in a report. If you ask questions about the report, listen to the tone and content of the response you receive.

Your Social Security office will have these reports on file for all Medicare-licensed facilities. Your state licensing agency will have the reports for all Medicaid-licensed nursing homes.

Be realistic

It's unlikely that any facility will meet all of your family member's needs perfectly. You and your family member need to decide what are your most important needs and preferences.

What to Look for in a Care Facility

There are many considerations in selecting a care facility, including the atmosphere and attitudes of staff, social and medical services, activities, and location.

Before visiting facilities, consider going through the following questions with your family member. Mark those questions which are most important to both of you. No guide can make the selection of a facility a "sure thing," but it can help to know what to look for and the questions to ask. Your individual situation will be one of the most important considerations in selecting a facility.

Atmosphere and attitudes

Atmosphere and attitudes are perhaps the most difficult factors to measure when choosing a facility, yet they are critical to a person's wellbeing. A beautiful building does not guarantee good care. How does the facility "feel"? One of the most important features is its atmosphere—the physical and social environment, but especially the staff. As someone said, "Brick and mortar make a building, but people make a building a home." A staff's kind and caring attitude is one of the most important factors in making residents happy. Observe carefully how staff interact with residents. Look for these things:

◆ Are staff kind, caring, and friendly? Are they patient and gentle with the residents? Do they treat residents with respect and dignity?

◆ Do staff interact and speak warmly to the residents and show affection by words and touch? Or do staff talk primarily among themselves?

◆ Are staff pleasant to you? Do they respond directly and courteously to your questions and comments?

◆ Are visits welcome at any time?

◆ Are volunteers and community groups encouraged to be involved in the facility?

◆ Is there sensitivity to individual resident's social, emotional, and intellectual needs?

◆ Does the staff member giving the tour speak to the residents as you pass by?

◆ Is respect given to the privacy needs of residents?

◆ Does staff respond promptly when a resident needs or asks for something?

◆ Do staff communicate with each other in a courteous and professional manner? Do they seem happy to be working at the facility?

◆ Are staff appropriately dressed?

Three important questions to ask about the atmosphere in relation to your family member are:

◆ Is the atmosphere one in which my family member will be comfortable? Some people prefer a cozy, homelike environment; some prefer one with a lot of activities; others prefer a more formal setting.

◆ Are there other residents with similar backgrounds to my family member? This can enhance compatibility. It is generally much harder for a person to adjust to a facility if the background of most residents—for example, socioeconomic status or culture—is significantly different from his own.

◆ If my family member visited the facility, was he comfortable with the reception he received?

The importance of the answers to these questions is reflected in one woman's comments about her 93-year-old friend who lived for 13 years in a care facility:

> The facility where my friend lived was very good, but Martha had few comrades because her mind was good until the end. This was not true for most people in the home. Mealtimes were particularly difficult for her because of this. Martha was fortunate to have one friend and confidante across the hall and did have a private room, which made a difference.

If your family member will be sharing a room, find out how residents are matched. The relationship a person has with a roommate can make a big difference in his adjustment to and satisfaction with living in a care facility.

Residents' appearance

Personal appearance is important to everyone's self-image. It also affects how staff and visitors respond to residents.

◆ Are residents appropriately dressed?

◆ Are the residents well groomed? Are male residents clean shaven?

◆ Are residents out of bed?

◆ Are residents who need personal assistance well-groomed and appropriately dressed for the time of day and season?

◆ Are residents dressed and their hair done in their personal styles, rather than everyone looking alike?

Location and physical environment

You and other family and friends will visit more often if the facility is conveniently located. The surroundings should be safe,

clean, pleasant, and homelike, with residents encouraged to personalize their space.

◆ Is the facility's location convenient for family, friends, and your family member's physician?

◆ Is the building safe, with well-lighted halls, handrails, clearly marked exits, and sturdy equipment?

◆ Is the facility clean, pleasant, and generally odor free?

◆ Does the building feel pleasant, cheerful, and homelike?

◆ Are various areas of the facility easily accessible for someone using a cane, walker, or wheelchair?

◆ Are there congenial and welcoming places for residents and visitors to meet, besides a resident's room?

◆ What is the noise level? Is it a level that will be comfortable to your family member?

◆ Does the facility have good ventilation and a moderate temperature?

◆ Can my family member have a space for solitude and quiet? For visits with family and friends?

◆ Is privacy provided in bathroom and bathing areas?

◆ If residents share rooms, how is privacy provided?

◆ Are there lounges, gardens, kitchens, and other areas and equipment for the residents' use?

◆ Is there a safe, secure outdoor environment?

◆ What security is provided? To what extent does the facility assume responsibility for the security of a resident's personal possessions?

◆ Are residents encouraged to bring their personal possessions? Do the residents' rooms reflect their personalities? Do residents have articles such as family photographs, a favorite bedspread, or wall decorations in their rooms?

People often feel a sense of loss when leaving their home. A room in a care facility cannot replace a person's home. Therefore, having a personalized space is important. If a part of what was "home" can accompany your family member, this often helps to make the adjustment easier.

Medical and social services

A move to a care facility often is prompted by a person's health care needs. If your family member needs therapy, for example, then it's important to look for a nursing facility with a good therapy program. These programs may include speech, physical, or occupational therapy, and treatment for chemical dependency. However, the social services provided to residents—and to family members—can be equally important. Most of the following questions apply primarily to nursing homes; however, some are equally applicable to a range of care facilities.

◆ Does the facility offer the services you need and want?

◆ Will your relative's physician visit the care facility?

◆ Are other medical services (dentists, pharmacists, optometrists, podiatrists, etc.) regularly available?

◆ Are the family and resident encouraged to participate in the development of the patient care plan?

◆ How often is the care plan reevaluated?

◆ How do residents register complaints or make recommendations?

◆ Is there a resident council where residents can express their concerns and viewpoints? If so, what is the level of participation?

◆ Is there a family council? What is the perceived role of the council in the facility? How often does it meet?

◆ Is a social service worker available to provide assistance to residents and families?

◆ Is there a program to support and involve families?

◆ Is there volunteer participation from the community? If so, how much?

The best care facilities encourage family and friends to be involved in the lives of residents and facility activities. A family council is designed to provide a forum for expressing concerns and making recommendations to the administration. Active participation usually means the administration and staff are concerned and receptive to dealing with issues presented.

Good care facilities also will encourage you and your family member, who is now a resident, to be involved in developing the care plan. Volunteers generally are most involved with the social service and activity departments. An active volunteer program often is a reflection of a facility's commitment to meeting the needs of residents.

Activities

Activities can be important in enhancing people's self-esteem. A varied and interesting activity program suggests the social, emotional, and spiritual needs of residents are recognized as being as important as their physical needs. Activities should be

appropriate for adults and structured around the capabilities and interests of residents. You will want to determine if your family member can participate in and will enjoy the activities. Activities offered at one facility may be better suited to your family member than activities offered at another facility. Ask to see the activity schedule, which usually is posted.

◆ Is there a varied and stimulating activity program? Or are activities boring and childish?

◆ Are activities offered that are interesting and meaningful to your family member?

◆ What intellectual and mentally stimulating activities are available to mentally alert residents? For example, are there speakers, discussion groups, or Bookmobile visits from the library?

◆ How are residents' spiritual needs met?

◆ Are residents supported in observing their religious preferences?

◆ Are there opportunities for residents to feel useful; for example, to do something for others, if they are able?

◆ What individualized activities are available for your family member?

◆ Are shopping trips or other community activities scheduled for those residents able to participate?

◆ If your family member is bedbound, how will his activity needs be met?

◆ Are there opportunities for both group and individual activities?

◆ Are there areas where residents can gather to socialize independently?

◆ Do all residents have access to the outdoors?

◆ Are activity and therapy rooms in use? Do you see residents participating in activities?

◆ Is someone available to assist with letter writing, opening and reading mail, or making telephone calls if your family member is unable to do so?

◆ Is assistance provided for residents to get to activities?

◆ Are family members encouraged to participate in activities such as special social events and holiday celebrations?

Meals

For many residents, mealtime is a highlight of the day. Ask to see a sample menu. If possible, observe more than one meal being served, and make arrangements for you and your family member to eat a meal with the residents. Observe whether residents who need help eating get the help they need.

◆ Is a menu posted?

◆ Is the facility serving what is on the menu?

◆ Is there a selection of entrees at each meal?

◆ Is food served that your relative likes?

◆ Are the meals well-balanced, attractive, and appetizing?

◆ Is the food tasty?

◆ Are the food portions adequate?

◆ Is the dining area cheerful?

◆ Is food served at the proper temperature—hot food hot and cold food cold?

◆ Are special diets available for persons with specific health problems such as diabetes or difficulty swallowing?

◆ Will the facility meet someone's special dietary needs based on religion?

◆ Are residents given enough time to eat?

◆ Are snacks provided to residents? If so, when? What are typical snacks?

◆ Do residents who need encouragement or assistance to eat get the needed help?

◆ Can family members arrange for guest meals? If so, what is the procedure?

◆ If residents need help getting to the dining room, will staff assist them or do they have to eat in their rooms?

◆ Is a tray available if a person cannot get to the dining room?

Policies

Facilities have policies regarding the use of personal furniture, conditions for admission, notification of the family when the resident's condition changes, visiting hours, and outings. Request a copy of the facility's policies and procedures and discuss them with the administrator, manager, or provider. Be sure you fully understand and are comfortable with them before your family member moves into a facility.

◆ Are visiting hours open (that is, may family and friends visit at will)?

◆ Are there restrictions on having visitors?

◆ Are out-of-town guests allowed to stay in a resident's room? Are accommodations available for overnight guests?

◆ Can residents bring their own furniture and mementos? Are there any limitations about what they can bring?

◆ Can food and drink be brought in for a resident?

◆ Can a resident have a pet in the facility? If so, what are the rules regarding pets?

◆ Can a favorite pet visit?

◆ Are young children encouraged to visit?

◆ If your family member smokes, is smoking allowed in the facility? Is the area safe and supervised?

◆ What is the policy for residents traveling outside of the facility?

◆ What is the policy regarding the use of restraints (chemical and physical)?

◆ Under what circumstances would a resident be asked or forced to move? How much notice is given? What about refunds?

- What is the policy for holding a room if a person is hospitalized or needs a higher level of care for a period of time?

- What is the policy regarding changes in medications? Who contacts the doctor? Who requests the changes?

- When is the family notified about changes in a person's condition?

- Can family members have access to a resident's chart?

- Who is responsible for contacting the primary care physician or house physician?

- In times of crisis, can the family visit during the night?

Your choice of a facility should be based on careful consideration of the questions on pages 204–213. While no facility is perfect, you can expect that most quality facilities will do well on your evaluation. Your decision should reflect this evaluation, together with your relative's preferences.

If time permits, plan return visits before making the final decision. As one family member stated, "A second visit should be made to a care facility for the same reasons you tour an apartment or house more than once before you decide to rent or to buy it. You are a consumer shopping for a way of life."

You won't be able to change your family member to fit a care facility. Therefore, pick one that will best "fit" your family member. The more you know about a facility, the more comfortable you will feel about a decision. However, even when you've made a decision, you may still wonder if you're doing the right thing. This is a common feeling.

PAYING FOR CARE IN A FACILITY

Facility care is expensive. Cost varies by facility, location, the care needs of your family member, whether he will be in a private or shared room, and the amenities a facility offers. Your most desired facility may be out of the question because of cost, or the facility may be full and have a long waiting list. As you consider costs, keep in mind the perspectives offered by two family members:

> We tried to keep mother at home. But when she needed 24-hour care, the cost of bringing in the professional help she needed was twice as expensive as to have her in a care facility.

> Staying in a care facility is costly, but it is not as expensive as a night in a good hotel, and the "guest" is receiving food and nursing services.

You will need to assess your family member's financial resources, including income, property, savings, stocks, bonds, and insurance. Also, find out if he has a long-term health care insurance policy. If he does, make sure you understand under what circumstances the policy will cover expenses, what level(s) of care it will cover, and for how long it will provide coverage. If his financial resources are inadequate, how much, if any, can family members realistically contribute?

Government health insurance programs can help pay for nursing home care and, in some states, adult foster care, residential or assisted living care; however, they have very specific requirements.

Medicare

Contrary to popular belief, Medicare covers only a very small portion of nursing home costs. It has limits on the amount of time and circumstances under which it pays for care. It pays only for nursing care that it defines as "skilled" and its definition is more restrictive than that applied to the level of care a facility offers. Federal guidelines for Medicare limit coverage to people who have the potential for recovery. Most people in nursing homes need primarily intermediate or personal care services.

Medicare also pays only if the nursing home is certified by Medicare. Even if the older person is receiving skilled nursing care, Medicare will not pay if the nursing home is not Medicare certified. Some nursing homes choose not to be Medicare certified; Medicare will not cover the cost of care for people in these facilities.

The physician, hospital discharge planner, or the nursing home admissions coordinator or director of nursing can help determine what, if anything, Medicare will cover. Because rules governing Medicare are revised frequently, it's advisable to check current Medicare policies. You may obtain additional information from your local Social Security office.

Medicaid

Medicaid helps low-income people of all ages pay for medical expenses, including nursing home care, when they have exhausted their own funds. In some states, assistance may also be available for adult foster care, residential care, or assisted living. Because of limited incomes and high medical costs, many older people in nursing homes eventually qualify for Medicaid. Medicaid covers nursing home care for eligible people as long as their condition merits it.

Medicaid eligibility and benefits vary from state to state, but a person must have a limited income and limited assets or resources. When his assets have been spent down to a required level, Medicaid may then be available, provided his income does not exceed the "Medicaid cap."

If your relative does not have the financial resources to pay for nursing facility care, he can apply to Medicaid for assistance. If the application is approved, the nursing home resident must contribute his monthly income, except for a small personal needs allowance and income allowed for the spouse residing in the community. Medicaid will pay the balance.

It's very important that spouses know federal and state laws regarding division of assets and limits on "spend down." Spouses of nursing home residents no longer need to become impoverished to pay for a mate's care before they can use Medicaid. But if the spouse is unaware of the laws and spends everything for care, the impoverishment will not be reversed by the government.

If your family member's financial situation is substantial, Medicaid coverage probably will not be available and it will be necessary to pay for care from the person's income and financial reserves. Some elders resist spending their money for care, especially if they have worked hard to leave an inheritance.

Because Medicaid payments to facilities in some states are lower than those paid by Medicare or private-pay patients, many facilities do not accept people on Medicaid, or they place a limit on the number of people on Medicaid.

If there is any chance that your family member will need Medicaid, be sure you

fully understand Medicaid's rules and regulations, especially in regard to "spend down" and "transfer of assets."

To learn more about the specific requirements for qualifying for Medicaid, or to complete an application, contact your local social services or welfare office. Social workers at most nursing homes also can help you. If you are an adult child of the person entering a care facility, you are not legally responsible for the costs of your family member's care; however, his spouse is responsible if income and resources are above the exemption limits.

Veterans Administration

The Veterans Administration (VA) Veterans Aid and Attendance Program can help offset nursing home care costs for eligible veterans. If your family member was in the service during wartime, inquire about the program to determine whether he qualifies. For more information, contact your local VA office.

HMO Contracts

If your family member belongs to a managed care health plan that contracts with particular nursing facilities, make sure the facilities you are considering have contracts with your relative's HMO.

After you select a care facility, be sure you thoroughly understand all financial arrangements and the facility's contract agreement before you sign it. This is a legal contract; therefore, you may want to have a lawyer review it before signing.

MOVING DAY: WHAT CAN YOU EXPECT?

The day of admission is often difficult for all family members. Emotional strain and apprehension are common feelings. You may feel guilt or remorse. Your family member may feel abandoned, angry, sad, or resentful. Entering a care facility means leaving behind a familiar and comfortable environment. Time helps most people work through these feelings.

Staff can assist in making the transition less stressful. Ask about the best time to make the move. Mid-morning often is recommended.

Ways to Ease the Transition

Even with careful planning, the move still may be rocky. Once a decision is made for placement, make a list of things you can do to make the transition as smooth as possible for your family member—and for you. One family, for example, planned a "housewarming party" shortly after their mother entered a care facility. Here are some other suggestions.

Personalize your family member's room

Make his room as homelike as possible before he moves in. Ask your family member to choose familiar and important items to bring—for example, family photos and favorite decorative items. Personal possessions and furnishings help provide a sense of continuity. Expect some grieving as your family member makes choices about what to bring, sell, or give away.

Remember his favorite clothing

If you're helping someone prepare to move, clothes may be the last thing on your mind. However, clothes are among the few personal belongings a person can keep after entering a facility. Clothes are also a form of personal expression, and the opportunity to make daily clothing choices provides a needed sense of control.

In deciding what to bring, ask yourself whether your family member likes it, whether it's easy to put on and take off, and whether it's easy to care for. Mark clothing clearly to avoid laundry loss.

Prepare in advance as much as possible

For example, complete necessary paperwork. Mark your family member's clothing with his name. Mark or engrave other personal items, including furniture, television set, or radio. If your relative wears dentures, ask the dentist to engrave the dentures with a name or Social Security number. Tape his name on his eyeglasses.

Make a written inventory of all items your family will be bringing into the facility. Update the inventory when items are given to your family member or removed.

Have more than one family member present

If paperwork has not been done beforehand, try to have at least two family members present—one who can do the necessary paperwork and another who can be with your family member.

Plan to spend the day

Spend most of the first day with your family member. This will help him feel less abandoned and provide needed reassurance. It also gives you an opportunity to meet staff members who will be providing the care to your family member.

Schedule your next visit

Before you leave, make plans for your next visit and make it as soon as possible.

ADJUSTING TO LIFE IN A CARE FACILITY

Once a move has been made, an adjustment period follows. The first few weeks will be the most difficult. It may take three to six months for your family member to adjust. Even once he has adjusted, there will be good days and bad days. Recognize it is a time of change for everyone.

If this was a move your family member did not want to make, at first he may be angry and his goal may be to "leave and go home." Try not to take the anger personally and resist the natural tendency to say that where he is living is now home. Instead, let him express his feelings of loss and pain. Depending on the situation, it may help to talk about what he must be able to do to return home—for example, dressing himself or walking 20 feet. Rather than ignoring or brushing off feelings, talk about them. The four R's to helping someone adjust are: reassurance, routes, routines, and relationships.

Reassurance. Be present and available during the first few weeks. You can help reduce a major source of anxiety—the fear of being abandoned. You probably are the "piece of security" in an environment that feels insecure.

Routes. Your family member may experience uncertainty about getting around in a facility, such as to the dining and activity rooms. This is especially true for the person who has Alzheimer's disease or other dementia. You may need to accompany him again and again to show how to get from one place to another.

Routines. Achieving some mastery of routines and "learning the ropes" bolsters self-confidence.

Relationships. Your family member may need help interacting with staff and other residents. Introduce him to other people. Your frequent presence and interest in other residents also may increase your family member's chances as a potential friend because the other residents enjoy your attention, too. Meet, talk with, and convey messages of appreciation to staff. When staff have good feelings about you it generally will carry over to your family member.

The move to a care facility may be as difficult for you as it is for your relative. Family members experience a range of emotions. The intensity of reactions depends on the circumstances leading to placement, your family member's response to the move, and past and present relationships among family members.

Feelings of loss, guilt, and fear often come into sharp focus during this adjustment period. Many of these feelings result from seeing the losses and declines experienced by your family member. It also may represent to you, as well as to your family member, the final stage of life and mark the beginning of mourning and bereavement.

Get support for yourself and share your feelings. Grief over your own losses needs attention. Once you have begun to face your own feelings, it will be easier to be more supportive of your family member's experience of loss.

Because there still is a social stigma associated with care facility placement, it's no surprise that feelings of guilt often are a part of the adjustment process. If you find yourself feeling guilty, you likely feel you have broken some underlying rule and you expect to be blamed and punished. An example of such a rule is "A good daughter should take care of her parents." The daughter may be totally committed to this rule, but unable to provide the direct care for practical or emotional reasons, and feel guilt as a result. Another person may be ambivalent about this rule and feel guilty for having mixed feelings. Often families manifest their guilt by being overly protective of their older family member or critical of staff, or by not visiting.

If you experience guilt, try to identify the rule, acknowledge any mixed feelings you may have, and rewrite the rule to make it more realistic and appropriate to the current situation. Most guilt rules are black and white, inflexible, and impossible to conform to completely. When they are examined rationally and in light of the current situation, guilt may diminish and more positive feelings surface. It is helpful to reach out to others for validation of your reassessment of the rule.

Here are suggestions for coping with the changes, adjustments, and feelings that placement may bring:

◆ Assess family relationships so you can be more realistic about the cooperation and support you can expect from other family members.

◆ Acknowledge the feelings you have and share what you are experiencing with others. Bottling up your feelings will only push them deeper and create more distress.

♦ Talk with others about their experiences. It can help you feel less alone and assist you to cope.

♦ Seek help with unresolved feelings that continue to be difficult to handle. Facility staff or a family support group may be helpful. If you still feel unable to cope with your feelings, professional counseling may be beneficial.

♦ Join a caregiver support group. Look in the newspaper for times and location of meetings.

If the care facility is large, it also may have a support group for family members. If you have questions about the care your family member is receiving or conditions in the facility, request a conference with the appropriate staff member. Mutual understanding is the first step to resolving a problem.

Your Role in the Care Facility

Moving a family member into a care facility is not the end of caregiving; it's a continuation of your caring. Your role is just as important as if you were the hands-on caregiver. The difference is that now you can focus on meeting the emotional needs of your family member, which you probably did not have the time to do before. There are several things you can do to make a difference in the life of your relative who lives in a care facility.

Monitor care

An important role you have is ensuring that your family member gets the best care possible. Residents whose families are involved in their care have higher morale and receive better care. One family member offers this advice: "As you monitor the care of your family member, keep in mind you are concerned only about one person. The staff is responsible for many residents." One important way to monitor your family member's care is to participate in care plan conferences.

Attend care plan conferences

Most care facilities are required to develop a plan of care for every resident. Family members can assist in preparing the care plan, with the resident's permission. The care plan outlines the therapies, activities, nutrition, and other actions to be carried out to help the resident reach or maintain optimum functioning and wellbeing. A plan should include personal goals for your family member and a way to measure whether the goals are achieved.

Participating in care plan conferences is another way to keep in contact with the needs of your family member and the concerns that arise in relation to his care. You can provide valuable information about your relative's needs, interests, and background, particularly if he is unable to do so. You also will learn more about how the facility will provide care and about any concerns staff may have. This also is an opportunity to discuss any concerns you may have. One daughter talked about the benefits the care plan conference also had for her father:

> The patient care plan meeting with my dad was a major turning point. He was impressed that people were concerned about how he felt about the care he was receiving. It also made a major change in staff understanding my father's sight and hearing limitations, and in recognizing him as a person with problems who would cooperate if approached appropriately. Dad later asked several times about the team of people who were supposed to help him get well. When I explained to him that the dietitian was in the kitchen preparing food he could eat, the physical therapist was helping him with exercises, etc., he made more attempts to communicate his needs and participate in his care.

Advocate

Another significant role is serving as advocate for your family member. This role is critical if your family member cannot advocate for himself. To effectively act as an advocate, it's important to know two things: the personnel structure of the care facility, and procedures and channels for dealing with concerns and problems.

Build relationships with staff

Your family member may live in a care facility for a long time. Good communication and a positive relationship with staff members can reduce misunderstandings and conflict. Try to get to know them as individuals and give appreciation and praise for good work. As one spouse said, "It's just as important to say something nice when care is good as it is to speak up when care is poor."

Concerns and problems will arise, even in the best of facilities. And, no matter how many precautions are taken, accidents and mistakes happen. Consider what one wife had to say:

> I don't know why I expected everything to be so perfect in the nursing home. When he was at home, Joe fell several times. He wandered away twice. And yet, when he fell once at the nursing home, I was so upset. I then reminded myself, accidents do happen—it wouldn't have mattered where Joe was."

The manner in which you approach staff about concerns is important. Do not assume the worst until you have investigated. Seek out the facts and try to understand all sides of an issue. For example, a daughter said, "I discovered my mother complained about care to get my attention…and to 'push my guilt buttons' about my having put her in the nursing home."

Approach staff with an attitude of "I'd like to talk about a concern." Demands and accusations tend to put people on the defensive. Provide constructive criticism and give a reasonable time for staff to respond to issues and concerns you raise. You might even ask, "When can I expect a response in regard to my concern about…?" If you have difficulty resolving concerns and problems with the facility, contact the local ombudsman.

Get involved in facility activities

Attending some activities may encourage your family member to participate more in other activities and events in the facility. If you have time, volunteer at the facility. If there is a family council, consider getting involved. Family councils provide a means

to bring concerns and issues to the attention of administration and to offer recommendations, assist in planning programs for residents, and receive and give support.

Staying in Touch

For residents, time often revolves around visits from others. Visits are important. They provide reassurance that family and friends still care. In fact, residents whose families are involved generally have higher morale and receive better care.

Making your visits meaningful

Staff can meet health, safety, hygiene, and nutrition needs. However, family and friends are particularly important in meeting the emotional and social needs of a resident. You also are a link between the person's past and present. Here are some suggestions for making your visits meaningful:

◆ To prevent disappointment, talk to your family member about expectations and limitations regarding visits. You can give your family member a feeling of control and choice by asking when he would most like you to visit, within the limits of your schedule.

◆ Schedule your visits. Scheduled visits give him something to look forward to and help avoid conflict with facility activities in which he participates.

◆ Plan short and frequent visits, particularly if your family member is frail and tires easily or has a short attention span. Regular visits also provide opportunities to observe how he is doing.

◆ Try to avoid visits during scheduled activities, unless you will be participating with your relative in a facility's activity.

◆ Find out from the staff if there are times when visits may be more difficult. For example, the morning is often a busy time.

◆ Plan one-on-one visits. This provides the person with some intimate contact. If your family member is confused by groups, one or two visitors at a time also will be less confusing.

◆ Encourage family and friends to visit frequently during different times of the day. School-aged children can drop by to say hello or to share some drawings after school. A brief stop before or after work can be meaningful.

◆ Take your family member out, if possible, to dinner, religious services, community events, and for home visits, walks, or drives to places he previously enjoyed. Don't be surprised if, after your family member has adjusted and accepted life where he is living, he asks to go "home" to the care facility during an outing. If your family member suffers from Alzheimer's disease or a similar disorder there may come a time when leaving the familiarity of the facility is too difficult.

◆ Join in facility activities with your family member.

◆ Plan to do things with your family member that he can no longer do alone. A son said:

Dad's vision is really poor, but he is still mentally alert. He gets frustrated with the small print so I bring in the newspaper or

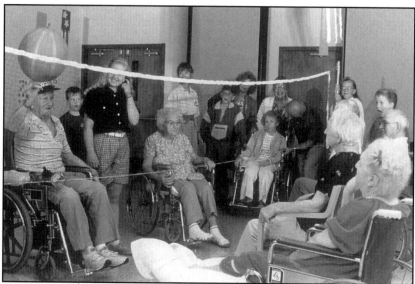

magazine articles and read them to him. Afterward, there's plenty to talk about. Not only is this activity stimulating to him, but it is also rewarding to me.

A daughter shared:

The days mother gets a letter she's more "up." Because of her paralysis, she can no longer write letters. During many of our visits, I write letters for Mom as she dictates to me. This keeps letters coming from family and friends to her.

Sometimes it can be difficult to visit, particularly if your family member does not remember who you are, cannot communicate, or has a severe hearing loss. Remember, visiting can include more than talking. In such situations, it may be more meaningful and less frustrating to do something with your family member—listen to music, go for a walk in the neighborhood, find a craft project you can do together, eat a meal together, give a manicure, look at family photographs, play a board or card game, or go out for (or bring in) ice cream cones.

If your family member forgets you have visited, don't take it personally. Changes in brain function rob many residents of their ability to record and remember visits. Focus on the pleasure the person received "for the moment" during your visit.

Touch. Try using touch. It is one of the most powerful means of communication and can be particularly important when a person no longer comprehends speech. Holding hands, putting an arm around the person's shoulder, giving a massage, stroking the person's arm, or brushing his hair can communicate caring, affection, and that the person is valued. One daughter commented:

> During the more than two years Mother was in the nursing home, we often sat holding hands while I talked and she responded in ever more limited fashion as her disease progressed. I kissed and embraced her frequently. However, the hair-combing sessions were among the most precious of our time together. When we could no longer carry on a conversation, touching and looking at each other in the mirror provided reassurance that a line of communication still lay open between us.

If you are frustrated or don't know what to do when you visit, speak with the social worker or activities director. They may have some helpful suggestions to make your visits mutually pleasant and rewarding.

How often to visit. "How often should I visit?" is a question that often arises. There is no simple answer. Family members offer some insights:

> Visit often enough to maintain a relationship with your family member, but not so often as to interfere with the person's adjustment to his new living arrangement.

Recognize that no matter how often you visit, it may never seem like it is enough to your relative. Time may fly by for you, but to residents, time often goes by slowly.

Keeping in Contact When You Can't Be There

Even if you can't visit regularly, you can still stay in touch with your family member. Frequent letters and telephone calls are one way. If your family member has poor vision, try using a black felt tip pen and print in large, block letters on off-white or light yellow paper. This may help him to be able to read your letters.

Some families use video visits. They talk to the person on videotape and record special occasions such as a trip, a grandchild's graduation or wedding, or a family gathering. Letters and videotapes have the benefit of being something your family member can keep and enjoy rereading or replaying again and again.

You also may be able to find a local volunteer who will visit or take your family member out occasionally. The social services or activity departments of facilities may be able to identify a volunteer. The local area agency on aging also can give you information about community agencies that have volunteer "friendly visitor" programs.

SUMMARY

Making a decision about placement of a family member in a care facility is difficult. It's even more difficult if you are confronted with the need to make a decision quickly at a time of crisis. Although it's a decision most of us hope we never have to make, there are times when a care facility is the most appropriate living arrangement for an individual. It can enhance an older person's quality of life and relationships between family members. One daughter, whose mother had been living in a care facility for several months, said:

> I think my mother is actually happier than when she was living with me, where she laid on the couch most of the day. In the care home there are people around her—not just me. She is involved in exercise classes and other activities. What I considered a last resort several months ago, I now know was the best decision, for both Mom and me.

If you have given careful thought to the decision, examined options, involved the older person in decision making as much as possible, and decided that a care facility truly is the best option, be confident that you have made the best decision possible.

Overview

Chapter Eleven

Making Decisions About Driving

Are you concerned about an older family member's driving? Are you reluctant to raise the issue with the person? It can be difficult to talk to an older person about his driving or to know what to do if an unsafe driver continues to drive.

Mary shares her father's situation:

Dad was very independent. Three years ago he had an auto accident, which was a real turning point. He ran a stop sign. Dad was lucky; no one was hurt. He continued driving. Then he got a letter from his insurance company, which said he had to be examined by a doctor. The doctor said Dad was very confused and would have to take a driver's test. We knew Dad couldn't pass the test, but it was having to pay for

high risk insurance that made the difference. Dad understood (about the high cost) and said, "No, I'm not going to pay for it." He stopped driving. It was months later that Dad said, "It feels like someone has cut off my arms and legs." It's hard… It's one of the big last freedoms.

If you're older, you may at some time face a decision to limit when or where you can drive or to give up driving completely. These are not easy decisions.

This chapter explores the significance of driving in our lives, age-related changes that can affect driving safety as we age, and what to consider when approaching a family member about his driving.

THE FACTS ABOUT OLDER DRIVERS

As a group, people age 65 and older have fewer accidents than any other age group. But they also drive fewer miles each year than drivers of other ages, and the picture changes when you consider accidents per mile driven. For example, people 75 and older are more than twice as likely to be involved in accidents-per-mile driven than the average driver.

Older people tend to have more accidents in driving situations that require a high degree of perception, problem solving ability, and immediate reaction and decision making. The most common problems are failure to yield right-of-way, incorrect lane changes, and improper turning—particularly left-hand turns and turning from the wrong lane. Older people are seldom involved in accidents that result from speeding, driving under the influence of alcohol, or other reckless driving.

When involved in a car accident, older people are more susceptible to injury and death. What may be a minor accident for a young, vigorous person is often serious or fatal for an older adult.

When they experience a decline in their abilities, most older people alter their driving. They may drive only during daylight hours, avoid heavy traffic times, limit the geographic area in which they drive, or limit driving to roadways that are less complicated. Helen, age 75, is an example:

I hadn't driven at night for a long time, and I quit driving long distances several years ago. I made the decision, totally on my own, to give up driving when I was 72 because I became increasingly tense while driving. It was difficult not to have the freedom a car gave me—to go where I wanted when I wanted to go—but at the same time I felt relief.

The Influence of Age-Related Changes

Most older people are safe drivers; however, age-related changes may contribute to problems with driving for some people. Common changes include the following:

◆ Reflexes and coordination become slower.

◆ Perception declines. Most older people don't see or hear as well as they did when they were younger.

◆ Recovery from glare takes longer. For example, it takes longer for eyes to return to normal vision at night when oncoming headlights temporarily blind them.

◆ Processing of information slows. Perceiving a situation, analyzing the information, making the necessary decisions, and executing an action within traffic speed may take longer. This is especially true in

complex driving situations; for example, those requiring right-of-way and yielding, and at intersections. Common behavior changes are driving slowly and braking at every intersection, or driving without awareness of other drivers.

◆ The tendency to tire easily increases. Older people are more likely to experience fatigue and reduced alertness when driving long distances.

Medications can affect skill and judgment behind the wheel. Any medications that affect mental alertness, reaction time, or vision can affect driving skills. These include sleeping pills, tranquilizers, sedatives, pain medication, muscle relaxants, some antidepressants, and non-prescription cold, antihistamine, and sinus remedies.

Strokes are also a common cause of cognitive, perceptual, and physical impairment that can make a person an unsafe driver. In particular, people with right hemisphere brain damage are especially at risk. Typical deficits seen include: left-sided neglect, loss of the left visual field, impaired judgment, decreased ability to problem-solve, and perceptual deficits. Particularly dangerous is the impulsive behavior and decreased appreciation of deficits that often accompanies this type of stroke.

Cognitive impairment from Alzheimer's disease and similar disorders is associated with poorer driving performance, increased risk of accidents, and getting lost while driving.

The Significance of Driving

How important is it to be able to drive? What does having your own car mean? How would you feel if today you had to surrender your driver's license? How would not being able to drive affect your lifestyle and day-to-day activities?

Driving is more than just a means of transportation, of getting from one place to another. Driving symbolizes independence, the ability to control your own life and time, spontaneity, convenience, competence as an adult, and membership in the mainstream of society. It's a link to friends, social events and activities away from home. Because of all the things driving may represent, it can be difficult to give up the keys. John, age 94, said:

> The day the doctor told me I had to give up driving because of my poor vision was the most difficult day of my life. I felt as though my world was coming to an end. I had always been independent and took care of myself. I felt as though the doctor had just given me a life sentence in prison.

Even when a person voluntarily makes the decision to stop driving, it is usually difficult. This is exemplified by the story a granddaughter tells:

> My grandmother is 96 years old, feisty, frail, and clear-minded. When she was 83 years old, her parked car was totaled when someone crashed into it during an ice storm. It was a hit-and-run case. Buying a new car seemed too costly, so she quit driving. She

still laments her loss of independent transportation, and occasionally, she will still say she wants to get her driver's license.

Most people do not have to give up driving with increasing age; however, many face some curtailment of driving. For those who do give it up, it can cause significant changes in their lives and it can cause great sorrow. This loss is even greater if the change is not voluntary. It's normal for a person to feel sadness and anger and to wonder, "How can I ever manage to do the things I have been doing if I can't drive?" Even the person who feels a sense of relief from not having to drive may still experience a sense of loss.

In rural communities and suburbs, loss of driving can have a tremendous impact. Generally, there are few alternatives to the personal automobile for transportation. There may be no bus, taxi, or senior/volunteer transportation program available. To give up driving may mean becoming dependent on the goodwill of neighbors, friends, and family. Family members may live at a distance or work full time, making it impractical for them to provide transportation. Some older people who know they are having problems with driving say they continue to drive because they believe they have no choice—alternative modes of transportation are not readily available or at all.

SIGNS OF UNSAFE DRIVING

Behavior that may indicate a person's driving threatens his personal safety and that of others includes:

◆ Has difficulty following instructions and directions.

◆ Coasts to a near stop in the midst of moving traffic.

◆ Drifts into other lanes of traffic.

◆ Stops abruptly without cause.

◆ Presses simultaneously on the brake and accelerator or confuses the two pedals.

◆ Delays changing lanes when obstacles appear.

◆ Fails to appreciate the frustration, exasperation, or irritation exhibited by other drivers toward his driving.

◆ Does not signal when turning or changing lanes.

◆ Has received an increasing number of driving citations or warnings.

◆ Does not check "blind spot" before changing lanes.

◆ Has accidents, near misses, or "fender benders."

◆ Gets lost in familiar places.

◆ Fails to obey traffic laws, road signs, or signals.

◆ Drives against traffic, on the wrong side of the road.*

◆ Has difficulty seeing pedestrians, objects, and other vehicles.

◆ Is increasingly nervous when driving.

◆ Becomes flustered in traffic or by more aggressive drivers.

◆ Fails to yield the right-of-way or yields the right-of-way inappropriately.

◆ Drives significantly slower than the posted speed or average speed of traffic.

◆ Turns from an improper lane or at an improper time or pace at intersections (especially when turning left).

◆ Straddles lanes.

◆ Ignores or coasts through stop signs.

◆ Backs up after missing an exit.*

◆ Falls asleep or gets drowsy while driving.

◆ Ignores other drivers or road hazards.

◆ Does not react to emergency situations.

* These are examples of driving behaviors that definitely indicate dangerous driving performance.

When any of these signs appear, it's time to assess the situation. Don't wait for an accident. Also, if your family member is having problems related to daily living—such as hygiene, grooming, and paying bills—he may also be having difficulties with driving.

THE FAMILY DILEMMA

It's common for family members to worry about the safety of their older relatives who drive, as well as the safety of others, but at the same time be reluctant to raise concerns or take action.

Family members may rationalize: "Dad only drives in the neighborhood," "My spouse only drives short distances to the grocery store and church," "Everyone in the neighborhood watches out when Mom is behind the wheel." Or the family may be reluctant to do anything because, "Driving is so important to Dad. If he can no longer drive, he will give up." Imagine how it feels approaching a family member about possibly giving up driving when the person has said to you, as Rose stated, "I would be lost without my car. It happens to be my only pleasure. I'm in it most every day, not only to go to the grocery store and the post office, but to enjoy the beauty of the outdoors."

In some cases, a family member can be intimidated by an older relative who is aggressive by nature and becomes more so as a result of a dementing illness.

Sometimes older adults express concerns about their ability to drive. If this occurs, consider it a timely moment. Listen to the concerns expressed and be open to a discussion. Sometimes, we are the ones who find it hard to consider that our family member is having difficulties, because we want to think of our parent or spouse as strong and independent. For example, a 52-year-old son shares:

My mother had always been a good driver. One day she said to me that she thought she didn't see well enough to drive anymore. I told her I thought she was still okay. She was about 73 at that time. I saw her again in about six months. She said, "I made a bad mistake. I am going to stop driving before I hurt someone." She wouldn't tell me what she had done. Later, I was visiting with the neighbor across the street. She said that Mom had missed her driveway and driven across the lawn and down onto the street. So Mom was smarter than me. She knew she was a risk to others and voluntarily stopped driving.

In a relationship where one spouse does not drive, it can be particularly difficult to accept that the driving spouse is no longer a safe driver because of the changes it will bring for both of them.

Often, families are not aware of their relative's driving problems until after the death of his spouse. Unknown to the family, the couple was driving as a team, with the passenger acting as co-pilot. Although one person was behind the wheel, the other gave directions and served as eyes and ears.

Role changes are inevitable when a person can no longer drive. For families, this requires a delicate balance between performing functions previously carried out by that person while at the same time protecting the person's self-esteem and preserving his independence as much as possible.

This decision is made even more difficult when family members disagree about what action to take. One daughter-in-law said:

I felt that the most important thing next to protecting the public was to preserve my father-in-law's dignity. My husband fixed the car so that it wouldn't run. That was where we left the situation. However, it really became a "control thing" for my sister-in-law. About three weeks later, when my sister-in-law visited, the car went. I could really detect a rapid decline in my father-in-law's abilities after that point. I think he gave up. The car was his last possession, as he saw it.

Note: If you think that all your family member needs in order to drive is someone to ride along and serve as a "co-pilot"—e.g., alert him to hazards, read the traffic signs, shift the gears, or serve as a navigator—this is not a safe option.

When a Person is Cognitively Impaired

The issue of driving is even more complicated when your family member is cognitively impaired, for example, suffers from Alzheimer's disease or a similar disorder. Because of impaired brain function, the individual often does not recognize his deterioration or appreciate the potential driving risk. Carl's wife stated:

I knew for months my husband's memory was failing. Carl had been losing things and accusing me of stealing them. He had some trouble driving, but I thought he was okay driving during the day and in familiar places. But one day when he left home to drive to the nearby grocery store, he turned the opposite direction out of our driveway. I thought he had probably decided to go somewhere else first.

Several hours later the police called from a city over 100 miles away. Carl had run a stoplight, hit another car, and seriously

injured several people. By the time we got to the police station, Carl had forgotten he was involved in an accident. He was adamant that someone had stolen his car.

Like Carl, a person who is cognitively impaired may insist, "I am a good driver," because this is truly all that he can remember. He simply has no memory of the recent close calls or even a major accident he caused while driving. Another person tells the story of her neighbor:

> I went to check on Elizabeth, an older neighbor. The state was trying to take away her driver's license. What I found out was that they had just taken her to court because she had hit a motorcyclist, her fault. She claimed that it wasn't her fault— the car just did it! This wasn't her first wreck. There had been a series of accidents. Her license was suspended, but they didn't fine her. I'm wondering if she will drive anyway since she still has her car.

The chances are that Elizabeth will drive anyway since no one lives with her to monitor her access to the car, which was parked in her garage. It's likely she also will not remember that her driver's license was suspended.

The question in regard to driving and Alzheimer's disease is not if a person should give up driving, but when. Studies show that people with Alzheimer's disease are likely to rate themselves as highly capable of driving when they are not.

Usually a family must make and carry out decisions when an older relative has Alzheimer's disease or a similar memory disorder. It is unrealistic to expect the older person to do so. Jillian said about her difficult situation:

> My grandmother and I had always been close. As a result of a series of small strokes, changes occurred, which included her driving down streets in the wrong lanes. We tried talking with my grandmother about her unsafe driving, but to no avail. Finally, I had to remove her car from the premises. We talked with her about the reasons she could no longer drive and made plans for meeting her transportation needs. For weeks my grandmother was angry and accused me of stealing her car. Of course, it hurt, but I also realized that my grandmother probably felt as though her car had been stolen, and because of the disease, it was unrealistic for me to expect her to fully comprehend the true situation.

WHAT YOU CAN DO

There is no one answer in regard to "what to do" if you are concerned about a family member's driving. Families and professionals have found the following suggestions useful in addressing concerns. What will work best depends on your situation, whether your family member's cognitive abilities are intact or impaired, and your relationship. In all cases, you will want to consider the following:

◆ Evaluate the person's driving skills.

◆ Seek support from your family member's doctor.

◆ Approach your family member in a positive way.

◆ Explore transportation options.

◆ Report to the state licensing agency.

If your family member's driving ability is impaired because of Alzheimer's disease or a similar memory disorder, you will need to take a more active role in making decisions about his driving and preventing access to the car. (See pages 245–246 for more information on this topic.)

Evaluate Driving Skills

It's important to check your concerns against your relative's driving performance. Before you decide the time has come for a person to hang up the keys, or to modify when and where he drives, you want to be sure the person is truly an unsafe driver. A person's driving performance—not age—is what determines fitness to drive. The following are options for evaluating driving ability.

Observe driving performance

Ride with the person to identify if he is having problems with driving. In addition, check the car. Small dents, fender benders, and paint from other cars or objects may indicate driving problems. In observing driving performance, be alert to any of the warning signs listed on pages 230–231, and try to answer the following questions:

Yes	No	
☐	☐	Is my family member alert to what is going on at all times when driving—i.e., notices and responds to real or potential hazards, pedestrians, traffic signals and signs?
☐	☐	Can my family member see things coming from the side of the car as well as ahead of the car?
☐	☐	Does my family member hear sounds of oncoming cars, horns, emergency vehicles, as well as sounds from the car itself?
☐	☐	Is my family member able to manage the steering wheel; gear lever; and brake, gasoline, and clutch pedals without problems?
☐	☐	Is my family member able to make the necessary and appropriate decisions while driving?
☐	☐	Is my family member able to respond quickly and appropriately to sudden situations?
☐	☐	Does my family member know where he is and how to get to the desired destination?
☐	☐	Can my family member drive and carry on a conversation at the same time?

You may find that your family member is driving safely within the acknowledged limits of his capabilities. However, if the answer is "No" to any of these questions, evaluate the problem further. Ask yourself, "Is the problem correctable?" For example, new glasses or cataract surgery may correct a vision problem that is creating driving problems. For some people, impaired vision that is not correctable may mean they still can drive, but on a limited basis (for example, during daylight hours); others may need to stop driving.

In assessing driving performance, you may find that a radio or conversing passengers may be distractions that create a problem. Marty tells this story about his mother and the differences between his observations and those of his sister:

> My sister was concerned about Mom's driving. Although Mom had not had an accident, Sheila felt that Mom had too many near misses when she rode with her. On my next visit I rode with Mom and observed her driving. I did not see any problems. Mom did comment, though, that she now avoided freeway driving. Of course, Sheila thought I was denying the problems and insisted that we both ride with Mom together, so we would have the same experience. I had to admit there were some problems when we went together.
>
> To make a long story short, we discovered that there was a difference in Mom's driving depending on who was with her. Sheila's and my behaviors were quite different. Sheila engaged Mom in conversations,

and often also had the radio on. I like quiet in the car and would sit back and enjoy the ride.

Have your relative coach as you drive

An alternate approach to observing someone's driving performance is for you to drive and have the older driver, riding as a passenger, tell you who must yield and who has the right-of-way. For example, have him tell you what to do at two-and four-way stops and uncontrolled intersections.

Suggest a self-assessment

The American Automobile Association Foundation offers a 16-page booklet, *Drivers 55 Plus: Test Your Own Performance,* for self-evaluation of driving performance. This self-evaluation asks the person to respond to 15 statements, such as "I find it difficult to decide when to join traffic on a busy interstate highway." The person computes the score and is advised of its meaning. Then, the booklet offers suggestions for dealing with deficiencies and their causes. This "how am I doing" approach appeals to some people.

Get an objective evaluation of driving performance

A useful strategy, when available, is to get an evaluation at a rehabilitation center, Veterans Administration Medical Center, or hospital-based driving program. The doctor may be able to refer your family member to such a program. These programs often have rehabilitation therapists who objectively assess driving ability. The assessment generally includes a clinical evaluation and a road test of driving skills. The clinical evaluation assesses:

◆ mental status through psychometric testing and interviews.

◆ physical ability, including sensation, muscle strength, and range of motion of joints, particularly in the neck and trunk.

◆ visual function, including acuity, depth perception, peripheral vision, and contrast sensitivity.

The professionals in these programs do more than evaluate driving. When appropriate, they recommend adaptive devices and teach people how to compensate for their deficits. For example, glare-reducing glass, steering devices, hand controls, and other adaptations may increase driving safety and extend driving ability. Frank, age 70, whose legs were amputated as a result of diabetes, said:

> I thought my driving days were over when I lost my legs. There was no way I could operate the gas and brake pedals. During rehabilitation, I learned I could still drive and be a safe driver. Hand controls were installed, and with a few driving lessons, I am driving once again!

Driver rehabilitation specialists at your local hospital usually can refer you to agencies or car shops that specialize in adaptations.

After the evaluation, the evaluator meets with the driver (and family members, if appropriate) to discuss test results. Because health care professionals tend to be viewed as more objective than family, many people are more willing to listen to concerns about driving, advice and recommendations from a trained, impartial professional than from a family member. It's also much easier to say "A health care professional suggested I no longer drive because…," rather than "My daughter (son, wife) said I can't…" or "…took away my car."

Some people make their own decision to modify or quit driving after an evaluation. Driver evaluation programs do not have the authority to revoke a license. If appropriate and necessary, the professional may send a report to the state licensing agency recommending re-evaluation of the person's driving.

The Association of Driver Educators for the Disabled can provide a list of members in your state who offer driver evaluations or training for persons with disabilities. Write to: ADED, P.O. Box 49, Edgerton, WI 53534; (608) 884-8833.

Encourage enrollment in a refresher driving course

These courses can be a non-threatening way for a person to evaluate his or her driving ability and improve driving skills. Emphasis is on training safer drivers, not taking away anyone's license. Participants are taught the effects of aging and medications on driving, and the indicators that suggest they either modify or stop driving. To reduce resistance, describe driver refresher courses in a positive light—that they are a way to learn to compensate for aging-related changes, to learn about rule changes, and to brush up on driving skills. Refresher courses do not tell people they should not be driving.

AARP offers a defensive driving course developed specifically for older drivers, *55 Alive/Mature Driving,* throughout the United States. It consists of eight hours of classroom instruction. For information about the local course schedule, contact: *55 Alive/Mature Driving,* AARP, 601 E Street N.W., Washington, DC 20049; (202) 434-2277. Similar mature driver programs are also offered by the National Safety Council *(Coaching the Mature Driver)* and the American Automobile Association *(Safe Driving for Mature Operators).* These programs are open to adults of all ages.

Participation in these programs may also mean your family member is eligible for an automobile insurance discount. If you or another family member qualify to take the course, consider attending along with the person whose driving concerns you.

Seek the Support of Your Family Member's Physician

A physician can determine if a medical problem or medications could compromise your relative's ability to drive. In some cases, the problem causing driving difficulties can be corrected. For example, older adults report:

◆ I had nearly given up driving because I could not clearly see signs or pedestrians. Cataract surgery on both eyes opened up my world and gave me the confidence to drive safely once again.

◆ My doctor found that the source of my driving problem was the medication I was taking. It made me drowsy and affected my vision. He prescribed another drug which works fine.

◆ Pain in my right arm made it increasingly difficult to drive. I had limited my driving to going to the local grocery store, bank and medical appointments. The doctor said the problem was from an early injury. Following surgery and strength and flexibility exercises, I am now a safe driver.

If problems are not correctable, a doctor may be able to assess your family member's physical and/or mental abilities that are necessary to drive safely. However, there is disagreement about clinical measures for assessing driving ability. Therefore, a doctor may refer your relative to a driving clinic to help make a more accurate evaluation of driving skills.

Don't expect the doctor to be able to pick up problems with driving in a regular medical checkup. It's important to let the doctor know your concerns and to be specific.

For some people, a doctor's advice is the most influential. In one study, when older adults were asked who should talk to them about driving, many felt that the physician should, since "When the doctor says you can't drive anymore, that's definite." Many also reported that family advice alone would not influence their decision to quit driving. The doctor may be viewed as more objective than family. Also, "the doctor says I shouldn't drive" and "health reasons" can be more acceptable reasons for not driving. Again, remember that the doctor may not be able to determine driving safety at the office; use evaluations to provide the doctor with the facts. Use the doctor, if appropriate, for "listening leverage" on the driving issue.

A doctor can strongly recommend, but cannot force a person to modify when or where he drives or to stop driving. Some people will not listen to a doctor's advice. One daughter said:

> The doctor was great. He talked with Dad and advised him that because of the changes caused by his Parkinson's disease, the time had come that he should no longer drive. As we drove home, Dad said, "What does the doctor know? I'm in control of this body, and I decide what this body can and can't do. It's my right to drive!" Later the doctor wrote a letter to the Department of Motor Vehicles.

Many physicians will work with families when a family member is shown to have difficulty driving. In some states, physicians are required to report to the driver licensing agency any patient whose medical condition jeopardizes safe driving.

Approach Your Family Member With Your Concerns

The manner in which you approach your family member is critical. If you come across with an attitude of "getting him off the road" or with accusations of unsafe driving, you will have little chance for success. You are likely to provoke anger, defensiveness, and denial.

Your goal should be to preserve the independence of the older driver while protecting the safety of others. However, preserving independence does not necessarily mean the person will be able to keep driving.

Identify who has "listening leverage" with your relative

It can make a difference who gives advice. Ask yourself who is most likely to have "listening leverage" with your family member on this particular issue. It may be you. Or your relative may "hear" the concern better from another family member, friend, or doctor.

Be sensitive

Preserving self-respect is important. Try to be gentle and positive to minimize the threat to your relative's self-esteem. It's important to appreciate the significance of a driver's license to the older person. Concerns about driving need to be approached with sensitivity to both the symbolic meaning and practical significance driving has to the individual.

Empathize with and listen to your family member. The feelings a person has about the situation are real for him or her. Acknowledging you have heard your relative—what was said and his thoughts and feelings about a situation—will enhance communication. For example, one son said to his father, "It is a huge change in your life to no longer drive. I know I would be very sad and mad if I was not able to get myself around in my car. Let's talk about what I can do to make this easier on you."

Take responsibility for your concerns

You are more likely to be listened to if you present your concerns in terms of your own feelings and perceptions, rather than as though your older family member is a problem. Too often, "you" messages are given to older people. Using "I" messages, in which you express your observations as *your* concerns, is less threatening than "you" messages. Consider the differences in how you would react to the following two statements:

"You" message: "You're no longer a safe driver. You should not be driving."

"I" message: "I am concerned about your safety when you are driving. I also know how important driving is to you. This is why I am concerned...."
    (Give specific examples.)

"I" messages tend to come across with a tone of caring. "You" messages, on the other hand, put people on the defensive because they sound accusatory, authoritarian and dictatorial. "You" messages come across as though the speaker knows "what is best" and has already made the decision.

"I" statements are also difficult for another person to argue about because they are your feelings and perceptions. If done correctly, they do not come across as "I am

right," whereas "you" messages can easily result in an argument about who is right. A caring approach will move a discussion farther than will a "I know what is best for you" attitude.

Choose your words carefully

In focus groups, researchers found that the words you use may make a difference. They found older drivers did not respond well to use of the word "restriction"; instead, they preferred talking about the "requirements" or "conditions" for safe driving.

Be prepared for negative reactions

Be prepared for the response you are likely to receive from your family member. Remember, it's hard to look at modifying or stopping driving if you are not ready to do so, or if you perceive yourself as a good driver.

Anger or hostility may be directed at you. Although it's not easy, prepare yourself for this reaction and try to understand that even though anger may be directed at you, these feelings generally result from the pain of the situation. Try to accept the anger without engaging the person in a heated discussion. For example, you might say something like, "I'd probably be angry too if someone talked to me about no longer driving."

Explore Transportation Options

When a person must give up driving, find out what is most important for him to be able to do and to attend. And, most important, do not judge the person's identified priorities. Jack, 87, tells his story:

When my driver's license was limited to daytime driving, it was difficult because I could no longer take my lady friend to the Friday night dance. My son said, "Dad, I don't know why you can't go. Let's look at how we can make sure you still can kick up your heels on Friday nights."

Carol tells how she almost blew it with her dad:

When I asked my dad what he still wanted be able to do that he thought he could no longer do, he immediately said, "Go to the pool hall." I'm afraid I viewed going to the pool hall as frivolous and that it would be better if he didn't go there anyway. To me, what was most important was that he get to his medical appointments, and get groceries and other necessities. I almost said, "Dad, don't be foolish." Fortunately, Harry gave me a kick under the table before the words came out. Dad's whole mood changed when Harry said to him,

"Let's see what we can do to get you to the pool hall. When would you like to go down there?"

Giving up the car keys doesn't have to mean a person must now stay at home. It's important to find ways to help your family member stay involved in activities outside of the home. Emphasize that he doesn't have to be housebound and isolated unless he chooses to be. Some older people want options that do not require calling upon family members and want to maintain continued privacy and control over their "comings and goings."

Before talking with your family member, be aware of transportation services in your community, and transportation that family, friends, and neighbors might provide. Questions to pursue and to answer with your older family member include:

◆ Are there friends or family who are willing and available to provide transportation? And, if so, when and to what?

◆ What buses serve your area? Does your family member view public transportation as an option?

◆ Is there a special transportation program for senior citizens available in the community?

◆ Is taxi service available?

◆ Are volunteer drivers available through an organization to which your family member belongs?

◆ Could someone be hired to provide transportation, as needed?

◆ Could your family member keep his car and pay someone to drive it?

◆ What are your family member's preferences?

It's also important to recognize and acknowledge the limitations of alternate transportation—it is not always available, it may not provide access to the places your family member wants to go at the times he wants to go, it may take time to learn "the ropes," and it may be expensive. Potential alternatives include:

- public transportation
- taxi service
- hire a driver
- bartering
- carpooling
- senior/volunteer escort or transportation services
- a motorized three-wheeled scooter or three-wheeled bicycle

Public transportation

If your family member has not used the public transportation system, it may be helpful to have someone travel with him a few times to the places he wants to go. Having to make transfers, waiting for another bus, and watching for the correct transit to take may seem complex and overwhelming at first. It's important to address problems your family member may have with public transportation. These might include:

- steep stairs
- crowded bus with no available seating
- movement of a bus before getting seated and fear of falling
- distance to the transit stop
- no available seating and/or protection from the weather while waiting for a bus
- difficulty in hearing announcements over the intercom
- concerns about safety

A bus may not be feasible if it requires walking a distance to catch it, and your family member has mobility limitations. Many of these same issues also apply to the use of a train or subway system. Some communities have vans or buses that pick up people with disabilities at their homes.

Keep in mind that people with cognitive impairment probably cannot learn to use a public transportation system and may have trouble with alternatives.

Taxi service

Lillian, age 84, wrote the following after a stroke and before back surgery:

I'm no longer driving. I sold my almost new (2,500 miles on it) Toyota Camry and am using our local paratransit taxi service (30 one-way rides per month; 24-hour advance notice; not limited to medical trips) to meetings, concerts, theater, and the beauty shop.

Some people don't want to use taxis because of expense. In this situation, some families have found it helpful to talk with their family member about the cost of keeping a car: gas, maintenance, repair, and insurance. They then put that amount of money away to spend on taxi service, and other forms of transportation. Sometimes people find that the cost of operating a car is higher than taxi service. Consider the experience of 76-year-old Margaret:

> We sold my car and put the money from the sale in what I call "my travel account." We also put into the account the amount of money my son figured I spent yearly to operate my car. Not only have I been able to take a taxi wherever I want to go, but each year I have also been able to fly somewhere and visit family or friends.

Some families have found they were able to set up a fund with the taxicab company, with deductions automatically coming out each time their family member used a taxi. Pauline found sharing taxi rides was an option for her:

> Robert, my neighbor, quit driving a few months before I did. One day when I was talking with him about how I didn't like to rely on my family for transportation, Robert suggested I take the taxi when he took one to town. It's great! We plan ahead for our appointments, and we shop together. We save money! And, we have a lot of fun together! And, it feels wonderful not to have to depend on my family.

Some communities offer reduced taxi fares to older people.

Hire a driver

One family hired a responsible teenage boy to take their dad to the pool hall three times a week after school. They found it worked out well:

> Danny, the neighbor boy, earned some money and Dad got to the pool hall three times a week when Danny got out of school. Also, on Sunday afternoons, Danny would frequently call Dad and ask him if there was any place special he would like to go—drives in the country were Dad's favorite. Danny would drive and Dad would buy lunch. A really nice relationship developed between Dad and Danny. Dad gave the car we thought he'd never sell to Danny as a gift when Danny went to college. Danny never failed to see Dad when he returned home from college…and usually they took a drive in the countryside.

If this is an option, you might want to find out if this arrangement would affect the driver's or your family member's automobile insurance (if your family member still carries it).

Bartering

Just because someone doesn't drive, doesn't mean he can't contribute. Your family member may be able to help out with gas, provide lunch, or offer a service such as child-sitting for a driver who has young children. Bartering can be another possibility for getting transportation needs met. Terry tells this story about his 85-year old mother:

> A neighbor was willing to drive Mom the few places she wanted to go, but the neighbor would not accept any payment. Mom was not willing to accept the neighbor's goodwill without paying for it. Mom

would say, "I've always paid my own way and I'm not about to stop now." Yet, there was no transportation service in the small town where Mom lived.

Mom and the neighbor finally worked things out. Mom loves to bake. So, they agreed that Mom would bake for the neighbor's family—bread, rolls, cookies, or whatever she wanted—twice a month in exchange for transportation. So far, this has worked for two years. Mom also gets a lot of rave reviews for her baking from the neighbor's family, which I think has done more for her self-esteem than if the neighbor had accepted money for providing transportation.

Carpooling

Identify other people who attend the same recreation activities, club meetings, or church or synagogue services as your family member. Find out if there is someone who lives nearby or travels near your family member's home on their way to the activity and could pick him up.

Senior/volunteer escort or transportation services

Local organizations such as senior citizen centers, churches, and synagogues often provide transportation. As part of a community service project, university students may provide volunteer transportation services.

Contact the local area agency on aging about transportation services available to older adults. Some transportation programs only operate a few days a week, serve a specific area, or provide transportation for specific reasons, such as for medical appointments and treatments, and shopping for groceries.

A motorized three-wheeled scooter or a three-wheeled bicycle

Although a scooter or bicycle cannot be driven long distances, for some older people it may substitute for a car to go to the corner store or to visit a nearby friend, particularly when walking is also difficult. Some motorized scooters are built ruggedly for outdoor use. Keep in mind, however, that some disabilities that make it unsafe for a person to drive a car, could also make driving a scooter unsafe. Be sure to check your local laws regarding use of scooters on sidewalks.

Meeting the transportation needs of your family member may require a combination of transportation alternatives. Rich said about his dad:

Even though Dad can't see very well and doesn't drive, it doesn't stop him. He's always "on the go." The Senior Van picks him up three times a week to go to the senior center and for their noon meal. Friends are always picking him up to do something. A neighbor takes Dad grocery shopping when she is going to the store, or if he's too busy, she picks up the things he needs. And if he wants to go somewhere on the spur of the moment, he calls a taxi.

When he comes to see us, he now takes the bus, rather than drive. We try to convince him to fly—it is so much quicker. But he says he doesn't like the "nothingness that's between him and the ground when he's in a plane." Since Dad is a people-person, he enjoys meeting people on the bus as well as watching the countryside.

You and your relative also may want to re-evaluate the location where he lives and its accessibility to shopping, services, and recreation. While moving may be difficult, living within easy access to what is needed and enjoyed might enhance independence. Some older people choose to move into a retirement complex where transportation is provided on a regular basis to local stores, trips are arranged to special community events, and arrangements can be made for medical appointments.

Report to the State Licensing Agency

Sometimes it's useful to seek re-examination of a family member's skills by the driver licensing agency. Although reporting someone may seem drastic, sometimes it is the only way. Some older people simply will not listen to a family member, the doctor, or anyone else.

All states have a procedure whereby unsafe drivers of any age can be reported to the licensing agency. But states do vary in their procedures and testing programs. For information about state policies and driver re-testing programs, contact the local licensing agency. You may want to find out:

◆ how to file a report and the information required.

◆ what happens after a report is filed.

◆ if your name would be kept confidential.

◆ what happens if your family member protests being retested.

◆ what is involved in retesting.

◆ how might the agency involve you personally in regard to actions resulting from the filing of a report.

Generally, a driver's license can be suspended on the basis of a written statement from a physician. In most states, the person filing a report has to reveal his or her name, but confidentiality is maintained.

In some states, the Department of Motor Vehicles offers a restricted license. This license is granted to individuals who have demonstrated the ability to drive safely to places they need to go in order to sustain themselves, for example to the store, church, bank, post office, senior center, and doctor's office.

There can be advantages to seeking retesting. It provides an objective opinion. It can remove some of the burden from a family and avoid a family confrontation. The licensing agency becomes the "bad guy" if a person's driver's license is revoked or limited, and the family can be more supportive of the person in regard to this life change.

Be prepared, though, for your family member to pass the road test even if you know he is impaired. Then there are new issues to deal with.

DON'T EQUATE GIVING UP A DRIVER'S LICENSE WITH GIVING UP THE CAR

When someone must give up driving, all too often family and friends encourage him to sell the car. Because the car has a symbolic meaning, for some people it is important to keep the car even if they never drive it. On a practical level, some people feel less dependent if they can offer their car when they must depend on others for transportation. What's important to them is the ability to offer the car for others to drive, not whether it is actually used.

Whether it is feasible for a person to keep his car may depend on several factors, including insurance. Insurance companies may agree to insure a car even if the elder owner has relinquished his or her driver's license. The insurance company will generally want to know who can be expected to drive the car. If a son drives his mother's car during infrequent visits, the insurance company may insure the car and calculate the insurance based on that limited use. The premiums should be lower than if the car was in regular use. The premium is assessed on the age of the driver (under 50 versus over 50). If the son is living in the house with the parent, the insurance company would prefer to insure the car with the son.

If the elder owner of the car has given up his or her license but persists in driving without a license, the insurance company would be uncomfortable about continuing the policy for visiting relatives.

Check with your automobile insurance company to verify the rules in a specific situation.

WHEN YOUR FAMILY MEMBER WHO SHOULDN'T DRIVE INSISTS ON DRIVING

It's important to involve older family members in decisions about driving. However, when a person has a dementia, such as Alzheimer's disease, family members need to take an active role in making and carrying out decisions.

People with Alzheimer's disease or a related disorder simply may not remember that they can no longer drive. Arguing or giving explanations about why the person no longer can drive usually does not work. You are likely to get more frustrated, and so will your family member. Families have found many of the following actions—which are also suggested by the Alzheimer's Association—to work for them.

Get a prescription from the doctor that states "no driving"

Show this to your relative when he insists on getting behind the wheel.

Distract the person

Depending upon the person's severity of memory loss, distraction can be an effective approach to preventing unsafe drivers from being on the road. When your family member insists on driving, try to get his attention focused on something else. For example, one wife would say to her husband, "I was just fixing a bowl of your favorite ice cream. Let's eat it first." Another wife would say, "We can't drive now. The car needs to be repaired."

Control access to car keys

Do not leave car keys in view of your family member. Give him a different, but similar-looking set of keys or have a lock-smith file the part of the key that turns the ignition. The person can still enter the car, but will not be able to start it. Some people, however, may become frustrated and angry when "the keys won't work."

Disable the car

A car mechanic can show you how to quickly disable a car—remove the distributor cap or battery or unplug the starter wire—so it won't run and what to do to get it to operate again. Another option is to install a "kill wire," preventing the car from starting unless a switch is thrown. If your family member lives alone, this may not be a good option. A son said:

> We knew how important Dad's car was to him. I'd never seen him cry so hard as the day we told him he could no longer drive. He finally agreed not to drive, but said that he wanted to keep his car in his driveway. Since we didn't know if he would remember that he was not to drive, as a precaution, we made his car inoperable. What we didn't count on is that a week later he would call a mechanic to repair his car.

Move the car

For some people, seeing the car is what triggers the desire to drive. Try parking the car where your family member doesn't see it but where you can have easy access.

Sell the car

You might use the excuse that the car cannot be repaired or that the car is no longer safe to drive.

SUMMARY

In addressing driving concerns, it's important to remember that:

◆ Driving is *not* a right; it's a privilege which the state may grant or withhold.

◆ An older driver does not automatically equal an unsafe driver. Do not hassle the older family member who is driving safely. Age is not the most important criterion for determining an unsafe driver.

◆ When asking a person to give up driving, we are asking a great deal.

◆ Driving and owning a car have symbolic meaning as well as practical significance.

◆ It's important to work with your family member, so that it is his decision.

◆ If your family member is putting others at risk by his driving, or is cognitively impaired, you need to take an active role in the decision.

◆ Public safety is a high priority. How well a person drives affects the lives of everyone else on the road. Act if you must!

CHAPTER TWELVE

Helping a Family Member Handle Finances

Older family members sometimes need assistance managing their finances The assistance needed may be minimal—reading the fine print, preparing checks, setting up a bill-paying system—or more extensive. Those who are homebound but able to direct their personal finances may need someone to implement their directives. A few older people with severe disability may need someone to manage their finances entirely.

For couples, the person who handled the finances may have died or may be ill, and the spouse may need to assume the personal finance duties.

When someone has Alzheimer's disease or a related dementia, eventually someone else must take over his financial matters. In such situations, it is crucial to do financial and legal planning early to guarantee a safe financial future for both the impaired person and yourself, the caregiver.

This chapter discusses the importance of planning ahead, ways to talk to your family member about financial concerns, useful financial tools, and guidelines for helping a person with finances.

PLANNING AHEAD

It can be difficult to determine whether a family member is capable of making sound financial decisions. Many families don't discuss finances until a crisis occurs—and then it may be too late. Once a person is mentally incapacitated, options are reduced and procedures become more complicated and costly. And professionals—from social workers to court-appointed conservators—may become involved.

Planning ahead requires anticipating situations such as dependency, disability, incapacity, and death, and exploring ways to deal with them. It can create anxiety for everyone.

Despite these anxieties, there are good reasons to plan ahead. Although it will not reduce the emotional pain that accompanies disability, loss of mental capacity, or death, planning ahead can:

◆ help you avoid crisis decision making.

◆ make decisions easier in difficult times.

◆ reduce emotional and financial upheaval.

◆ ensure that a person's lifestyle, personal values and philosophy, and choices are known if he becomes unable to participate in decision making.

◆ increase the financial management options.

◆ reduce disagreements among siblings about "what Mom and Dad want" and how to handle their assets.

Planning ahead does not prevent all problems, but it does help to reduce stress and prevent unpleasant surprises and heartache. It also enables you to act more effectively if a crisis does occur, and reduces the probability that you will need to take more intrusive, restrictive actions.

TALKING ABOUT MONEY

If you haven't talked about money matters before, you may be reluctant to begin. Talking about finances has a high "discomfort index." Talking about potential incapacity can be even more difficult than talking about death. None of us likes to think of ourselves or someone else as not being able to make decisions or handle personal finances.

Approaching your family member about financial issues takes thoughtfulness, caring, and determination. Using the following strategies increases the likelihood he will listen to you, producing a positive discussion:

◆ Know why you're talking.

◆ Look for natural opportunities to talk.

◆ Find a low-stress time and location.

◆ Acknowledge your family member's feelings.

◆ Anticipate his response.

◆ Express positive intentions.

◆ Respect your family member's right to make choices.

Know Why You're Talking

Ask yourself why you are bringing up the subject of finances with your relative. Do you want to raise the issue or do you want him to do what you feel needs to be done? Are there reasons to be concerned about his ability to manage his finances either now or in the future? Are you merely curious? Are you concerned about inheritance? Are you concerned about your own financial future? Once you are clear about your purpose, you will be in a better position to raise financial issues with the person.

Look for Natural Opportunities to Talk

One way to begin a discussion is to share your preferences and plans in the event of your own serious illness, incapacity, or death. Remember, mental incapacity is not just related to aging and illness. A debilitating accident could happen to anyone, regardless of age. Parents may question the motives of adult children who express concern about parental finances and planning, but have not made plans themselves.

Talking about plans you have made for yourself may help create an atmosphere in which your relative may feel more comfortable sharing his thoughts with you. You might say, "I've been thinking what if…." Then ask, "What would you want done if you ever experienced that situation?" Or, "I've been thinking about what would happen if I were… I would like to talk with you about it."

Find a Low-Stress Time and Location

When and where you hold a discussion can have a tremendous impact on the outcome. Avoid emotionally demanding times. Raising the subject during a relaxed, shared activity may help to diffuse tension when the conversation turns to money.

Acknowledge Your Family Member's Feelings

Remember, it's difficult for many people to talk about finances, especially when discussing potential incapacity and the inability to manage one's finances. Talking about potential loss of control can be even more difficult for a person already experiencing health changes. He may feel grief, anger, frustration, or uncertainty.

Feelings are likely to be particularly strong if the person fears giving up control. Be sensitive to and acknowledge feelings and preferences, recognize the person's need to be in control, and do all you can to maintain his dignity.

Try "stepping into the person's shoes" and see how a situation looks and feels from his perspective. Ask yourself, "How would I feel if I were in Dad's (Mom's/my spouse's) situation?" Give the person your attention; listen to what he says and communicate your understanding. A person who senses empathy and understanding is more likely to listen to what you have to say.

Anticipate His Response

Ask yourself, "How is he likely to respond?" How has he responded to sensitive issues in the past? Is he likely to respond matter-of-factly, become emotional, deny and avoid discussion, become angry or suspicious, or create guilt by saying something like, "All you care about is my money"? Then prepare for the worst, as well as plan for the best, that might happen.

Rehearse or practice what you might say. Consider having someone else play the role of the person, responding as you think he might respond. Consider strategies you can use to de-escalate potential arguments and keep the discussion calm (see chapters 3 and 4 on communication). Practice not becoming defensive.

If you know the discussion will not be easy, be prepared. Express your concern, then say, "Could we schedule a time to talk about my concerns?"

Express Positive Intentions

When you start the discussion, express your good intentions and willingness to listen. Set the right tone. Don't say or imply "I know what is best for you." Telling your relative what to do is likely to create anger, resentment, and resistance. Being well informed about options, resources, and problems that can occur if planning is not done, and sharing that information, is the best way to work with someone.

Make it clear you are acting out of concern, not self-interest. An effective way to express this concern is to use "I" messages: "I'm worried that if something happens to you, I won't know what to do…."

Respect Your Family Member's Right to Make Choices

Respect your relative's right to make choices as long as he is capable of doing so. His view of what is best may differ from yours. This does not mean that anyone is wrong; differences of opinion may result from different experiences, values, and attitudes. It's essential for an open discussion to show respect for his choices, even if you disagree with them. Unless he lacks capacity for effective decision making, do not assume that you know what is best for him.

If your family member refuses to talk about financial concerns or denies the need for such discussion, you cannot force communication. What you can do is to acknowledge his feelings, share the reasons you are concerned, and ask him to consider the possibility of a discussion at a later date. Consider, too, that the person may feel more comfortable talking about the concerns you have raised with an attorney or a financial adviser.

USEFUL FINANCIAL TOOLS

Families provide most help informally. However, there are also financial tools available, including joint bank accounts, power of attorney (non-durable and durable), living trusts, appointment of a representative payee, and conservatorship. Since the effects of each are very different, it's important to identify the needs of your relative and the most appropriate tool.

The goal is to choose the least intrusive intervention that will enable your family member to remain as independent as possible. Court intervention should be used only if less restrictive means are inadequate.

The following discussion is not a substitute for legal advice. It's to acquaint you with the tools available. Because you want to be sure the steps taken provide the desired results and benefits, with the least risks, you may need to consult a lawyer about your specific situation.

When Your Relative Is Capable of Making Financial Decisions

Three legal tools—joint bank accounts, power of attorney, and living trusts—can be used to plan ahead for possible future incapacity or to give another person legal authority to conduct financial transactions on one's behalf. These tools must be completed by your family member while he is still fully capable of making financial decisions. They are generally uncomplicated, can be implemented quickly, are revocable in most cases, and do not affect your relative's right to self-determination.

Tara found these tools useful in her dad's situation:

My father is capable of making financial decisions. Because of severe arthritis and poor vision it has become difficult for him to write checks and to transact business away from home.

Three years ago he put my name on his checking account and gave me power of attorney. It's worked well. Dad still has control over his money. I just do what he wants done.

Joint bank accounts

A joint bank account can provide an easy way for you to sign checks and pay bills for a family member. Yet he will still have a sense of control, particularly if he retains the checkbook.

A joint account can be set up by putting someone's name on an account either as an "additional authorized signature" or as "joint owner with right of survivorship." An account with the latter designation means that when one owner dies, the account belongs to the survivor. This designation on an account may supersede what is written in a will, should it be different.

A joint account is not without problems. Because anyone named on a joint account can deposit to and withdraw from it, a joint account requires considerable trust. Some states also permit creditors of the helping relative to get some or all of the person's funds in a joint account. If not properly handled, a joint account can present complications in terms of taxes, eligibility for government benefits (e. g., Medicaid and Supplemental Security Income), and disposal of funds at the death of either

party. To avoid such complications, a helping relative should not deposit any of his money into the account or withdraw money for personal use.

Power of attorney

A power of attorney is a written document in which a person (called the "principal") gives another person (called the "attorney in fact") legal authority to act on his behalf in financial transactions. It can be a useful tool for the person who is capable of directing his finances, but needs assistance in conducting personal business. The person does not lose the right to manage his finances, but rather extends that right to someone in addition to himself.

It's critical to have trust in the person to whom a power of attorney is given because abuses are possible. If this is a concern, one or more people can be appointed as co-attorneys-in-fact, requiring two or more signatures on all transactions. Another method of maximizing security is to retain control over the original power of attorney document. Since financial institutions, such as banks and stockbrokers, will only honor and recognize the original power of attorney, retaining the original reduces the potential of abuse.

The person who has a power of attorney has only those powers specified in the document. The power can be limited to a specific purpose (for example, selling the person's car or signing checks only on a particular bank account) or it can be broad, giving someone authority to conduct all financial transactions. It should state clearly and in detail what authority is being given.

The person granting the power of attorney determines the extent of the power granted. He should also anticipate the temporary absence, illness, incapacity, or death of the attorney-in-fact with a backup arrangement for an alternate or successor attorney-in-fact. The person granting the power of attorney must be mentally competent and fully understand the effect of the written agreement, that is the responsibilities and powers he is giving to another person, at the time of signing the document.

The power of attorney must be in writing, signed, and notarized. Standard forms are available in bookstores. If the power of attorney is to be used for real estate transactions, it should be recorded in the county recorder's office of the county where the property is located.

The person authorizing a power of attorney can revoke it at any time. When revoking such power, it's a good idea to send written notification to anyone with whom the attorney-in-fact has done business, as well as to the attorney-in-fact, and to record the revocation in the county where property is located.

A power of attorney may end if the person granting it becomes mentally incapacitated and loses decision-making ability (unless it is a durable power of attorney; see below). It also terminates upon the person's death, or upon the expiration date specified in the document if the period ends before the death or incompetence of the person.

Some financial institutions recognize only a power of attorney drawn upon their forms; therefore, it may be necessary to complete their individual forms.

Durable power of attorney. A durable power of attorney does not terminate if the person granting the power becomes mentally incapacitated. Usually a durable power of attorney becomes effective after it is signed. However, it can also be written such that it has "springing power," that is, it goes into effect only if the person becomes incapacitated or incompetent. However, such "springing" effectiveness (so named because the authority of the attorney-in-fact springs into effect when the principal loses mental capacity) can be difficult to recognize and might not be honored by the bank and other institutions. A durable power of attorney also must be executed while the person understands the effect of the power of attorney.

The durable power of attorney can avoid conservatorship or guardianship proceedings in the event of incapacity. In many states, medical and health care can also be managed by a durable power of attorney.

State laws vary regarding a durable power of attorney; thus, it should be drawn up by an attorney licensed to practice in the state where the person lives. In many states, all powers of attorney are presumed to be durable under state law unless limited in the wording of the power of attorney document.

Kelly shares her story about the benefits a durable power of attorney had in her situation:

My mother suffers from Alzheimer's disease. She is no longer able to manage her money or make wise financial decisions. Although it was tough to see a very capable woman become so forgetful that she couldn't remember to pay her bills, it was easier because Mom had executed a durable power of attorney when her mind was sharp. We were told that if this hadn't been done, we might have had to go to court. That would have been really hard.

Living trusts

A living trust is one way a person can assure management and protection of assets if he becomes incapacitated in the future. A trust is a three-party arrangement whereby designated assets are transferred from one person (the grantor) to another person (the trustee) who holds and manages the assets for the benefit of the third (the beneficiary). The grantor, trustee, and beneficiary may be the same person. The trust agreement contains specific instructions about the management and distribution of the assets to the beneficiary.

Trusts are either revocable or irrevocable. A revocable trust remains in a person's control during his lifetime, then passes to the beneficiary upon his death. The trust can be revoked at any time. An irrevocable trust is controlled by the trustee. The grantor loses control of the assets. Assets in a living trust avoid probate.

A lawyer's help is important in setting up a trust to protect everyone's interest. It's particularly important that the person drafting the living trust is knowledgeable about restrictions on Medicaid eligibility for beneficiaries of living trusts, particularly if there is any possibility the person may need long-term care.

When Your Relative is Incapable of Making Financial Decisions

Options are fewer, more complex, and more intrusive if you have not made advance plans and your relative becomes incapacitated. Two legal tools available in this case are representative payee and conservatorship (also called "guardianship of the estate").

Representative payee

If your relative is unable to manage his Social Security, veteran's pension, railroad retirement, or public benefits checks, a representative payee may be appointed. Checks are then written to the payee on behalf of the beneficiary.

This device is most useful when the person's expenses can be covered by the benefit check(s), since the representative payee is not empowered to gain access to the person's savings accounts or other assets. (If lack of trust in the helping relative is not an issue, direct deposit of the monthly income checks into a joint account is generally convenient.)

To arrange for a representative payee status, contact the appropriate agency for an application form and instructions. Medical confirmation that the person is unable to manage benefit payments is required. The benefits office determines whether a payeeship is appropriate, based on evidence of the person's incapacity. Notice is sent to the payee, who can object. The representative payee is given instructions on how funds are to be held, managed, and disbursed, and any accounting that is required.

Conservatorship

Sometimes called a *guardianship of the estate* or *guardianship of the property,* a conservatorship is a court process whereby an individual secures the right to manage another person's financial affairs after that person has become unable to do so, and a durable power of attorney or living trust is not in operation. Obtaining a conservatorship is a serious step and should be used only as a last resort.

Ambrosia stated:

My grandmother's income was $1,000 per month, but she was spending nearly $2,000 each month ordering magazine subscriptions, entering prize contests and shopping by television. Her savings were quickly disappearing and her credit card balances were growing. She had 50 magazines coming each month, including four subscriptions for the same magazine.

Grandma was adamant she had won the big prize. She showed me the statement "You Are A Winner" in big, bold letters on the flyer she received. It did no good to show her the small print that read "If you have the winning number." I tried many times to talk with her. Nothing worked. This behavior was so unlike her!

I had no choice but to seek a conservatorship over my grandmother. It was emotionally painful, but necessary.

A conservatorship can be created only by action of the court. An attorney must file a petition with the court and a judge decides if the older person is legally competent to manage his own affairs or if a conservator should be appointed. In many states, a court hearing is held only if someone objects in writing to the court.

A person is generally considered competent if he understands the nature and consequences of his actions. Poor judgment, a non-traditional lifestyle, or personal neglect does not constitute incompetence.

A family member may serve as a conservator. For a large or complex estate, an attorney may be appointed. A public guardian may be appointed as a conservator when no one else available. A person can designate in advance who he wants the court to appoint as conservator, should the need arise.

Once a conservator is appointed, the person loses the right to make decisions about his finances. However, other rights (to vote, to marry, to write a will, and other personal decisions) remain intact unless a *guardian of the person* has been appointed.

The conservator is responsible to the court and must make an annual accounting to the court. Most states require the conservator to purchase a bond (insurance policy) equal to the value of the impaired person's estate. Thus, there are several expenses associated with a conservatorship—filing fees, legal fees, bonds, and accounting costs. A conservator may receive a fee set by the court for services and reimbursement for expenses incurred for estate management and for the accounting. A conservator may be removed and replaced by the court that appointed the conservator.

The *Oregon Nursing Home Guidebook* offers important advice to families considering a conservatorship:

> It is always important for family members to examine their motives for seeking conservatorship. Sometimes it is very hard to separate concerns about inheritance from concerns about protecting an older person's money for his own needs and wants.

> It is also important, though sometimes difficult, to accept that in a person's old age, they may choose to spend their money in ways that do not meet with their children's approval. An older person may legitimately choose to do things that he would never have considered in his younger years. Families considering conservatorship must try to be sure that the problem they are attempting to resolve is not simply a conflict between personal values.

GUIDELINES FOR HELPING

Some people have difficulty accepting help with finances. Giving up control over money is often difficult because it means another loss of responsibility, independence, and freedom. If you are trying to help, you may find it's a delicate balance between providing assistance and assuming control. The situation is further complicated when tension and misunderstandings develop between family members.

In helping a family member handle his finances, your intent should always be to assist, not to take away control. Tension may be reduced by following these guidelines.

◆ **Give your family member as much control as possible.** Utilize your relative's capabilities. Too often when a person becomes frail, we tend to focus on what he can no longer do. It's equally important to focus on what he can continue to do. For example, while your mother may need assistance in managing property and paying large bills, she may be able to pay for groceries and small purchases. To most people, it's important to have some money in their pocket and to control how financial decisions are made—what money goes where.

◆ **Involve him and keep him informed.** As much as possible, involve your family member in planning and making decisions. Even when he may not be able to make or remember a decision, keep him informed (unless giving such information tends to create anxiety or agitation). Keeping a person informed about decisions and actions will often help ease his mind that things are being done as he would have chosen.

◆ **Respect his financial privacy.** Your relative will likely need some privacy in his financial matters, just as in other areas of his life.

◆ **Accommodate changes.** Review options periodically as your family member's capabilities, assets, and situation change.

◆ **Keep complete records.** A good bookkeeping system in which you record all income and expenditures is important. If you are unsure about how to do this, consult with an accountant. Letting other family members know that books are open to their inspection builds trust.

◆ **Keep his money separate from your own.** To avoid confusion, have a separate account for your family member's money.

◆ **Balance financial statements.** Reconcile bank statements each month with the checkbook. Some caregivers have found it helpful to have the older person, when possible, or another family member check the arithmetic and initial bank statements.

SUMMARY

Remember, taking away a person's control over finances is a very serious matter. When you must take action, take only those steps absolutely necessary to help the person.

If you suspect that a time may come when either yourself or a family member may not be able to manage personal finances, make plans in advance. Consider what legal instruments will be best for your particular situation. And, seek legal advice to help you make the wisest decisions. Although it's often difficult to talk about these matters, people facing disability generally are relieved to learn there are ways to retain control.

CHAPTER THIRTEEN

Recognizing and Responding to Depression

Depression is disabling. It can cause physical problems and disrupt a marriage and family. Despite its many symptoms, depression in older people often goes unrecognized.

Two years ago, Albert's wife of 54 years died. Shortly thereafter, his closest friend died. Albert has become increasingly forgetful and uninterested in family activities. His children are concerned that "father has become senile."

Mrs. Jensen, 74, has always been active. In the last few months she's withdrawn into her home, isolating herself from family and friends. Formerly pleasurable activities are no longer enjoyable. She's tired much of the time, but has difficulty sleeping.

Mr. Jones' life revolved around his work. Since retiring eight months ago, he feels lost and useless. He's neglecting his appearance, and drinking more.

For Albert, Mrs. Jensen, and Mr. Jones, life has lost its joy. They are suffering from depression. However, they are not likely to seek help. They may fear being labeled "crazy" or "weak," or may be too depressed to take action.

This chapter will help you understand depression in later life, recognize signs of depression and intent to commit suicide, and know the actions you can take if you suspect someone may be depressed or contemplating suicide.

IMPACT OF DEPRESSION

Living with a depressed person is not easy because depressed people tend to turn inward, not think about others, and sometimes become hostile. As a family member, you may feel as though you are being driven away.

When faced with the challenge of helping a depressed person, it's important first to understand depression yourself. You will then be better able to respond in helpful and caring ways.

What is depression?

Depression is one of the most common emotional disorders. It can occur in anyone—young or old, male or female, rich or poor. The term "depression" is used to describe a range of conditions, from a low mood to severe depression. Regardless, sadness is a predominant feeling. Occasional feelings of unhappiness and feeling "down" or in a "blue mood" are normal. But when the feeling goes beyond normal mood swings and adversely affects one's life, the problem is depression, an illness.

There are many ways to describe depression. One way is by its severity—mild, moderate, or severe. Mild depression is the most common, but it also requires our attention because even a mild depression can deepen or persist. Severe depression can be life-threatening. Health can fail rapidly. In fact, depressed people appear to be more susceptible to infection and other illnesses, and their recovery from illness takes longer than for people who are not depressed. Many people who commit suicide are depressed.

Mild depression is a brief, temporary sadness that is a normal reaction to stress, tension, frustration, and disappointment. It does not seriously interfere with a person's functioning or daily activities. Professional treatment may not be needed. A person primarily needs emotional support, an opportunity to talk, or a change of pace or environment.

A moderate depression is more intense and lasts longer. It is often caused by a loss or an upsetting event. Daily activities become more difficult, but the moderately depressed person usually can still meet daily responsibilities. Professional help may be necessary.

A severely depressed person shows marked behavior changes and loss of interest in the outside world. Often a chemical imbalance is involved. His ability to function is impaired and he is unable to cope. Professional treatment is necessary.

How Depression Differs from Grief

It can sometimes be difficult to tell the difference between depression and grief. For example, both depressed and grieving people experience sadness, tearfulness, sleep problems, and appetite and weight changes. However, there are differences. It's important to understand these differences so that you can better recognize when a person may be depressed versus grieving and offer the most appropriate support.

Characteristics of depression. Depression may not have a specific trigger. Also, depressed people tend to be passive, remaining "stuck" in sadness for a long time. They have generalized feelings of helplessness, hopelessness, and emptiness. They lack interest in previously enjoyed activities.

It is common for a depressed person to have low self-esteem and a lack of confidence; he usually feels like a failure, unattractive, and unloved. He is likely to be unresponsive and humorless, incapable of being cheered up even temporarily. He is likely to resist help and support.

Depressed people have difficulty identifying or describing their feelings. They tend to cry for no apparent reason, but crying does not bring relief. Inappropriate or excessive guilt is common. A person may dwell on past failures.

Characteristics of grief. Grieving is a normal part of recovering from loss. Grieving is an active process; the person gradually progresses through the sadness toward recovery.

A grieving person experiences a range of feelings, including emotional pain and emptiness. He cries for an identifiable loss and crying provides relief. He is more likely to accept support than a person who is depressed. A grieving person usually can be persuaded to participate in activities, particularly as he begins to work through the grief. He will sometimes be able to laugh and enjoy humor.

With grief, self-esteem usually remains intact; the person does not feel like a failure, although there may be such feelings related to the specific loss. Any feelings of self-blame and guilt relate directly to the loss, are episodic, and resolve as healing occurs. The grieving person is not likely to be suicidal.

Sometimes grief evolves into a serious depression, particularly when the grief process is blocked or mourning over a loss is increasingly turned inward. Sadness for weeks, even months or years, after a loss or unwanted change is to be expected. But when intense sadness continues, when the person becomes "stuck" in sadness, or when he is increasingly unable to function on a daily basis, the bereavement has turned into depression. When thoughts of self-blame associated with a loss—for example, the "I should haves" common with the death of a loved one, become excessive or prolonged (last longer than six months), chances are the bereavement has become complicated by depression.

Types of Depression

Depressive disorders come in different forms, with three of the most common types known as major depression, dysthymic disorder, and bipolar disorder.

Major depression. Major depression differs from the normal "feeling down" mood in several ways. A major depression is pervasive, persistent, and intense. It interferes with normal social and physical functioning. The person is not simply sad. Rather, he experiences an exaggerated sadness coupled with pessimism—he feels the sadness will persist indefinitely regardless of what might be done. There is a loss of pleasure in life.

One woman described her depression as:

I felt like I was walking around in wet cement that kept getting harder and harder.

Another person said:

While depressed, I felt like I was in the middle of a black cloud that was getting blacker. I lost all feeling. I just didn't care about anything or anyone.

Some people who experience a major depression have only one or two episodes in a lifetime. Others have recurrent episodes and require ongoing medication.

Dysthymic disorder. This is a form of depression in which the person is chronically depressed—depressed two years or longer without a break in the depression of at least two months. The symptoms tend to be less severe than with a major depression, but can keep the person from feeling well and functioning effectively. Without adequate treatment, depression is more likely to become chronic.

Bipolar disorder. This condition involves emotions at two extremes or poles with the person going from depressive "lows" to manic "highs." It's frequently referred to as *manic depression.*

In the depressive phase, the person suffers from symptoms typically associated with depression. During the manic phase, the person experiences a marked increase in energy, insomnia, elation, and increased irritability. Mania often affects thinking, judgment, and social behaviors.

What Causes Depression?

People get depressed for different reasons. There may be one factor or many.

Understanding the cause is important since it will determine the most appropriate help. You will be better able to assist a depressed person, or even prevent depression, if you recognize factors which can put an older person at risk for depression. Some of the following are common to people of all ages; others are more frequent in later life.

Heredity

Studies show that some depressive disorders, particularly bipolar disorder, are hereditary. Genetic factors, however, usually do not show themselves for the first time in late life.

Biochemical Imbalances

Chemical imbalances in the brain as we age can increase vulnerability to depression. A proper balance of brain chemicals is necessary to maintain normal mood. An imbalance of certain brain chemicals is associated with depression. This imbalance can have many causes, including physical illness, medication, and chronic stress. Medication can correct the imbalances.

Drugs

Depression can be a side effect of one medication or the interaction of two or more medications. Among these are medication for high blood pressure, sedatives, tranquilizers, and anti-Parkinson and anti-inflammatory drugs. A depression may develop immediately or may not show up for months after starting a medication.

Because alcohol is a central nervous system depressant, it can cause depression or intensify an existing depression. Some depressed people turn to alcohol for relief, but it may mask the symptoms of depression.

Illness

Sometimes depression can be a symptom of a physical illness, or sometimes the changes caused by an illness can trigger depression. Medical conditions that can actually *cause* depression include thyroid disease, pernicious anemia, brain tumor, Parkinson's disease, cancer (particularly cancer of the pancreas), uremia or kidney disease, and electrolyte imbalance.

Depression often is a reaction to illness, especially one that produces chronic pain, disability, and dependence. Medical conditions associated with changes in body image— for example, strokes or amputations —are particularly threatening.

Medical conditions that provoke greater anticipation of loss of function, disability, or death—such as cancer, Alzheimer's disease, or cardiovascular disease—also can bring on depression. People who pride themselves on being independent and self-reliant may be particularly susceptible to depression when illness means increased dependence on others.

Personality

People who have low self-esteem, are highly self-critical, consistently pessimistic, unusually passive and dependent, or easily overwhelmed by stress tend to be more prone to depression. People who are highly resourceful are less likely to become depressed than those with low levels of resourcefulness. And, if they do get depressed, they are more likely to recover quickly and are less likely to have a relapse.

Sensory Loss

Loss of sight and hearing can trigger depression. These changes affect a person's

ability to function in the physical environment, but also can lead to isolation and being dependent on others. Even a slight hearing loss, for example, can be emotionally upsetting if it interferes with understanding others. Many people withdraw from group interaction when they become hard of hearing.

Stress

Living in a highly stressful situation over time, such as taking care of a spouse with dementia, living in poverty, or experiencing declining health, can cause depression. Inability to adjust to a major life change— death of a spouse, divorce, death of an adult child, chronic illness, retirement, a forced move from one's home—can precipitate depression.

The later years are often a time of loss. As one older person said, "The older I become, the more goodbyes I have to say as older friends and relatives die one by one." Older people also are more prone to multiple losses occurring in rapid succession. And sometimes their support networks are fragile or non-existent.

Perceived loss of control often leads to depression. People who believe their actions make no difference may develop a sense of helplessness. A person who feels both helpless and hopeless is at greater risk of suicide.

Seasons

Research shows that the short days of winter with less light, particularly in rainy, cloudy regions, can trigger a low-energy type of depression in susceptible individuals. This condition, called seasonal affective disorder (SAD), is an extreme form of the "winter blahs."

Signs of Depression

Recognizing the symptoms of depression is the first critical step in helping the depressed person. Unfortunately, depression in older people is frequently misdiagnosed or considered to be a natural part of aging. Sometimes people expect that "to be old is to be depressed." Depression is neither inevitable nor normal in late life.

Here's why depression can be more challenging to recognize in older people.

Age-related changes

Signs of depression sometimes look like normal age-related changes. Stooped posture, reduced physical activity, increased sleep problems, and loss of appetite (caused by a decline in taste sensation) are problems experienced by many older people who are not depressed.

Denial

Older people tend to deny or hide being depressed. Many grew up in an era when people did not talk about feelings. They may feel that to be depressed is a sign that they are "weak" or "crazy." They may even be fearful that being depressed means they will end up in a mental institution or nursing home. You need to observe changes in a person's appearance and behavior, rather than rely on what he says.

Atypical signs

Depression may be dominated by moods other than sadness, such as agitation, irritability, or anxiety. The person may complain, pace, and be easily angered. Paranoia and suspiciousness are also common. Sometimes depression is expressed through hostile behavior. This is particularly important to recognize because such behavior can alienate family members and interfere with helpful assistance. One daughter said:

> I remember my mother being hostile toward her grandchildren whom she once loved dearly. She was more likely to behave like that than to complain about feeling depressed.

Older depressed people frequently report memory problems that are greatly out of proportion to reality. Some will appear more confused than depressed. A common mistake in diagnosing depression in older people is to confuse depression with dementia (memory loss or impairment in mental functioning as a result of changes in the brain).

Older people are more likely to express emotional distress in terms of bodily symptoms. Vague complaints of aches and pains (for example, "I feel like I don't have any blood"; "My body just feels heavy and weak"), unfounded fears about a serious illness, or complaints about health problems for which there is no medical basis can signal an underlying depression.

Physical Illness

Physical illness can mask depression and depression can mimic physical illness. Many physical illnesses have symptoms similar to those produced by depression, for example, weakness, fatigue, social withdrawal, and appetite changes. This can sometimes lead to a misdiagnosis of a physical illness when depression is the problem. When depression coexists with an illness and goes untreated, it can worsen or complicate the medical problem. Even if a person has serious medical problems, treating a depression will help the person cope better.

Diagnosing Depression

You should not try to make the diagnosis of depression yourself. But you need to be aware of common signs and know how to locate and use available health care resources.

There is no single sign that identifies depression. Rather it is determined by a cluster of symptoms. A serious depression affects the entire person: physical well-being, feelings, thoughts, and behavior. The main features are a persistent sadness for at least two weeks and a change in usual behavior and mood. For example, the once socially active woman becomes reclusive; the man who has always taken pride in his appearance dresses in a slovenly way.

If you are wondering whether someone you know is seriously depressed, check the list on page 268 for signs you may have observed. The more signs you check, the more likely the person is suffering from a serious depression. If several of these symptoms have been present for two weeks or longer, or if the person's day-to-day functioning has been affected, help the person to get a professional evaluation.

You may also find some clues indicating a person is depressed if you listen carefully to what he says. Verbal statements such as the following are often associated with depression and suicide.

◆ I just feel down in the dumps. Nobody cares.

◆ No matter what I do, I can't do anything right.

◆ I just don't feel like doing anything.

◆ No one wants a dreary old person around.

◆ My life is worthless.

◆ I'm tired of living.

◆ What's the use of living?

◆ My family would be better off without me.

◆ There's nothing to live for anymore.

◆ I feel like an empty shell.

As with other signs of depression, it's important to compare such statements with the way the person typically has behaved in the past. If he previously has been satisfied

---

SIGNS OF DEPRESSION

Physical Signs

☐ Aches, pains, or other physical complaints that seem to have no physical basis

☐ Marked change in appetite (or weight loss or gain)

☐ Change in sleep patterns (insomnia, early morning waking, sleeps more than usual)

☐ Fatigue, lack of energy, being "slowed down"

Changes in Thoughts

☐ Feelings of hopelessness, pessimism

☐ Feelings of worthlessness, self-reproach, helplessness

☐ Inappropriate or excessive guilt

☐ Inability to concentrate, slowed or disorganized thinking

☐ Forgetfulness, problems with memory

☐ Indecisive

☐ Recurrent thoughts of death or suicide

☐ Thinks he would be better off dead

Emotional Signs

☐ Pervasive sadness, anxiety, or "empty" mood

☐ Apathy (lack of feeling)

☐ Decreased pleasure or enjoyment

☐ Crying for no apparent reason

☐ Indifference to others

Changes in Behavior

☐ Loss of interest or pleasure in previously enjoyed activities, including sex

☐ Neglect of personal appearance, hygiene, home, and responsibilities

☐ Difficulty performing daily tasks; ordinary tasks are overwhelming

☐ Withdrawal from people and usual activities; wanting to be alone

☐ Increased use of alcohol and drugs

☐ Increased irritability, argumentativeness, or hostility

☐ Greater agitation, pacing, restlessness, hand wringing

☐ Giving away possessions and putting closure on relationships and tasks

☐ Suicide attempts or talking about suicide

---

with life, he may be seriously depressed. Coming from someone who always has been pessimistic and negative, these phrases may not be as significant. However, consider the possibility that the person has been depressed for a long time. Sometimes depression can develop so slowly as to seem natural. Without treatment, a depression can continue for months or even years.

TREATMENTS FOR DEPRESSION

Depression is highly treatable. Over 80 percent of depressed people can be treated effectively and their symptoms alleviated within weeks. However, many depressed people never receive proper treatment, and undertreatment is a common problem. Without treatment, depression can last for weeks, months, or even years.

The earlier a depressed person receives help, the sooner the symptoms will be alleviated and the quicker the recovery. When depressed people who suffer from a medical problem are treated for both conditions, improvement in their physical health and overall wellbeing is better than for people who are treated for the medical problem alone. Treatment of the depression also can increase a person's will and capacity to cope with an ongoing medical problem.

Although several treatments are available, the most appropriate treatment will depend on the cause and severity of the depression, the availability and practicality of various treatments, and the person's medical condition. There are three basic types of treatment: medication therapy, psychotherapy, and electroconvulsive therapy. These treatments can be used alone or in combination. Antidepressant medication and psychotherapy together are often more effective than either treatment alone. Psychotherapy not only enables the person to feel understood and supported, but also increases his willingness to take medication.

Finding the right treatment can take time. No two people are alike in their response to treatment. A treatment should be evaluated regularly so that appropriate continuation and/or changes can be made.

Medication Therapy

Antidepressant medications are especially effective in treating the symptoms of severe depression: lack of pleasure, sleep and appetite problems, and loss of energy. They work by bringing the level of brain chemicals involved in depression back into balance.

Some people, particularly those with recurring forms of depression, need ongoing medication to prevent or alleviate further episodes, much as the diabetic requires insulin. For others, a short period of drug therapy is adequate. Because older people metabolize and excrete drugs more slowly than young adults, they may require lower initial and maintenance doses. Usually it takes an older person longer to respond to an antidepressant medication. It may take two to six weeks or sometimes longer before the antidepressant takes maximum effect.

Sometimes people will stop taking a medication when they begin feeling better, thinking the medication has done its job. This can cause a recurrence of the depression in a few days. People are frequently maintained on an antidepressant medication for several months or longer after improvement to help prevent relapses.

Antidepressant medications should be used with caution to avoid adverse side effects. The potential for adverse effects is even greater when a person is taking multiple medications. Even mild side effects should not be ignored because they can make a person resistant to taking medication.

Antidepressant medications fall into four categories: selective serotonin reuptake inhibitors (SSRIs), tricyclic antidepressants, monoamine oxidase (MAO) inhibitors, and "mood stabilizers," including lithium. A person's history and behavior may suggest a lack of certain brain chemicals and the use of a particular type of medication. Sometimes it takes more than one try to find the medication that works best.

Selective serotonin reuptake inhibitors

Selective serotonin reuptake inhibitors (SSRIs) are the newest of the antidepressant medications, and they are safer and better tolerated. In most cases, the SSRIs are the first-line of treatment for depression. Side effects can include both over-activation and sedation, excessive sweating, and sexual dysfunction, all of which are reversible. However, many people experience no or few side effects.

Tricyclic antidepressants

These were the mainstay of therapy prior to the availability of the SSRI's, but are used much less today because they take longer to work and side effects are common, particularly in older people. Side effects include sedation, dry mouth, and reduced blood pressure upon standing. Also, these medications are more likely to worsen memory and concentration problems in older people. However, the tricyclic antidepressants can be useful in select circumstances, for example, if the person is not able to tolerate SSRIs or is agitated.

MAO inhibitors

MAO inhibitors are generally reserved for people who do not respond to other types of antidepressants. Patients on these medications have to follow a careful diet to avoid a dangerous side effect involving high blood pressure.

Mood stabilizers

Mood stabilizers are particularly effective for bipolar disorder. They lower the euphoric highs and alleviate the depressive phase. These medications are also helpful with some cases of recurrent major depression. Lithium, the initial medication used to treat bipolar disorders, is still used frequently. Medicines developed for seizure disorders have also shown positive results.

Psychotherapy

Psychotherapy, or talk therapy, usually is used to treat mild to moderate depression, but also can relieve severe depression. It involves working with a trained professional to solve problems that contribute to depression. It can be particularly helpful when depression is triggered by loss and grief, low self-esteem, or problems with relationships.

Antidepressant medication may bring a person sufficiently out of a depression to face problems, and psychotherapy can then help the person develop better coping responses. Psychotherapy helps people examine the underlying causes of depression and develop skills to better manage the factors that contributed to their depression.

Age is not a determining factor in the success of psychotherapy. Older people respond well to psychotherapy; however, it may not be practical for those who have a significant hearing loss, are memory impaired, or are homebound.

There are many mental health professionals who provide psychotherapy. They are psychiatrists, psychologists, clinical social workers, licensed counselors, and pastoral counselors. Psychotherapists can also help people deal with and adjust to difficult life changes such as loss, chronic illness, and caregiving.

The three major psychotherapies, which may be used singly or together, are cognitive therapy, behavioral therapy, and interpersonal therapy.

Cognitive therapy

Cognitive therapy helps people change negative thinking. It is based on the premise that mood is determined by the way a person interprets an event rather than the event itself. Depressed people tend to view themselves, their environment, and their future negatively. Cognitive therapy helps them monitor their thoughts, identify negative thought patterns that increase their vulnerability to depression, and restructure their thinking in positive ways.

Behavioral therapy

Behavioral therapy emphasizes the importance of daily experiences and behavior. Depression occurs when a person experiences several unpleasant events or too few pleasant events in his life. The goal is to increase the positive events. The therapist guides the person to develop skills or access resources to make this possible. The "pleasant events" are determined individually.

Interpersonal therapy

Interpersonal therapy focuses on relationship problems and role conflicts that contribute to the development of the depression. Therapy addresses the person's way of relating to significant people in his life and helps the person change negative patterns and develop effective communication and relationship skills.

Electroconvulsive Therapy

Many people have difficulty accepting the idea of electroconvulsive therapy (ECT), yet it has saved the lives of people who otherwise would have starved to death or committed suicide. This therapy may be considered for situations where a person is severely depressed and dangerously suicidal, when no other treatment has worked, or when the person cannot take antidepressant medications because of serious side effects or a medical problem contraindicates their use.

With ECT, a brief pulse of electricity is passed between electrodes on a person's scalp. A series of treatments (6 to 12 treatments are typical) are given over several days, producing changes in brain function that can quickly bring a person out of a deep depression. Modern methods have reduced the risks of ECT. The major side effects are some mild memory loss and confusion for a short time after each treatment. Treatments are generally given in an outpatient setting.

HELPING THE DEPRESSED PERSON

You play a critical role in helping a depressed family member return to full functioning. However, there is a fine line between "helping" people to get well and "enabling" them to remain depressed. Sometimes helpers unknowingly reinforce depression; for example, if attention is primarily given to the person when he is depressed or complaining. Consider the following guidelines as you reach out to help.

Encourage Treatment

One of the most important things you can do is to encourage the person to get a medical evaluation. However, expect to take an active role in getting a person in for evaluation and treatment. The nature of depression—low energy, lack of motivation, and helpless feelings—makes it difficult for depressed people to take the initiative to seek treatment. Recognize, too, that the older person may have been socialized to view depression and seeking help as a sign of weakness or personal failure, and therefore may deny being depressed or may resist help.

Because depression can cause confusion and forgetfulness, it also may be helpful to accompany your family member to the doctor.

Don't force the person into treatment or threaten to institutionalize him. Helping someone overcome depression should be positive, healing, and designed to return him to normal functioning. It should never be held over him as a threat or punishment. In talking with him, it's important to communicate your concern and caring and to give hope. For example, you might say:

Dad, I love you and I am concerned about you. In the last month I have seen you

losing weight. You are no longer going out with the group, and your weekly bowling game has always been so important to you. I know this has been a difficult time but there is help available that can help you feel better.

Avoid putting yourself in a power struggle with the person who refuses help. He has a right to remain depressed even though it is uncomfortable for you, as well as him. Only when the person's life is in danger should you intervene without permission.

Get Expert Help

When someone close to you is depressed, remember you don't need to solve the problem all by yourself. Your best strategy is to locate and use the resources available to you.

When to get help

It's better to seek help early than wait for a crisis. It will be less stressful for everyone. Here are some signs that professional help is necessary:

◆ You're wondering if it's time for professional assistance. This usually means it is time.

◆ The depressive symptoms persist for more than two weeks.

◆ Depression is interfering with the older person's daily functioning and activities.

◆ The person's health is threatened by the depression.

◆ You observe signs of potential suicide.

◆ What you have done doesn't seem to be working and you don't know what else to do.

◆ You find yourself getting pulled down by the person's depression.

Where to get help

The availability of mental health services varies by community. If the person lives in a rural area, you may need to take him to a larger city for evaluation and development of a treatment plan.

Whenever possible, consult with a professional experienced with the elderly. Most important, select a professional who is knowledgeable about mental health issues in later life and believes older people can recover from depression. Ask specifically if the professional has a background or training in geriatrics or mental health issues and aging. If a geriatric specialist is available in the older person's community, that's usually a good place to start. Find out whether Medicare will pay for the professional's services.

Here are some additional resources you might contact for assistance:

◆ **The person's physician.** Whenever depression is suspected, a first step is to arrange for your family member to have a complete physical examination to uncover any physical illnesses or medications that may be contributing to the depression. Go with him or call the doctor beforehand. Be assertive and tell the doctor the changes you have observed. It's unrealistic to expect a doctor to be aware of these changes in your relative.

◆ **Community mental health center.** Some centers provide a broad range of professional mental health services, including crisis intervention, at a reasonable cost. Some mental health centers provide outreach programs through senior centers.

◆ **Private mental health professionals.** This group includes psychiatrists, medical doctors who specialize in mental health treatments and can prescribe medications; psychologists, people who hold doctorates in psychology and specialize in psychological testing and therapy; and other mental health specialists (for example, psychiatric nurses, individual and family therapists, and social workers) who have specialized training in counseling and helping people cope with their problems.

◆ **Local and state hospital geriatric programs.** Hospital geriatric programs provide in-patient diagnostic work-ups and treatment.

◆ **Clergy trained in counseling.** Many clergy have been trained in counseling techniques. If the older person has been active in a church or synagogue, he may be more receptive to help from this source.

◆ **Area agencies on aging.** Your local area agency on aging may be able to provide you with a list of agencies and professionals specializing in geriatric mental health problems.

Get Help for Yourself

Because dealing with a depressed person can be frustrating, you may benefit from professional help. It's important to take care of yourself and not let the depressed person's behavior "get to you" or "drag you down." As one daughter said,

I didn't know who was being affected more by Mom's depression, Mom or me. After every visit I was a wreck. It seemed that nothing I did made a difference for her. And I'd end up feeling depressed!

A mental health specialist can help you to better understand depression, to deal with the frustrations and negative feelings you may have about the depressed person's behavior, and to learn what your role should be in speeding his recovery. Your seeking help may also serve as a "bridge" to get a resistant person to accept professional help.

Listen and Validate Feelings

A person who is depressed needs to be listened to and understood. As one person said, "The opportunity to talk helps to get the sad out of you." Ask what is happening in the person's life and then really listen. Give the person a chance to talk about his feelings. Acknowledge the difficult situation(s) he has experienced and the "hurt" he may feel. For example, a son said to his father:

Dad, you've been through so much in the last few months with the company cutting your position and your not being able to find another job. This must be painful for you. I know how important your work has always been to you. If this had happened to me, I would feel as though I had been stabbed with a knife and it's twisting

deeper and deeper. I'd be angry, wondering how the company could do this to me after I'd worked faithfully for 34 years. Is this somewhat how you're feeling?

A daughter said to her mother:

I know that the move from your home to living in one room probably has been very difficult and filled with sadness. There must be many special memories associated with your home and a lot of things you have had to give up. What has been most difficult for you?

Allow repressed anger and despair to be expressed. By listening you show concern and openness, and you will likely be told more. Older people experience many losses, some permanent, which can cause depression. Allow the person to move through the grief process at his own pace. If you rush him, he may stall and become "stuck" in the middle of the process.

Look beyond the loss itself to the meaning the person attaches to it. For example, a move from one's home to a care facility may be interpreted as "I'm no longer useful," or "My family doesn't love me." Or the person may feel a total loss of control or see only more sadness in the future.

Don't try to talk the person out of his feelings. It will only make him feel worse if you try to get him to cheer up or quit thinking about problems. Avoid moralizing, telling him to try harder to get well, or pressuring him to "put on a smile," "snap out of it," or "pull yourself together." Such remarks imply that depression is willful.

Pep talks actually tell depressed people that their feelings are wrong or not important and that you really are not listening. Pat answers tell people that things are really simple if they would only try. *Depression is not simple.*

Avoid statements like "Look at all you have. You can still...." "You've had a good life. Count your blessings," "You have everything to live for," "You are much better off than...," or "Don't worry. It'll all work out." Such statements do not communicate caring or understanding; rather, they smother the person's efforts to talk things out.

Build a Supportive Environment

Support from family and friends is critical. It helps keep the person from giving up or withdrawing further. Offer help when needed but avoid doing everything, which might increase the depressed person's feelings of helplessness.

People often find it difficult to be around a person who is sad, negative, or complaining. You may have to educate family and friends about depression and the person's feelings and needs. Upbeat, positive people who understand depression are particularly helpful.

Set up a system of calling and visiting on a regular basis. Spending focused time with the person can show genuine caring and attention. Scheduling special time, rather than just dropping in, gives the person something to look forward to.

Maintain support during and after treatment. Your continuing encouragement will support the efforts of the mental health professional. When therapy has ended, your support is important as the person begins to use his newly acquired coping skills.

Practical help, such as transportation to a clinic or assistance with bills, may help speed the person's recovery. Or perhaps you might be able to change a situation contributing to the depression. One daughter said:

What a difference it made when we moved Mom down to a first floor apartment. She had become isolated, then depressed, after a fall down the stairs. Being on the first floor removed her fear and lifted the depression.

Structure Activity

Depression responds to structure and physical activity. If you can get depressed people involved in doing things, they generally begin to feel better. Exercise, such as walking, can make a difference, particularly for the mildly or moderately depressed. However, you may have trouble getting a depressed person motivated.

A depressed person tends to feel like a failure. It's important for him to experience success, to do something well. Try to find activities that reinforce pleasant events and build a sense of self-worth and adequacy. Point out his strengths in the process. You can help the person to succeed by assisting him to set small, reachable goals through incremental steps that have immediate results.

Give the Person Control

Encourage as much control and decision making as the person can handle, but don't overwhelm him with decisions. Taking away power unnecessarily only reinforces a depressed person's feelings of inadequacy. Provide choices, but don't push or intrude more than necessary. Respect his autonomy. Because many depressed people have difficulty with decision making, you need to maintain a delicate balance.

Learn about Medications

Be aware of any medications the person may be taking that could contribute to depression. If he is being treated for depression with an antidepressant medication, know the therapeutic and side effects, any precautions to follow, and what you can expect so you can quickly spot any problems. Be aware of how antidepressants interact with other medications he may be taking. If a problem develops, talk to the doctor about it.

Be Alert to Signs of Suicide

Every depressed person is vulnerable to the risk of suicide, even someone you think would never take his life. Therefore, it's important to be alert to potential signs of suicide and to know what to do if you suspect a person may be contemplating taking his or her life. Try to remove instruments of suicide, if possible.

Be Watchful at Holidays

Holidays and anniversaries can be particularly difficult for a depressed person. A past loss linked to the day may seem more poignant. Or the joyousness of a holiday like the Christmas season may serve only to deepen, perhaps by contrast, feelings of sadness or aloneness. Be especially watchful of a depressed person at these times and for the month following.

HANDLING SPECIAL PROBLEMS

In this section we discuss tools for handling special problems, including what to do if the person denies being depressed, helping from a distance, and identifying and responding to a suicidal person.

If the Person Denies Being Depressed

You may see many signs of depression, yet your family member may firmly deny it, blame the symptoms on stress or physical illness, and become angry that you would even think of him as being depressed. He may resist any help. There are no easy ways to deal with resistance; however, here are some tools to help reduce the tension:

- **Visit a mental health professional for yourself.** The therapist will give you assistance in problem-solving, information about how to approach the person, and help you work through your feelings.

- **Identify someone the person trusts.** Enlist the help of anyone who has listening leverage and influence with the depressed person: physician, pastor, neighbor, friend, or another family member. Many older people are more likely to accept treatment by a mental health professional if it is prescribed by their own medical doctor.

- **Focus on what the person acknowledges as a problem.** Ask the person what he sees as the problem and address this concern rather than the depression itself.

- **Concentrate on depression as a medical illness.** The physical aspects of depression may be more acceptable to the person than "mental" issues. Therefore, focus on the physical symptoms—

problems with sleep, appetite, and fatigue. Remember, a first step in evaluation is a thorough physical examination.

Explaining that depression is a medical condition and is often caused by illness, medications, or biochemical factors may relieve the person of a feeling of shame and make evaluation and treatment more acceptable. For example, you might say, "You may be 'feeling down' as a result of a chemical imbalance."

◆ **Encourage the person to get a medical check-up.** You can help by being willing to make a doctor's appointment and taking the person to the appointment. Once you are in the doctor's office, respect the person's autonomy by giving him private time with the doctor.

◆ **In talking with the person, use "I" rather than "you" statements.** With "I" messages, you speak about your feelings and identify the specific behavior changes you have observed. For example, say "I know you feel that you're fine, but I am concerned because you seem to be tired most of the time. I'd like you to see your doctor to reassure me that you're okay," or "I am worried about you because you have stopped going to the senior center and to church."

"You" statements sound dictatorial and tend to create defensiveness and resistance. "You" messages are usually orders or commands, like "You are depressed and you must quit denying it and go to the doctor" or statements that lay blame on the person, like "You brought this all on yourself." Sometimes these remarks give solutions or deny the person's feelings: "If you'd do…then you wouldn't be depressed," or "You shouldn't feel depressed. You have so much to live for."

Sometimes it's necessary to wait for a crisis before the person recognizes the depression and the need for help. Be patient and don't give up.

Helping From a Distance

When you are separated geographically from the depressed person, it becomes more of a challenge to help. The following tools may make the task less complicated:

◆ **Learn about resources.** Use the telephone to find resources in the older person's community such as a mental health center, the person's doctor, a physician specializing in geriatrics, the local area agency on aging; the local senior citizen's center, or an outreach worker to make a home visit and "bridge" the older person to a mental health specialist. Use these resources for both information and referral.

◆ **Encourage the older person to follow up on a specific contact you make.** Then check his response and progress by telephone. Before you talk with his physician, get the older person's permission. This encourages a sense of control. Sometimes, however, a person will not give permission. If you ask for it and are told "no," another approach is to tell the person, using an "I" statement, that because of your concern and worry you plan to call his physician. At least he will know what you're doing.

◆ **Maintain regular contact.** Make frequent telephone calls and really listen to show you care. At times, it can be difficult to listen to negative or pessimistic talk, but

it's important to encourage communication. Send letters, audio and videotapes, family photos, and other surprises. They help the person feel cared about.

◆ **Find a local support person.** Seek out a person in the community you can trust to monitor the wellbeing of your family member. Ask the support person to provide you with accurate information about the depressed person's condition and progress. Be willing to pay for this help if you need to. You may find it helpful to hire a private care manager.

Responding to a Suicidal Person

Factors that put a depressed older person at high risk for suicide are:

◆ Severe personal loss, such as health or a significant person

◆ Feelings of hopelessness and helplessness

◆ Living in isolation

◆ Prior suicide attempt

◆ Alcohol or drug abuse

◆ Detailed suicide plan, including the means, time, place, and method

◆ A readily available lethal weapon

The clues to suicidal intent are generally more subtle with older people than with younger age groups. The following are common warning signs that a depressed person may he contemplating suicide:

◆ **A sudden upswing in mood.** A sudden improvement in mood may occur because the depressed person has reached a decision to end his life and may have formulated a plan to do so.

◆ **Talking about suicide.** It's less common for older people to talk directly about suicide, but when they do, listen and take action. Verbal clues, however, are likely to be more indirect, for example:
— You won't have to worry about me much longer.
— Here, take these things. I won't need them anymore.
— There's just nothing to live for.
— I need to tie up loose ends.
— My time has come.

◆ **Feeling hopeless and helpless.** A person who expresses a sense of worthlessness, helplessness, and hopelessness through words or actions will often begin to think of suicide as a way out of the situation.

◆ **Unusual behavior.** A sudden or dramatic change in behavior that is not characteristic of the person should be treated as a warning flag for suicide. The following are examples of actions that may indicate suicidal intent:

— He suddenly writes a will and puts personal affairs in order whereas previously he resisted doing so.

— He stockpiles medications or makes sudden requests for sleeping pills.

— He shows new interest or disinterest in church and religion.

— He has been active in the community but suddenly resigns from all organizations.

—He gives away important possessions.

—He has always been known as a "penny pincher" but he gives away large sums of money.

—He sells his home and other possessions without plans for replacement.

—He displays uncharacteristic acts of affection; makes amends for things that have happened in the past.

—He increases his use of alcohol.

—He is preoccupied with death.

A time to be particularly vigilant is when a person is coming out of a deep depression. This is a time of suicide. Earlier the person may have felt suicidal but was too paralyzed to act on these feelings. Now, he may have the energy to commit suicide.

The three most important actions to take to prevent suicide are to listen, ask questions, and get professional help:

◆ **Listen.** Listening is what suicide prevention is all about. Be aware of both obvious and subtle expressions of suicidal intent and take these expressions seriously. Never ignore remarks about suicide. Most important is to be accepting, non-judgmental, and supportive. Encourage the person to confide in you.

◆ **Ask questions.** You need to ask questions to assess the risk of suicide. Asking questions about suicide will not give a person the idea to take his life. In fact, asking questions often provides the opportunity for the person to express emotions that if not expressed might prove fatal.

You can ask general questions such as "How is your life going?" or specific ones like "Have you considered harming yourself?" "Have you thought about ending your life?" or "Are you thinking about suicide?" Don't be afraid to say "suicide"; the mere mention of the word will not create a desire to act it out.

If the person denies that he is wanting to die, the potential for suicide is probably low unless the person is an alcoholic, drug abuser, or psychotic (a mental disorder in which the person has irrational beliefs, is extremely impulsive, and has an impaired sense of reality). If the person hedges, responds with self-accusations, or admits to having suicidal thoughts, the potential for suicide is high. Immediately ask these questions:

— How would you take your life?

— Do you have the means available?

— When would you do it?

Asking specific questions about the plan is important. The person who has a plan and a method available is at greatest risk.

◆ **Get professional help.** If there is a risk of suicide or if you are uncertain about the person's intentions, get professional help immediately. At this point, the decision to

get help may have to be taken from the person. Realize that you may have to discuss that forced decision with the person at a later time. Often, however, the person is relieved, not angry, about the decision.

The resources listed below will provide help to the suicidal person. Emergency services are also available in many communities that enable you to get immediate intervention assistance.

Crisis lines and organizations. The volunteers who staff these services receive special training to handle potential suicides and can assist you in getting help. Keep their telephone number where it is easy to find in case of an emergency.

Mental health clinics. These clinics will give immediate attention to suicide threats, whether or not the person is already a client. Most mental health clinics have a 24-hour telephone number that you can call in case of an after-hours emergency.

Hospital emergency room. A person who threatens or attempts suicide will

receive immediate care in most hospital emergency rooms. Many hospitals have staff available 24 hours a day as part of the inpatient mental health unit. If you cannot get the person into an automobile and to the hospital, call an ambulance.

Police or other emergency service agency. If other resources are not available or you cannot decide what to do, call 911 (or the emergency number in your area) or your local police. You will get assistance in deciding what to do, and help in dealing with the immediate crisis. To intervene with the high-risk person:

◆ Act decisively.

◆ Remove the method or weapon.

◆ Summon help.

◆ Remain with the person. Do not leave a suicidal person alone. (If not possible, try to get the person to agree to a verbal contract that they will not take any action for a specific period of time.)

If the person is not at high risk for suicide, keep monitoring him. Reapproach with questions about suicide if his mood or activity level deteriorates further or suddenly shows an upswing. Keep in frequent contact at least by telephone. If possible, arrange to have someone visit or have him see someone daily or every other day. Try to keep the person away from alcohol. The combination of alcohol and depression places a person at higher risk for suicide.

☙

MYTHS AND FACTS ABOUT DEPRESSION AND SUICIDE

MYTH: Depression is a normal part of aging.

FACT: To be old is not to be depressed. An attitude of "I'd be depressed too if I were old" is the major barrier to helping a depressed older person. Depression should not be accepted as inevitable in later life. Unfortunately, the belief that depression is normal in later life stops many people from getting needed help.

MYTH: Older people cannot benefit from therapy.

FACT: Depression is treatable at any age. Older people also respond well to short-term psychotherapy.

MYTH: People who are depressed either lack willpower, are psychologically weak, or are putting on an act.

FACT: To be depressed is not a person's fault nor is it a sign of weakness. It's as real as a heart attack is real. Depression is an illness involving genetic, biological, and environmental factors. However, some older people believe depression is a sign of a weak character and feel ashamed.

MYTH: People could control their depression if they just had the right attitude.

FACT: The causes of depression are complex. However, a depression is not a condition people can simply will or wish away. They cannot "pull themselves together" and get better. While some people can manage their depression through self help, others need professional assistance.

MYTH: People who talk about suicide seldom take their lives.

FACT: A person who talks about suicide is at high risk of taking his life. Suicidal statements or acts should be taken seriously.

MYTH: Asking a person if he or she has thought about suicide increases the risk that the person will attempt suicide.

FACT: Inquiring about suicidal thoughts in depressed people does not increase the risk. In fact, by asking you are likely to save a life. Many people who have thought about suicide are relieved when asked.

MYTH: Older people who attempt suicide usually do so only to gain attention or to manipulate family members.

FACT: Older people seldom attempt suicide as a means to get attention or as a cry for help. Depression underlies up to two-thirds of suicides in the elderly. Most suicide attempts made by older people are well planned and usually successful.

SUMMARY

Depression is one of the most treatable emotional disorders. Resources are available to help people move out of their depression and back toward a happier life. Your job is to locate and use the assistance available to you. You can help manage the depression, but remember that you are not responsible for the cure.

You also may need to accept that no matter how much you might want to, you cannot replace the losses or undo the changes in your relative's life, nor "make him happy." You need to be realistic about what you can do and about your own personal limits.

Healing the emotions is all too often viewed as a sign of weakness, yet we don't consider it weak to go to a doctor when we experience physical pain. Just as it's okay to seek help in healing our bodies, we (must) seek help in healing our minds.

R. D. Colen
Health, November 1988

CHAPTER FOURTEEN

Helping Memory-Impaired Elders

Providing caregiving to a family member who has a dementing illness such as Alzheimer's disease can be particularly stressful. As the disease progresses, the person not only requires increasing supervision and assistance, but also becomes impaired in thinking, language, reasoning ability, and social behavior.

Research shows that if a care receiver has dementia and exhibits emotional disturbances and behavior problems, caregiver stress tends to be higher than if a care receiver has only physical disabilities.

Not everyone exhibits behavior problems, but they are a common consequence of the illness. Special techniques can improve the quality of life for both the care receiver and the caregiver.

A 1994 Harvard Health Letter Special Report on Alzheimer's Disease stated:

> Caring for the Alzheimer's patient is one of the toughest jobs in the world. Families who learn everything they can about the disease are better equipped to handle the demands, but there is no secret formula for meeting the day-to-day challenge.

This chapter provides an understanding of dementia, ways to cope with the resulting changes, and general care and management guidelines. It also presents approaches for handling specific problems and for communicating with memory-impaired individuals.

SENILITY VERSUS DEMENTIA

For several years Ray had known he was having memory problems. He compensated for his forgetfulness by writing himself notes of once-familiar names, telephone numbers, and things he had to do.

Sometimes he became annoyed when people tried to help by reminding him. He silently worried about becoming "senile." He was, after all, 64 years old.

Recently, Ray encountered a detour while driving home from the neighborhood grocery store. He arrived home two hours late. He had become lost three blocks from home. He felt frustrated and afraid, but he covered up by telling his worried wife that he ran into an old friend.

Ray's work suffered. His employer suggested an early retirement. Ray felt worthless He mistakenly believed and accepted his problems as the inevitable result of aging. He is not alone.

Many people, including some health professionals, share this myth and label older adults who have memory problems as "senile." Others fear that aging leads to "senility" or loss of memory.

Getting older does not necessarily mean losing one's intellectual abilities. Actually, the word *senility* has been used erroneously. It is derived from a Latin word which means "to grow old."

Dementia is the more appropriate word to describe significant progressive loss of mental abilities experienced by some older people. Symptoms of dementia include: impairment in thinking, learning, memory, and judgment; and changes in personality, mood, and behavior.

Dementia is the result of a disease process Although it is more common with advancing age, it is not a normal part of growing older.

Dementia is more common in industrialized societies today than it was 100 years ago because a greater proportion of people survive into the older age ranges. The age group 85 and older is the fastest growing group in the United States.

Most people experience some changes in memory as they grow older. For example, information processing and recall are slower, and it may take more time and effort to learn new information. However, these changes do not interfere with a person's daily functioning.

Memory also can be affected by many other factors, including stress, fatigue, illness, grief, or an overload of information. Frequently people do not remember something because they didn't concentrate in the first place, and the information didn't get filed in the brain's memory bank.

Adults concerned about their forgetfulness should ask themselves, "How did I know I forgot?" The answer: "Because I remembered later." In a dementing illness, these memories cannot be recalled because they have been erased from the mind.

Confusion and cognitive impairment sometimes can be caused by treatable illnesses, reactions to medications, drug toxicity, alcohol abuse, depression, poor nutrition, infections, and metabolic disorders such as a thyroid problem. When cognitive impairment is due to an underlying medical condition, the dementia may be partly or completely reversible. Early evaluation is important, because treatable condi-

tions may become irreversible if left undiagnosed and untreated.

Any memory loss that interferes with a
person's lifestyle, work or daily functioning
should be evaluated. A variety of diagnostic
tools exist to help physicians assess
whether a memory problem is significant.
Finding the cause of memory loss is critical
to appropriate treatment.

Causes of dementia

The onset and course of dementia depend
on the nature of the particular disease
causing it. Symptoms can vary widely, and
no two afflicted persons follow precisely the
same course or rate of progression.

Alzheimer's (Alz'-hī-merz) disease is the
most common cause of dementia in the
United States. In Alzheimer's disease, the
nerve cells are destroyed throughout the
cerebral cortex, the outer layer of the brain.
Often the first symptoms include difficulty
remembering recent experiences. This is
because early in the disease process, the
brain loses the ability to "record" new information, experiences, and events.

As the disease progresses, afflicted individuals lose more and more of their memory and other abilities. Eventually, they are
not able to function independently. The
time from onset to total disability may vary
from three to 20 years.

A diagnosis of Alzheimer's disease is made
by ruling out all other causes of the symptoms. As of 2000, there is still no way to be
certain of a diagnosis of Alzheimer's disease
without a brain biopsy or autopsy. However,
if comprehensive diagnostic testing is done,
one can be fairly certain that a diagnosis of
"probable" Alzheimer's is accurate.

Currently, there is no known cure or prevention for Alzheimer's disease. Medical
researchers, however, are making great strides
in understanding the disease and helping
the patient and family to function better.

The second most common cause of
dementia is vascular dementia. The inter-
ruption of blood supply to the brain results
in small strokes. Vascular dementia progresses in steps—the person may lose some
functioning with a small stroke (or accumu-
lation of small strokes) and stay at that level
of impairment until the next ministroke.
The person may even appear to improve
slightly for a time.

The symptoms experienced depend on
the area of the brain that has been damaged.
Some cases of vascular dementia progress
over time, but others do not.

Progressive dementia may also be caused
by Pick's Disease, Huntington's Disease,
Parkinson's Disease, AIDS, or other relatively
rare conditions.

THE FAMILY'S ADJUSTMENTS

Not only the patient suffers from the effects of dementia—the family, too, is greatly affected. Coping with the changes and problems associated with a progressive dementing illness places tremendous stress on families. The "loss of the mind" is difficult for both the patient and the family to accept.

As dementia progresses, people slowly lose insight into their condition. For the family, however, losing the person they have always known, although he or she is still physically present, can be very painful. Family members have said:

> "It's like looking after a six-foot-tall two-year-old who is accustomed to doing what he wants to do."

> "It's very, very hard to watch someone you love die very, very slowly. We go through many emotions—hurt, anger (at them, at ourselves), frustration, bitterness. We feel helpless!"

> "It's like a funeral that never ends."

Denial is common early in the disease. The impaired person usually looks healthy, can talk about familiar topics, and sometimes even seems to improve. Many changes are subtle, and early in the disease people often are adept at compensating for memory loss. They may write themselves "memory notes," make light of the changes, blame others ("Who took my wallet?"), or attribute memory loss to stress or other pressures.

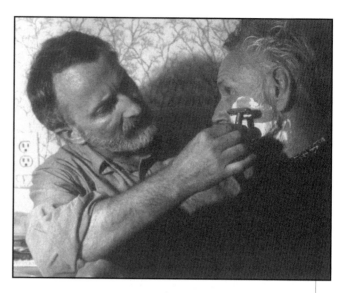

Family members may have attributed the person's inability to carry out tasks to laziness or stubbornness, and this led to arguments. When a disease is diagnosed, family members sometimes experience strong guilt feelings or blame themselves for not being aware of the changes earlier. However, the subtle beginnings of dementia are even difficult for the professional to diagnose.

Dementia also results in a gradual shift of tasks and responsibilities from the patient to the caregiver. These added responsibilities can be overwhelming.

Social and emotional isolation occurs for many caregivers. The caregiver may not be able to leave the person alone at home. The care receiver may become easily upset in public, may be unable to tolerate being around people, and/or may lose social graces. Friends and family may stop visiting if they do not understand the disease or if they find it difficult to see the deterioration in the person or to accept the behavior and personality changes.

Caregivers comment:

"To go out is scary, not knowing what I'll find when I get back. My last night away was four years ago."

"During the five years of caring for my husband, I only left home to purchase food and medications. I prayed nothing would happen while I was away."

"Usually, we just stay at home because I don't know how he will act. If we have dinner with friends, he may refuse to eat and want to go home, so our social life is negligible."

Some caregivers are inclined to hide their family member's illness. Although explaining the disease may be difficult, it helps if family, friends, and neighbors understand the person's behavior and the stress of caregiving. People need to know:

◆ Dementia causes the brain to fail, just as diseases of the heart and kidneys cause those organs to fail.

◆ The disorder is not contagious.

◆ People afflicted by the disease are not "insane" or "crazy." The disease causes a gradual deterioration of the mind. This means that people increasingly are unable to remember, use good judgment, control their behavior, and perform seemingly simple tasks like dressing themselves.

Caregivers must be realistic about what they can do. Eventually, the person may need round-the-clock care and supervision. No caregiver can provide total care without help.

GENERAL GUIDELINES

The amount of care, supervision, and help a memory-impaired person needs will depend upon the extent of the disease. The following guidelines will help to improve the quality of life for everyone involved.

Keep expectations realistic. Know what you can expect from the memory-impaired person. Keeping expectations realistic reduces frustration for everyone. Trying to force the person to do something he cannot do, or does not want to do, will only make a situation worse.

Psychological testing may be helpful. It can identify the cognitive abilities still intact and provide a realistic measure of what the person can do. Your family member's physician may be able to direct you to professionals who can provide such testing.

Maintain a calm atmosphere. Being rushed, around a lot of activity, or in a chaotic environment tends to increase confusion and restlessness. Even small amounts of excitement can cause agitation for some individuals. For example, it's often more difficult for the person to eat a meal if the television is playing, or if young children are running around.

The more secure and comfortable a person feels, the less likely behavior problems will occur. If the person becomes upset or resistant, it's important to remain calm. If necessary, remove the person from an upsetting situation to a quiet, unhurried environment.

Avoid confronting or overloading the person with stimulating experiences. Alternate activity with quiet times throughout a day and over a week.

Keep your voice calm and reassuring. Your tone of voice and the feelings expressed are as important as your words.

Be consistent. Avoid changes and surprises. People with a dementing illness generally do best in familiar, well-organized environments and with consistent routines. Many have difficulty coping with change, even seemingly minor changes like rearranging the bedroom furniture.

Create a routine by doing things the same way at the same time every day. This will make it easier to get through everyday tasks (e.g. bathing, eating, and dressing). If you go on walks, go out the same door, at the same time, and use the same route.

Establish early a schedule of daily activities based on the person's lifelong patterns, if possible. Plan more difficult tasks for the person's best time of day. Keep in mind that the memory-impaired tend to have short attention spans—30 minutes or less.

Post the schedule. Not only will this help the person who can still understand the written word, but it will also make it easier for anyone who provides assistance in the home.

When you must make changes, prepare and support the person but avoid lengthy explanations. Take care when you plan a trip or vacation. Some people become agitated and more confused in strange, unfamiliar surroundings.

Simplify tasks. Tasks that previously were easy for the person may become too difficult. Reevaluate skills when the person becomes frustrated by a task or refuses to cooperate.

Breaking down complex tasks into simple steps and giving step-by-step instructions may enable the person to continue to do some tasks. For example, the person may be able to partially set the table as long as the items are dealt with one at a time.

Demonstrating each step also may help—for example, brushing your teeth with the person. Occasionally, a person who is helped with the first step of a familiar activity can then complete the activity. For example, when you assist with putting on one sock, the person might be able to put on the other sock and (perhaps) even the shoes.

Think of parts of previously enjoyed activities that the person can still do. For example, the person who enjoyed cooking (but for whom cooking is now too complex) may still be able to mix batter, wash the vegetables, or tear lettuce for a salad. The former gardener may find satisfaction in raking the yard or watering plants.

Limit choices. Reduce confusion by limiting the choices the person has to make. For example, remove seldom-worn or out-of-season clothing from the closet. Limit the number of food choices and put out only the utensil(s) the person will use at mealtime.

Use repetition. Memory-impaired people need frequent, calm reminders. They simply may not remember what they are told because the brain no longer has the ability to retain information. Be prepared to repeat the same instructions daily, sometimes several times in succession.

Remind with brief, simple statements; avoid lengthy explanations. When repeating, do not remind the person that you said it before. Don't use phrases like "Remember, I told you yesterday" or "I've already told you four times." Give the same brief answer each time the same question is asked.

The person may remember some tasks and information from repetition. Don't assume he will forget promises you have made or places you have said you will take him.

Use memory aids. The success of memory aids depends on the severity of the disease. In early to moderate cases of memory impairment, memory aids can help promote better orientation. Signs, clocks, calendars, seasonal decorations, and a schedule of the day's activities reinforce memory.

Give cues. For example, put labels on drawers, cupboards, appliances, and doors. When the person can no longer comprehend the written word, replace word labels with pictures. Mark off days on a calendar with a large felt pen so the person will see the current date.

Autographed photographs may help the person to remember family members and close friends. However, expect fluctuations in the person's ability to recognize people, even close family members. Don't take it personally when you are not recognized.

It's often beneficial to instruct family and friends when the person may no longer recognize them. Let them know that the lack of recognition is due to the disease and not the impaired person's feelings toward them, and that some individuals deteriorate to the point where they don't even recognize themselves in the mirror.

Encourage recognition rather than recall. It's easier to recognize rather than to recall information. Limit the demands for recall of facts, names, and schedules. For example, post a schedule of the day's activities. Name events and give the names of family members and friends who visit.

Say to a person who has difficulty remembering you, "I'm Jane, your daughter. I'm here to visit with you." Avoid saying "Who am I?" when the person can no longer remember who you are.

Make the environment safe. Safety is a major concern in activities and the environment. Family members continually need to be aware of sources of danger.

Don't expect the person with dementia to take responsibility for his or her own safety. Even a mildly impaired person may have lost the judgment needed to avoid accidents.

Three potentially dangerous activities are smoking, cooking, and driving. Other potential dangers are high windows, stairs, swimming pools, power tools, appliances, knives, hot water, matches, razor blades, cigarette lighters, firearms, poisons, and plants. Lock up potentially dangerous items.

The memory-impaired person may not know the difference between what is and is not edible. Make sure that poisonous items like cleaning fluids are not accessible. Remove items that resemble food, such as plastic fruit or rocks in a jar that they might mistake for candy.

Memory-impaired people sometimes forget they are smoking or forget to put a cigarette out. If possible, encourage the person to give up smoking. Otherwise, supervise the smoking. Keep matches and other smoking materials out of reach.

The stove may be turned on and forgotten or flammable materials put in the oven. Removing knobs from the stove may solve the problem. Or remove the fuse or open the circuit breaker when you're not cooking. If you have questions about how to make a stove inoperable, consult your utility company.

Lower the temperature setting of your hot water to prevent burns. Check the temperature and depth of bath water before the person enters.

Install grab bars in the bathtub and shower and by the toilet. Use a rubber mat or no-skid

decals on the bottom of the bathtub to prevent falls. Don't use bath oils that make the tub slippery.

Observe when the person begins putting inappropriate items in his or her mouth. If this occurs, remove things like plants, buttons, small knickknacks, and other items that might be swallowed.

Remove locks on bedroom and bathroom doors to prevent the person from accidentally getting locked in a room. Lock windows or limit the amount they can be opened so the person cannot climb out. Install locks on outside doors to prevent the person from leaving unnoticed.

Awakening in the dark can be disorienting. Installing nightlights in the bedroom, hallway, and bathroom and/or a strip of glow-in-the-dark tape from bedroom to bathroom increase nighttime safety and help orient the person.

Be sure that stairs are made safe to prevent falls. Remove any objects the person might trip over, such as scatter rugs, footstools, and electrical cords.

Because memory-impaired people are at greater risk for accidents, it's helpful to know first aid procedures. Contact the Red Cross about classes.

Use reminiscence. Reminiscing about the past may help the person become involved in what he can remember. It also builds self-esteem since the past generally was a time when the person felt independent and productive.

People who seem to have little memory often respond to discussions about significant personal experiences (e.g. weddings, births of children, hobbies) in their past and unique historical events (e.g. the Depression). Old photographs, special holidays, and familiar songs often evoke memories and reminiscing.

Approach the person slowly, from the front. Moving quickly, pushing or pulling the person, and approaching from behind may startle the person and stimulate agitated or hitting behavior and resistance.

Treat the person as an adult. Include the person in conversation and in adult activities. Avoid talking "down" to the person and talking about him as if he isn't present. Avoid treating the person like a child; when treated like a child, a person is more likely to respond with childlike behavior.

Maintain an attitude of respect and dignity and allow the person to be as independent as possible, even if tasks are not done as well as you would like. A person with dementia still needs to feel that his dignity and self-esteem remain intact.

Reassure and praise. People with dementia also need a feeling of success and self-esteem. Provide praise for tasks accomplished.

Look for concrete activities that give a sense of accomplishment and fun. Small accomplishments amount to tremendous victories for people who have impaired memory.

Maintain a sense of humor. Families find a sense of humor especially helpful in dealing with trying situations—for example, discovering garden tools in the refrigerator, or finding their family member has removed all of his clothing to use the toilet just after having struggled to get him dressed. Try to have a good laugh occasionally. Laughter and humor have positive effects on physical and mental health.

APPROACHES TO SPECIAL PROBLEMS

Dementia can cause a person to act in different and unpredictable ways and challenge the caregiver. In dealing with a difficult behavior, accept the behavior as a reality of the disease, try to work through it, and do not take the behavior personally. There is no one "best approach" that is guaranteed to work. You may need to be prepared to try several approaches. However, it can help to keep the following eight principles in mind:

1. Difficult behavior is not willful.

2. Understand the world of the person with dementia.

3. Person loses the ability to learn and to "record" information and events.

4. The past becomes more real and lovable than the present.

5. Emotions and feelings remain largely intact.

6. The person cannot change. We must change our behavior or the environment.

7. Connect. Don't correct.

8. Use distraction.

Difficult behavior is not willful. Irritating, rude, stubborn, and socially inappropriate behaviors are usually beyond the person's control. Blaming the person or viewing the behavior as "being done on purpose," can set a caregiver up for a destructive pattern of anger and frustration.

Key elements in responding effectively to difficult behavior are: (1) recognizing that the person is not deliberately being difficult, (2) defining the behavior, not the person, as the problem, and (3) looking at the behavior as *reflecting a need,* rather than simply as a problem.

Try to understand the "why" of the behavior. Behavior usually does not occur in a void. There is a reason for it. The behavior serves a purpose, but is not done "on purpose."

Understand the world of the person with dementia. Try to view a situation through the "eyes of the person" and understand his or her perceptions, thoughts, and feelings. If you can do this, you will be in a better position to develop strategies to address a difficult situation. One approach that some caregivers find helpful is to view the person as always right—right from *his* point of view.

For example, a radio talk show playing in an adjoining room may seem like people are in the next room. A tree branch brushing against a window when the wind blows may seem like somebody is trying to break into the house. Ice cubes dropping into the bin of an automatic ice maker may sound like something has broken. The woman who no longer recognizes herself when she looks in the mirror may accuse her husband of "having another woman in the house." Shooting and violence on television programs may seem real.

Person loses the ability to learn and to "record" information and events. It's easy to get frustrated when a memory-impaired person has said he would wait but then does not, or agreed to give up driving or to

move, then is adamant the next day that "no such agreement was made." It's important to remember that, early in the disease process, dementia "steals" from the person the ability to "record" information and events.

The person may not remember your visit a few hours earlier or an event that he attended and enjoyed. Sometimes family and friends feel it's not worthwhile to visit or to engage the person in an activity because "it won't be remembered anyway." It becomes important to look at the "joy for the moment" that is created.

The past becomes more real and lovable than the present. As a dementia progresses, it increasingly erases memories. "Today" for the person may be what was 10, 20, or 40 years earlier. The person may talk about a family member or friend, long dead, as though she is alive. People in the current surroundings may not be recognized as who they are: A grandchild may not look familiar; a daughter, who looks like her mother, may be misperceived by her father as his wife; and a nephew may be misperceived as the person's brother.

Emotions and feelings remain largely intact. People with dementia are memory-impaired, but not non-feeling. They can feel love, caring, joy, embarrassment, and other emotions even if they cannot communicate. Sometimes, a feeling will be remembered long after an event has occurred.

For example:

It was the day of Abraham Lincoln's birthday, and the 16th U.S. president was being discussed at the adult day program. To the surprise of staff, a male participant recited part of the Gettysburg address. He received applause and a lot of praise. When his wife came to pick him up, he excitedly told her "I did it, I did it." But when asked what he had done, he could not remember. But the feeling of what had happened was still with him.

Emotions are very infectious, and people with dementia will often mirror the emotions of people around them. If you are tense, annoyed or angry, the memory-impaired person may exhibit the same emotion. People with dementia lose their memory, but not their sensitivity to the emotional climate of the environment.

The person cannot change. We must change *our* behavior or the environment. An important key in meeting the challenges of caring for someone with dementia is modifying the environment or one's own behavior—*not* trying to change the person's behavior. Trying to reason or rationalize also are not effective strategies. It's important to stay flexible. For example, if the person resists taking a bath in the morning, try later.

Connect. Don't correct. If a person says something you know can't be true—for example, "My mother is coming to see me today" and you know her mother died 20 years ago—don't argue about the correctness of what she said. Either let it go or look for the feeling behind the words. If the person seems pleased that "her mother is to visit," you might say something like, "Tell me about your mother." On the other hand, if she is upset, you might use distraction. The goal is to create a feeling of comfort and to connect with the person in a positive way.

Focus on feelings, not facts. If you argue about "the facts" or try to convince the person that he is wrong, you will likely make the situation worse and convey that you are unfriendly or not to be trusted. Try to connect with the person as a friend. For more information about what it means to "be a friend" in relating to someone who has dementia, read *The Best Friend's Approach to Alzheimer's Care.*

Use distraction. The person with dementia tends to be highly distractable. You can often interrupt difficult behavior or dodge potential problems by diverting the person's attention. And it can avoid a confrontation. For example, you might divert the person who "wants to go home" by saying, "Let's have lunch first." Avoid saying, "This is your home," because it is more likely to lead to a disagreement.

In addition to these principles for responding to challenging behaviors, the following approaches to specific problems may be helpful.

Repetitive Questions

The fifth time a person asks the same question within a short time can try anyone's patience, but it may help to understand that each time is like the first time to the person with a dementing illness. He may no longer be able to remember answers given to questions or that he even asked the question before.

Sometimes reassuring the person will reduce repetitive questions. Simple written reminders also may aid a failing memory, particularly in the early stages of dementia.

Look for a need that may underlie a repetitive question. For example, the person who continually asks, "When do we eat?" may be asking the question because he is hungry. Giving a snack, even though it is an hour before dinner, may stop the repetitive question.

Wandering

Individuals with dementia may become disoriented and lost—in their own neighborhood or when they are far from home. Any person who is ambulatory is at risk. Wandering is common and potentially dangerous. Traffic, weather, water, crime, missed medications, and exhaustion put the wanderer at risk.

The wanderer does not necessarily realize he is lost, may not remember where home is, and may not think of (or be able to use) a telephone.

Wandering behavior can be triggered by a variety of circumstances, including stress, medication, fear, and failure to recognize surroundings. Look for possible reasons for wandering behavior.

◆ Did the person previously enjoy walking and outdoor activities?

◆ Did the person walk to reduce stress in his life?

◆ Is the person bored?

◆ Is there somewhere the person wants to go? Is the person searching for something?

◆ Was the person trying to get away from someone, or from a situation that was unfamiliar or uncomfortable?

◆ Was there an unusual noise that attracted the person's attention, such as a fire truck going by, road construction, or the sound of a neighbor's saws and hammers?

◆ Was the person over-stimulated by activity or noise in the home?

◆ Was the environment changed at home, or is the person in a new environment?

◆ Does the person seem to be searching for some satisfaction? Calling out "I want to go home" or "Where is my mother?" may indicate a search for security.

◆ Is the wandering directed toward a goal? Commenting on the need to perform a task or gesturing as if cleaning or performing a task may indicate a need to do something or be busy.

Is there a pattern to the wandering behavior? The wandering may seem to have no specific cause other than being part of the disease process.

Some wandering behavior stems from the need to exercise. If this seems to be true, you may reduce the wandering by taking the person on frequent walks or providing other exercise such as raking leaves or sweeping the driveway. Regular exercise also can relieve tension and help the person sleep better.

A high fence with locked gates may allow the person to wander freely and exercise outdoors. This may be particularly important to the person who spent considerable time outdoors before the illness.

Approach a wanderer slowly and calmly. Offer reassurance. Walk with the person a short distance in the direction he is walking. Then gently ask him to walk you back home. Another strategy is to divert the wanderer to an enjoyed activity, for example, you might say, "We have cookies and ice cream inside."

Avoid hurriedly moving the person, scolding, restraining or using physical force. These approaches will generally make the person more agitated and confused. In fact, they may result in striking out behavior. Logic and reasoning generally will not be understood.

Sometimes, medication can help to lessen wandering behavior.

You may want to alert neighbors and local merchants to the memory-impaired person's problems and ask them to contact you if they see the person leaving the area.

Have the person wear an identification or medical-alert bracelet that gives his name, address, and telephone number and includes the phrase "Memory-impaired" or "Brain-impaired." Giving the diagnosis, such as "Alzheimer's disease" or "dementia," may not be as helpful because strangers who find the impaired person may not know what these terms mean. Simpler and more direct language helps others understand and deal more effectively with the wanderer.

The Alzheimer's Association has a program called "Safe Return" in which you may enroll a memory-impaired individual. Membership provides registration in a national database and access to a nationwide alert system of law enforcement agencies, a 24-hour 800 number to contact when the person is lost, an identification bracelet or necklace, wallet cards, and clothing labels. When a wanderer is discovered, the person who finds him can call the Safe Return number. The operator immediately calls the family members or caregivers listed in the database.

Preventive measures to safeguard your home include: installing locks at the top or bottom of doors where they are out of direct sight; disguising exits by painting doors the same color as the wall or covering the doors with curtains; installing electronic alarms or warning bells that jingle when outside doors are opened; or using dead-bolt locks that lock on the inside with a key.

A room with an expansion safety gate across the open door (often used for small children) may provide an area where the person can pace and explore safely. However, if the person is a "climber," such a gate could be hazardous.

Never leave the person alone in a parked car. He may wander away or cause an accident by starting the ignition or releasing the brake. Prevent the person from exiting a moving car by locking doors and using seat belts.

Wandering frequently occurs at night and may be the result of disorientation. Nighttime wandering also can be a sign of congestive heart failure. A medical checkup may be indicated.

Wandering at night can be particularly disruptive to the caregiver's sleep—and to the caregiver's physical and emotional well-being. Keeping the person awake and active during the day generally promotes better sleep at night.

If medication taken during the day to control behavior is making the person sleepy, talk with the doctor. Changing the medicine, or when it is given, may reduce daytime drowsiness and encourage sleeping at night. Make sure the person empties his bladder before going to bed.

The quiet and darkness of a home at night may also cause increased restlessness. Using a nightlight or playing the radio softly may help reduce wandering and confusion on wakening.

Sundowning

Individuals with a progressive dementing illness sometimes experience more confusion and behavior problems in the late afternoon and evening. This is sometimes called *sundowning.*

While the cause is unknown, sundowning may be due, in part, to dim light as darkness approaches, resulting in confusion. The impaired person may be tired and less able to cope with stress, or alternatively, may grow restless as activities gear down at the end of the day.

Evaluate the person's daily activities. Behavior problems may be managed by: lowering the noise level and decreasing activities in the evening hours; providing regular daily activities, such as exercise; restricting the person's intake of caffeine-rich liquids and foods; and increasing lighting in the evening and using nightlights.

It may help to alternate activity (including dressing, meals, etc.) with quiet time. Include a 30-minute rest period each morning and afternoon. Reduce all noise and distractions during this time (soft music may be the exception).

If the behavior occurs in the evening after a trip to a favorite restaurant, a friend's or family member's home, or elsewhere, it may mean the person can't cope with the activity any longer. Be prepared to gear down.

Catastrophic reactions

Memory-impaired individuals sometimes overreact when a request, task, or situation overwhelms their thinking ability. Stubbornness, pacing, wandering, and weeping are common reactions.

Rapidly changing mood, anger, and aggressive behavior also may occur. To the caregiver, it may seem childish that the person has become upset "over nothing."

Look for clues about what may be upsetting the person. Was the reaction the result of mounting frustration? Over-stimulation? Misinterpretation of requests, events, or activities? Inability to perform a task? Fatigue?

A catastrophic reaction can be triggered by: being asked to think of several things at once; small mishaps; strange noises, people, and places; a confusing, unpredictable environment; and scolding and arguing. Signs of an impending outburst may be refusals, restlessness, and blushing.

You can often avoid catastrophic reactions by simplifying a task, a request, or the environment. After minor mishaps, allow time for the person to calm down.

It may work to ignore the behavior, leave the room, and let the person be alone if he is acting out and there is no risk of injury. Otherwise, calmly remove the person from the stressful situation.

Divert the person from the situation with a favorite treat or activity. Do something familiar, like having a glass of juice or going for a walk. Soft music, holding hands, and rocking may be calming. Spending time with an uninvolved person also may help.

Avoid explanations, arguments, and restraints. These usually will only make the person more confused, angry, or combative. Feelings of distress may linger after the person has forgotten the situation. And remember, the behavior is beyond the person's control—and can't always be prevented, even by the most experienced caregiver.

Sometimes increased agitation and irritability are the result of internal discomfort—for example, pain or constipation—and the person isn't able to put his discomfort into words. Any sudden deterioration in functioning or behavior may be a warning signal of a fall or illness. Check with the person's doctor. Correcting even minor physical and medical problems often improves the person's functioning.

If you are alone and your safety is in jeopardy, don't hesitate to leave and call for help. Call 9-1-1 (or the emergency services number in your area) or the police. Explain that the person cannot help his behavior, but that the situation is getting out of control and you need help.

Seek professional help with reducing violent episodes and about how to cope with them if they do occur. Due to the progressive nature of dementia, aggressive behavior will lessen over time.

Hallucinations and delusions

Individuals with a dementing illness may see or hear things that exist only in their minds. For example, one person kept seeing a cow on top of the neighbor's house. Another saw rats running under her bed. Such hallucinations can be disturbing and a source of intense fear, or they may be a source of laughter and humor for the person.

Individuals may also express beliefs that things have been stolen or that someone is going to harm them. These delusions can make the person fearful and resistant to all attempts at care and help.

Respond calmly to what the person is *feeling* and provide reassurance. Remember that his experiences and beliefs are based on his reality. For example, you might say, "I don't see the cow on the roof, but it must be funny" (if the person finds the situation humorous) or "I didn't see the rats run under your bed. But, don't worry, I will take care of them."

Do not argue or try to reason. It usually makes matters worse. The person can't stop the hallucinations just because they're illogical or unreal to someone else, nor will he be able to remember your reasoning or rationally weigh your points.

It may help to touch the person gently and offer reassurance that you will see that things are all right. Some caregivers choose to ignore the behavior if the person is not upset and has forgotten the situation. Distraction may also work.

Medication may help to lessen the intensity, frequency, and anxiety of the hallucinations and delusions.

Hiding and losing things

Memory-impaired individuals sometimes lose things, hide objects, or put them in safe but forgotten places. They may not return items to their customary places, but be adamant that they always keep an object in a certain place. When the object is not in that spot, the person may accuse the caregiver or others of stealing his possessions.

Remain calm if accusations are directed at you, and remember that the person truly does not know that he did something with an item. His brain tells him that the missing item must have been stolen. It rarely works to try to convince the person otherwise. It's better to offer to look for what is missing. Look for lost items in dresser drawers, boxes, coat pockets, shoes, and wastebaskets and under cushions and mattresses.

Reduce hiding places by locking closets, cupboards, and rooms the person doesn't use. Keep important and valued items locked up. Hide a spare set of household and car keys in case your set disappears.

Be aware of common places where items are put. Check garbage cans before emptying if these become hiding places.

Bathing and grooming

Most people feel and act better when they are well-groomed. A checklist of activities—brush teeth, wash face, shave, comb hair—placed by the bathroom mirror will help some people early in the disease with grooming activities.

As memory loss progresses, some individuals resist bathing and changing clothes. Reminders about the necessity of these activities and using simple explanations may work.

Bathing instructions written by a physician on a prescription pad—"bathe twice weekly"—may help to persuade the resisting person to bathe. Avoid arguing as to whether a bath or shower is needed.

Recognize, too, that bathing may be frightening. The person may not be able to understand that someone undressing her is being helpful and not trying to harm her. Water rushing out the pipe, going down the drain, or hitting against her body may be fearful. Remember, the person's brain no longer processes information accurately.

You may need to lower your expectations about frequency of bathing when it becomes a hassle for both you and the impaired person. A sponge bath may be the best alternative. If the bathroom is warm and a calm atmosphere is created, the person may be more likely to cooperate.

Some families find it helpful to fill the tub with 3 to 4 inches of water before the person enters the bathroom, to use a shower chair for both baths and showers, to install grab bars, to use a shower head on a flexible hose, and to play soft music.

Bathing is a private activity, and for some people it is embarrassing to receive assistance. Allow the person to do as much as possible for himself. Most importantly, never leave the person alone in the bathtub or shower.

If possible, try to maintain the person's lifelong routine. For example, if the person took a shower before breakfast, try to follow this habit.

Simplify bathing and dressing. You can encourage dressing by laying out clothes in their order of use. When necessary, show the person what to do. There are many steps required to take a bath and get dressed. The person may no longer be able to remember these steps or to do them in the right sequence. Break down tasks into small steps and give step-by-step instructions such as "unbutton your shirt," "take off your shirt," etc.

Use clothes that can be put on and taken off easily and that help the person to dress independently. You can replace clothing that has buttons, hooks, snaps, ties, and zippers with slipover and slip-on shirts, skirts, pants, and shoes. This also means fidgeting fingers can't unzip or unbutton clothing in public.

Wash-and-wear clothing provides the easiest care. Don't argue if the person wants to wear the same clothing every day or insists on sleeping with a hat on. This is not harmful. If the person prefers to wear only one outfit, perhaps you can make life easier by buying another one just like it.

Mealtime

If you go out to eat, try to select a restaurant that is small, quiet, and familiar. Problems are more likely to develop in large, noisy, dimly lit settings. Depending on the degree of memory loss, the person may or not be able to order from a menu.

Sometimes the impaired person will eat only one food several times a day or will develop specific likes and dislikes. Accept the behavior if it doesn't interfere with overall nutrition and dietary restrictions. Eating only certain foods is better than eating nothing at all. If he is on a restricted diet because of a condition like diabetes or high blood pressure, you may need to put restricted food out of his reach.

Some individuals forget to eat. Others forget that they have eaten. Setting out a small tray of nutritious snacks or serving less food more often is sometimes a satisfactory solution.

With increasing brain deterioration, people frequently lose their coordination and table manners. They may lose the ability to use a knife and fork or to make proper food choices. For example, they might put gravy on salad instead of on potatoes.

Consistency at mealtimes, and a calm atmosphere without distractions, optimize functioning. Set the table in the same way, serve meals at the same time each day, and seat the person at the same place.

Remove unnecessary utensils, condiments and foods. A person may become confused if he has to choose between several utensils or foods. Sometimes it helps to serve only one food at a time.

Prepare the person's plate. Cut food into small pieces. Use finger foods when the person can no longer use utensils. Serve soup in a cup if the person has difficulty handling a spoon. Use a plastic cloth on the table, spill-proof containers, and smocks with the bottom edge turned up into a big pocket to catch crumbs.

Avoid foods the person may not chew thoroughly, such as nuts, popcorn, and raw carrots. Liquids and solids offered together may be confusing—the person may not know whether to chew or to swallow. Because he may lose the ability to judge temperatures, serve foods and drinks lukewarm, *not* hot.

Foods of a soft, even consistency (like purees) are easiest to swallow. Thin liquids (water, apple juice, coffee) are the hardest to swallow.

A person who has difficulty swallowing should sit up straight with his head tilted forward slightly—never back—and remain seated at least 15 minutes after eating. If he begins stuffing too much food into his mouth, remind him to swallow. Don't allow him to lie down or walk around with food in his mouth.

Learn the Heimlich method from a medical professional or the Red Cross. It can save the life of a choking person.

If you have to spoon-feed the person, it may help to talk with a nurse or speech pathologist who specializes in swallowing about the best procedure to follow. As the disease progresses, you may need to remind the person to swallow *after each bite*.

Contact the doctor if the person stops eating or begins losing weight. These may be symptoms of a complicating disease.

Incontinence

Caregivers report that incontinence is such a difficult problem to manage that it is often the "last straw," prompting care facility placement. However, there are many medical causes of incontinence, such as infection, that can be treated. Therefore, when incontinence begins, it's important to get a medical evaluation.

At first, loss of bladder or bowel control may occur only occasionally or during sleep. Later, the person may not be able to respond to the body's signal to void or to remember the acceptable places and ways to eliminate bodily wastes. A man, for example, may urinate in the closet or wastebasket, or on the sidewalk in town.

Establishing a regular toileting routine often decreases problems with elimination. You may need to remind the person every two or three hours, on rising in the morning, after meals, and before bedtime to go to the bathroom. It often works better to say, "It's time to go to the bathroom," rather than asking, "Do you have to go to the bathroom?"

Take the person to the bathroom at the time of day he usually has a bowel movement. Observe the person's behavior for cues. For example, sudden restlessness or picking at his clothes may indicate a need to use the toilet. Be aware when assistance is needed to undress or use the toilet.

Limit fluid intake after the evening meal. Getting the person up once during the night or placing a commode or urinal bottle near the bed may help prevent accidents. Using nightlights may also help increase the person's orientation and ability to find the bathroom.

When a regular toileting schedule does not work, use incontinence products. Special clothing with disposable pads, absorbent undergarments (sometimes called "adult diapers"), protective bedding, and disposable bed pads are available from medical supply, home health, and/or drug stores. Consult the physician or a nurse for additional products available for urinal and fecal incontinence.

When a person is incontinent, it's important to keep the anal and genital area as clean and dry as possible and to watch for signs of redness and irritation on the skin.

COMMUNICATING WITH THE MEMORY-IMPAIRED

The way in which a dementing illness affects communication will vary with each person and the progression of the illness. Early in the disease, communication isn't too difficult, although the person may have problems finding the correct word, especially nouns. The person may substitute names he cannot remember with what the items or people do. For example, if he cannot think of the word "coffee," he may tell you, "It's what I drink in the morning." If he cannot think of the word "garbage collector," he may say, "The guy who empties those big cans into that big truck." Language also may be punctuated with indefinite words like "thing," "this," "that," and "there."

As the disease progresses, communication becomes increasingly difficult. The person may have difficulty expressing himself in words, easily lose his train of thought, and lose the ability to understand what has been said. As a result, he may not be able to understand instructions or report physical needs, discomfort, or pain to caregivers.

Late in the disease, a person's vocabulary may be reduced to a few words. Some individuals may revert to speaking in their first language or use curse words. This is not done purposefully, but is a part of the disease process. When the person is no longer able to communicate verbally, be sensitive to nonverbal behavior—facial expressions, tone of voice, body language and eyes.

Many people with dementia are far more sensitive to a speaker's tone of voice and body language than to the actual words spoken. Therefore, it's important to be aware of *how* you are communicating, not just *what* you are saying. In addition, consider age-related changes in vision and hearing. Good lighting, a quiet environment, hearing aides, and eye glasses may help to increase the person's understanding of what you say.

If taking a message confuses the person, disconnect the telephone when you're out or unable to answer it yourself. Or use an answering machine or voicemail for callers to record their messages.

Kindness, patience and respect go a long way toward communicating effectively with a person who has dementia. Effective communication also requires flexibility. As the disease progresses, the person will change how he communicates, and you will need to change your expectations and how you communicate with him.

Experts suggest the following guidelines for talking with the person who has dementia:

◆ **Call the person by name.** Before asking a person to do something, address him by name to get his attention. In some instances, a childhood nickname may be better recognized than a given name. Some memory-impaired women may not respond to their married name because they no longer have a memory of the name or their marriage.

◆ **Speak slowly and clearly.** Memory-impaired people need more time to comprehend a message. Allow the person time to process information and respond.

◆ **Talk about real actions and objects.** People lose the ability to deal with abstract concepts, such as planning for the future, and using their judgment to avoid potential danger.

◆ **Keep statements short and simple.** Limit statements to one idea at a time, for example, "Your hair looks pretty," and "Please come to the table." Give instructions one-step at a time. Long sentences, complex instructions, and lengthy explanations are likely to overwhelm the person.

◆ **Be specific.** Statements that are specific frequently help the person grasp what you are saying. "Pick up your glass on the table" is preferable to "Pick up your glass" because it gives the person more specific information and may help to focus actions.

◆ **Keep questions simple.** Ask one-part questions—for example, "Do you want orange juice?"—that can be answered with a "yes" or "no" or by a gesture. Avoid open-ended questions like "What do you want to drink?" or "What do you want to wear today?" Also avoid multiple-choice questions, such as "Do you want tea or coffee, and do you want it now or with dessert?" Such questions increase confusion and stress.

Eventually, even questions requiring only a "yes" or "no" response become difficult for some people. When this occurs, say "Here's your orange juice" rather than asking, "Do you want orange juice?" Sometimes it's less confusing to provide the solution rather than asking a question.

Avoid quizzing the person with questions such as "Do you know my name?" "What is this I am holding?" "What day is today?" "Do you remember when…?" These questions generally create frustration and agitation when the person is no longer able to answer such questions.

◆ **Use names or nouns, not pronouns.** For example, don't say "Your best friend is coming to see you. She wants to make cookies with you." It's better to say "Your friend, Cynthia, is coming to see you. Cynthia wants to make cookies with you." Instead of saying "I found it," say "I found your wallet."

◆ **Use positive statements.** It's easier for memory-impaired people to understand what *you want* them to do than what you *don't want* them to do. For example, say: "Please stay inside with me" rather than "Don't go outside"; say "Let's go here" instead of "Don't go there"; and "Please sit in this chair," rather than "Don't sit there." You are less likely to get the desired response using negative words like "no" or "don't."

◆ **Use non-verbal communication.** Communication is more than just the use of words. Your nonverbal communication should reinforce your words. Gestures, pointing, demonstration, facial expressions, and visual aids help communicate what you want done. Using objects such as a comb or toothbrush will help identify activities. Sometimes pictures help convey an idea.

Be aware of your feelings and attitudes. They are often communicated unintentionally through tone of voice and facial expression.

Be sure your words and body language are consistent. If they contradict each other, the person is more likely to respond to your body language. For example, if your words say something sweet, but your body language says you are upset, your body language will usually carry the stronger message.

◆ **Use the person's vocabulary.** For example, if the person uses the word "potty" for toileting activities and "pee" for urinating, then use those words, too.

When the person no longer understands speech, touch can become the most meaningful way to communicate. Tender hugs, holding hands, gently combing the hair, and giving a massage can communicate acceptance, love and caring. Touch is also soothing and can provide comfort and reduce feelings of isolation. However, the need for touch must be met on an individual basis. Each person has a different level of comfort with touch.

Sometimes a person with dementia may misinterpret the meaning of a touch. If this occurs, respond with calmness.

There are distinctive techniques for communicating with people who have memory loss as a result of specific medical conditions such as stroke, Parkinson's disease, and Alzheimer's disease. Contact the appropriate disease-related organization for more information and materials.

SUMMARY

A time may come when the personal care and safety needs of the impaired person exceed the resources and abilities of the most dedicated caregiver. Care facility placement may be the next logical step.

If you face this difficult decision, realize you have not failed, broken a promise, or abandoned your relative. You have only given up the physical chores of daily care. As one nursing home administrator said, "Anyone can give a bed bath or help a person to dress, but only a family member knows the favorite treats, events, and memories that are meaningful to the person."

About the Authors

Vicki L. Schmall, Ph.D.

Dr. Schmall is the Executive Director of Aging Concerns, a non-profit organization in West Linn, Oregon. For over 20 years she worked at Oregon State University, where she served as the Director of the Program on Gerontology, then as the Gerontology Specialist with the Extension Service. She has worked extensively with caregivers and older adults for 30 years, and conducted several hundred workshops nationally and internationally for families and professionals. Dr. Schmall has authored over 100 publications, produced eight training manuals, and developed three videos and eight multimedia programs focused on family and caregiving issues, She also has been actively involved in the Oregon Trail chapter of the Alzheimer's Association from its inception. Her Ph.D. is in Family Studies and Gerontology.

Marilyn Cleland, B.S., R.N.

Ms. Cleland is a Caregiver Education Consultant with over 20 years experience in the field of caregiving for the chronically ill and elderly. She has developed education and training materials and video tapes for professional and family caregivers. The subjects of these materials have ranged from dealing with aggressive clients to working successfully with in-home help. She received her nursing degree and did post-graduate work at the School of Nursing, Oregon Health Sciences University.

Marilynn Sturdevant, R.N., M.S.W., L.C.S.W.

Ms. Sturdevant is a Clinical Specialist in chronic illness, loss and grief. She has over 30 years experience working with individuals, caregivers and family members who have been affected by chronic illness. Her experience includes "hands on" nursing care in hospital and nursing home settings as well as counseling, teaching, and leading support groups in hospice and oncology programs. She received her nursing degree from St. Francis School of Nursing and a master's degree in social work from Portland State University. Her most important learning came from being a caregiver for a mother with Parkinson's disease. At present she is a consultant in the field of long term illness and loss and grief in Portland, Oregon.